WATER MARGIN

WRITTEN BY SHIH NAI-AN

TRANSLATED BY

J. H. JACKSON

"Translation is a condition of order between nations, and therefore of places. In a still wider field it is the condition without which a common culture cannot exist."—J. Hilaire Belloc.

VOLUME TWO

THE COMMERCIAL PRESS, LIMITED

CHAPTER 34

STONE GENERAL DELIVERS A LETTER AT A VILLAGE INN; HWA JUNG SHOOTS A WILD GOOSE AT LIANG SHAN PO

WHEN general Chin Ming and colonel Huang Hsin surveyed the outskirts of the town they saw that Sung Chiang and Hwa Jung led one group of bandits, while Stunted Tiger and Yen Shun led another. They had about one hundred fifty men each.

Huang Hsin gave orders that the drawbridge be lowered, and the bandits be allowed to enter the town. Sung Chiang had previously issued an order that his men were not to kill even one people in the town, that they were first to reach the southern side of the town where to exterminate the family of magistrate Liu Kao. Stunted Tiger however took his men to magistrate Liu Kao's house and seized the magistrate's wife for himself. The magistrate's house was looted, and all the valuables, horses, cattle, etc. were taken away. Hwa Jung took his men to his own house where he took all his family and their possessions on carts. He announced that any of the men at his yamen might remain in their homes, or go with the bandits to the mountain, just as they wished. When all this had been done the bandits returned to the mountain with their loot, etc. Cheng Tien-shou had remained behind in charge of the stronghold, and when he saw the bandits returning with cartloads of loot he welcomed them to the main hall. After Hwa Jung had introduced Huang Hsin and the new comrades they all sat down.

Sung Chiang gave orders that Hwa Jung's family should be given proper quarters, and that the loot from magistrate Liu Kao's house should be equally divided among the bandits. Stunted Tiger had taken the captured woman to his own rooms.

In the main hall Yen Shun asked where magistrate Liu Kao's wife was and Stunted Tiger replied, "You must now let me keep her to be my wife."

"You may keep her," said Yen Shun, "but first she must come here as I have something to say to her."

"I also want to ask her a question or two," said Sung Chiang.

Stunted Tiger sent a man, who soon brought in Mrs. Liu Kao who was weeping and begging pardon.

"You vixen!" said Sung Chiang, "I saved your life on this mountain because you were the wife of the magistrate, but why did you return evil for my good? Now that you have been arrested what have you got to say for yourself?"

Yen Shun jumped up and said, "Why do you ask questions of this adulterous woman?" So saying he drew his sword, and killed the woman on the spot. When Stunted Tiger saw this he seized a sword, and advanced to fight with Yen Shun. Sung Chiang and the others however also arose, and intervened. Sung Chiang said, "Yen Shun has done the right thing in killing this woman. I saved her life, and sent her down the mountain to rejoin her husband, and yet she caused her husband to injure me. If you keep her it would only end in trouble. I will get you a wife later on, and you will then be satisfied."

"I am of the same opinion," said Yen Shun. "If we do not kill her she would do us further injury."

Stunted Tiger listened to all this, and remained silent. Yen Shun ordered the servants to remove the corpse, and then spread out a feast for celebration.

The next day Hwa Jung prepared the marriage of his sister to general Chin Ming under the auspices of Sung Chiang and Huang Hsin, Yen Shun, Stunted Tiger, and Cheng Tien-shou acting as go-between. All the dowry was prepared by Hwa Jung.

All this was done, and after the wedding there was general feasting for about five days.

About ten days after the wedding one of the bandit's scouts came up the mountain and reported that prefect Mu-jung at Ching Chou Fu had sent a memorial to the Minister of State denouncing Hwa Jung, Chin Ming, and Huang Hsin as rebels, and petitioning that a large army be sent to quell the rebels and the bandits.

Upon receiving this news, they held a general discussion and all agreed that their position on that mountain was not too secure and that if a large army had them surrounded, they could not avoid being captured.

"I have a plan," said Sung Chiang, "but I do not know whether you, my brethren, would approve of it."

"Let us hear it," they all cried.

To the south of this place there is Liang Shang Po with a circumference of two hundred miles, and in that area are the towns Wan Tzu Cheng and Liao Erh Wa. That district is now controlled by about five thousand bandits under the command of Ch'ao Kai, and the government troops dare not look them in the face. How would it be if we take all our men there, and join that gang?"

"As there is such a place," said general Chin Ming, "your proposal is admirable. But as we have nobody to recommend us would they be willing to admit us?"

Sung Chiang laughed aloud, and related the whole story from the seizure of the birthday presents unto the sending of a letter to him through Liu Tang and how he killed the woman Yen Po-hsi, and later joined the highwaymen.

Chin Ming was pleased at hearing this, and said, "So you are their benefactor! In that case there is no need for any delay, and we can go there at once."

That day all the details were discussed and arrangements made. All the women and children, valuables, clothes, stores, etc. were loaded on about ten carts. There were about three hundred horses available. All those men who did not want to go to Liang Shan Po were paid off, and allowed to go their own way. There were altogether about five hundred who agreed to go. These were divided into three companies, and they left the mountain separately, disguised as troops going to fight against Liang Shan Po. When everything was ready for departure all the buildings on the mountain were destroyed and set on fire. Sung Chiang and Hwa Jung took command of the leading company. They had flags on which was written: "Government troops for the arrest of brigands." So that on the way no one attempted to impede the progress of such a considerable force.

Sung Chiang and Hwa Jung rode at the head of their column; next to them were the carts containing the women, children, stores, etc., and bringing up the rear was the main force. They had gone about seven miles when they came to a place called Tui Ying Shan—having, true to its name, two equally high mountains on both sides of a broadway. As they were proceeding they heard drums and gongs on the mountains.

Hwa Jung said, "There are evidently brigands in front," and so saying he buckled his spear, got his bow and arrows ready for action. He gave orders that the main force should move forward, and stay with the carts in one body. The two leaders then took about twenty of the mounted bandits to make reconnaissance. They had only gone a few hundred yards when they saw about a hundred mounted men, following a youth, all in red. Balancing a halberd in his hand, this knight gave a challenge, "I will fight with you to-day, and see who must be the winner."

Instantly another young knight in white holding another halberd also led about a hundred mounted men, clad in white, down a small mound, to meet the challenge. Each side had its respective red and white flags. The roll of drums seemed to shake the very rocks. Grimly both knights gave reins to their steeds, and engaged in a deadly combat. After about thirty bouts neither leader gained any advantage.

Sung Chiang and Hwa Jung witnessed this contest from a distance and applauded the skill that was displayed. Hwa Jung urged his horse forward slowly until he was quite close to the combatants. He then noticed that one man had a leopard's tail on his halberd whereas the other had a spotted streamer of five colors, and during the contest these had become entwined so that the two weapons could not be separated. Hwa Jung reined in his horse, seized his bow, and shot an arrow, cutting the tangle and releasing the two halberds at the same moment. At this feat a shout of applause involuntarily broke from the throats of the two bodies of mounted men.

The two young knights stopped fighting, and advanced to Hwa Jung and Sung Chiang with a salute, "We request the name of the marvelous archer."

Returning the salute Hwa Jung answered, "This is Sung Chiang, my adopted brother. I am Hwa Jung, military governor of the Pure Wind Town."

The two young men dismounted, thrusted their halberds in the ground, and bowed down. "We have heard of your fame for a long time."

Hwa Jung and Sung Chiang quickly dismounted, and raised the two men to their feet. "We ask for your worthy names," they said.

The young knight in red replied, "I am Lu Fang, of Tan Chou. I am a great admirer of Lu Pu of the Three Kingdoms, and therefore I learned the skill with the halberd. People have given me the same nickname as Lu Pu, i.e., Little Marquis of Wen. Some time ago I took some unprepared medicine to Shantung, but lost all my capital in that venture, and I could not go back to my native village. Temporarily I took charge of the bandits here at Tui Ying Shan. A few days ago this worthy came, and wanted to take my stronghold by force. I proposed to let him occupy one mountain while I held the other one, but he would not agree to that. So every day we met, and fought about that matter. By an act of Providence our fighting has resulted in our fortunately meeting you."

Turning to the knight in white Sung Chiang asked for his name.

That person replied, "My unworthy name is Kuo Sheng, and I am from Chialing in Szechwan province. I was a trader in quicksilver, but one day a strong wind upset my boat on the Huang Ho (Yellow River) so that I could not return to my native town. Formerly at Chialing I was trained in the use of the halberd by a major Chang, and I became so skillful that people gave me the nickname Rival of Jen Kwei. I heard that at Tui Ying Shan there was a man who had held that place against all comers by the use of the halberd so I came here to have a trial of strength with him. We have been fighting for about ten days without either of us winning. We did not anticipate meeting you, but Providence has evidently favored us."

Then Sung Chiang told them about his affairs, and he suggested that they should come to amicable terms. Both men agreed to this, and all were pleased. By this time all the three contingents of the brigands had arrived, and Sung Chiang introduced the leaders. Lu Fang invited them all to go to his stronghold up the mountain, where he provided a banquet. On the following day Kuo Sheng invited the bandits leaders to come to his mountain, and there they had another feast.

Sung Chiang suggested that they should both go with them and join the brigands under Ch'ao Kai at Liang Shan Po. Gladly they agreed to this, and prepared their effects for an early departure. But Sung Chiang said that as they had now more than five hundred strong men their movements would be duly reported to Liang Shan Po by spies or scouts, and there they might suspect some hostile intention. So he suggested that he would go in advance with Yen Shun, and announce their proposal. They could come along afterwards, but not in one body, but divided into three contingents. The other leaders agreed to this plan as much better, and it was arranged that Sung Chiang and Yen Shun should have a start of a half day.

These two were accompanied by about ten men when they departed for Liang Shan Po. On the third day of their journey about noon they came to an inn, and as they were all tired Sung Chiang decided to stop there for food and wine. He gave orders that the horse's girths were to be slackened, and when this had been done they all adjourned to the inn. Sung Chiang saw that there were only three large tables and a few smaller ones. One of the big tables was already occupied by a man. He noticed that the man wore a turban in the shape of a pig's snout, at the back of which were two finely wrought copper rings of Taiyuan fu make. He wore a black silk gown with a white waist sash; had puttees and hempen shoes. Leaning against the table was a short cudgel, and on the table was a bundle of clothes. The man was about eight feet high; had a sallow complexion with prominent cheek bones; the eyes were clear, there was neither mustache nor beard.

Sung Chiang spoke to the waiter, "We have a large party, but we two will sit in your inner room. Will you ask that customer to be so good as to change to another table and let my men dine on that big one." To this proposal the waiter assented.

Wine was ordered; each man to have three big cups. Food was also placed on the tables. As several of Sung Chiang's men could not find seats the waiter went to the guest before mentioned, who looked like a petty officer, and said:

"May I trouble you, my good petty officer; but would you mind moving to another table so that the followers of these other honored guests may have a seat as we are short of room?"

The man was annoyed at being addressed in this way, and replied, "I was here first, whatever official wants me to move I won't move."

"You see he is so rude," remarked Yen Shun to Sung Chiang.

"Leave him alone," said Sung Chiang. "We must not follow his bad example."

Just then the man turned round, and seeing the two leaders, he laughed sneeringly.

The waiter said to him, "Sir, you may render a favor to our business here, and change tables."

The man banged the table and with an angry voice shouted, "You fool! You insult me because I am by myself, but even if the emperor himself came here I would not shift. You do not know me, but you will soon make the acquaintance of my fist."

"Why are you so angry?" said the waiter. "I have not said any thing to insult you."

"You dare not say any thing to me," the man roared.

Yen Shun could not endure this, and called out, "Fellow, you have rather coarse manners. You need not move, but why threaten the poor waiter?"

The man jumped up, and seizing his cudgel said, "I may have insulted him, but that is not your business. There are only two persons I give way to, and all others I treat like mud."

Yen Shun was excited, and seized a bench to use as a weapon. But Sung Chiang intervened as he saw that the man was not a common vulgar person. 'Let us not have a row about this," he said, and addressing the man he asked,

"I request you to tell me who are the two men whom you would give way to?"

"If I tell you that, you would be stupefied."

"But still I would like to know their names," insisted Sung Chiang.

"Well, one is Ch'ai Chin, the Small Whirlwind."

Sung Chiang nodded approvingly at this and asked who was the other one.

"He is even greater. His name is Sung Chiang of Shantung. He is called Welcome Rain."

A wink passed between Sung Chiang and Yen Shun at this, and the latter put down the bench.

The man continued, "Those two men I would give way to, but I fear nobody else."

"Stop, I know both of them," said Sung Chiang. 'But where did you meet them?"

"As you know them I will tell you the truth. About three years ago I stayed for more than four months at Ch'ai Chin's house, but never met Sung Chiang there."

"Do you want to know him now?"

"I am in fact now trying to find him."

"Who set you to do this?"

"His own brother."

Sung Chiang shook the man by the hands, and rejoiced. "As decreed by Providence you have met him, you might have failed although you traveled a hundred miles. I myself am Sung Chiang."

The man looked at him closely and saluted. "Heaven has favored me by this fortunate meeting with you. I might have easily passed you by and travel to look for you in vain at Sire Kung's place."

Sung Chiang took the man into the inner room, and asked, "Tell me the home news."

"Ah, senior brother, let me tell you, my name is Shih Yung and I am a native of Ta Ming Fu, Chihli province, and I was given the nickname of Stone General. Once I made a row with a person at a gambling den and killed him with my fist. I escaped to Squire Ch'ai's home for refuge. While staying there I heard so much of your fame that I set out for your home at Yun Cheng Hsien to make your acquaintance. There your younger brother informed me that you had gone to Sire Kung's home at the White Tiger Mountain. As I decided to go there, your brother gave me a letter for you; and he said that if I met you, I must tell you to go back home as quickly as possible."

Sung Chiang had a misgiving when he heard this, and asked, "How long did you stay at my home? Did you meet my father?"

"I only stayed there one night," said Shih Yung, "and did not see your father."

Sung Chiang then told him all about their plans of going to Liang Shan Po. The other suggested that he might be allowed to join them. Sung Chiang readily agreed to this, and then introduced him to Yen Shun. More wine was ordered as they all sat down.

Shih Yung soon got out the letter from his bundle, and handed it to Sung Chiang. It could be at once noticed it had been addressed in an unusual way—indicating trouble. The two characters "with peace," ordinarily used had also been omitted. Sung Chiang now had a great misgiving. Quickly he tore the letter out of the envelope, and read these in the latter part—"Father was taken ill and died in the first month of this year. The coffin is still in the house, and we wait until you return to bury him. Return at once with all speed. I, your younger brother shedding tears and blood from my eyes in writing this letter."

Now Sung Chiang burst into lamentations, and striking his breast he exclaimed, "Unfilial son! A wrongdoer! My father dies, and I have not done my duty. I am like an animal." He thus cried with a flood of tears, and banged his head against the wall in utter despair.

Yen Shun and the Stone General seized hold of him, but Sung Chiang continued to wail in a dazed condition and it was for some time before he could come to himself.

Yen Shun said, "Elder brother, do not give way to your grief so much."

"My affections cannot be restrained," said Sung Chiang. "I cannot forget about my father. He is no longer alive so I must depart this very night to my home. You must go to the mountain without me."

"Brother, your father is no more," said Yen Shun. "But even if you return home at once you will never see him again.

In this world parents do not live forever. So please make your mind easy, and again lead us to the mountain. When that matter is settled you can return home without any delay, and attend to funeral matters. I will accompany you there. There is an ancient saying, 'A snake without a head cannot go forward.' You are our head, and if you do not go with us they will not receive us."

"I cannot agree," said Sung Chiang, "because in going to the mountain you will delay me too much time. So I will write a letter stating all the details, and you can take the letter to Ch'ao Kai, and he will then receive the whole company. If I had not known about my father's death I would have gone with you, but as Heaven has given me the information, every day will be like a year in length, and it is imperative that I should return at once. I need neither horse nor companion but must start off straightway through the night."

Yen Shun, and the Stone General could do nothing further to change his mind. Sung Chiang asked the waiter for pen and paper, and while writing, he was weeping all the time. He wrote most emphatically that the company must be allowed to join the bandits. The letter was not sealed and was handed to Yen Shun. Sung Chiang was now ready to go, but Yen Shun asked him not to leave until Hwa Jung, Chin Ming, and the other leaders arrived. But Sung Chiang would not wait even for that, and instructed Stone General to explain the whole situation to the other leaders. He then set off.

Yen Shun and Stone General paid for the food and wine, and the latter then mounted Sung Chiang's horse, and took the men about two miles further along the road to another inn where they stopped. About 7 a.m. the following day the main body of the bandits arrived, and Yen Shun explained what had happened.

The other leaders were annoyed, and asked why Yen Shun had not asked Sung Chiang to wait.

Stone General explained that Sung Chiang was completely upset by the sad news, and in fact would have committed suicide, and would not agree to stay until they all arrived. He had hurried off at once to return to his home.

He had left a letter behind which would induce Ch'ao Kai to receive them.

Hwa Jung and Chin Ming read the letter, and then said to the leaders, "We are in a dilemma, as there will be difficulty whether we proceed or retire. We cannot go back, or separate our forces, so we had better go forward. We will now seal the letter up as we have all read it, and go on our way. If we are not received at the mountain then we can discuss some other plan."

So these nine heroes all set off again, and in due course reached Liang Shan Po. As they were proceeding amidst reeds and rushes they heard drums and gongs beaten on the lake and many flags were visible on the mountain. On the lake were two speedy boats. On the first was Lin Ch'ung with about fifty men, and on the next Liu Tang, the Red Haired Devil, with also fifty men.

"Who are you?" called out Lin Ch'ung. "Whose troops are you? How dare you come here to arrest us! We would kill the whole lot of you. You ought to know the reputation of us on Liang Shan Po."

The leaders dismounted at the side of the lake, and replied, "We are not government soldiers, but have come here to join you bandits. We have here a letter from Sung Chiang, the Welcome Rain."

Lin Ch'ung said, "You had better take the letter to that inn over there where you will find our leader Chu Kwei."

A blue flag was waved on Lin Ch'ung's boat, and a boat with three fishermen came out of the reeds, and upon reaching the bank two of them disembarked, and told the strangers to follow them. On the first boat a white flag was now waved, and gongs were sounded and both boats returned.

When Hwa Jung saw the way in which the brigands promptly obeyed orders he remarked, "It is no wonder that the government troops keep away from this place. How can our stronghold compare with theirs?" He and his company followed the two fishermen to the inn.

They were introduced, and sat down to a meal with wine. After Chu Kwei, the Speedy Courier, had read the letter he went to the arbor on the bank, and shot a whistling arrow across the lake. Instantly a fast boat emerged from the reeds and came along. He told the boatman to take the letter to the leaders on the mountain, and then ordered pigs and sheep to be killed, and a feast prepared for the nine guests. He also ordered that all the men should encamp about there for the present.

The following day about 7 a.m. Wu Yung came to the inn, and was duly introduced and they talked the matter over. He and Chu Kwei then invited the leaders to embark, and all the baggage, etc. was loaded on the fleet of about twenty boats that was placed at their disposal. Upon reaching the Golden Strand they all disembarked, and were met by Ch'ao Kai and many of the bandits. They then all went up the mountain, and gathered in the assembly hall. All the eleven leaders with Ch'ao Kai were seated along the left side of the hall. (Among them was Pai Sheng, the Daylight Rat who had escaped a few months ago from the prison at Chi Chou Fu.) On the right-hand side of the hall were seated the new nine leaders with Hwa Jung.

In the center was burning an incense urn over which they all took the oath. All the newcomers were then sworn in. They were all given quarters, and then there was general feasting for everybody. Over the wine Hwa Jung and general Chin Ming spoke highly of Sung Chiang, and gave full details of his adventures. They also described their meeting with Lu Fang and Kuo Sheng, and how Hwa Jung had cut the tangled streamers with an arrow. To all this Ch'ao Kai listened, and commented, but in his heart he doubted some of the statements made. He said, "To-morrow, I hope that you will give us an exhibition of your skill as an archer."

The following day the leaders agreed to go for a stroll, and view the scenery round the mountain. They had passed the third barrier when they heard overhead the cries of a flock of wild geese which was flying in single file.

Hwa Jung thought that as Ch'ao Kai did not seem to be convinced the previous day as to his skill in archery, so he would now show him a specimen of his shooting, and so gain Ch'ao Kai's respect. So he asked one of the archers to lend him his bow and arrow, and then turning to Ch'ao Kai he spoke, "When I said that I cut the streamers binding the two halberds together I thought that perhaps some of you did not believe me. Now you see that flock of wild geese overhead. I do not wish to boast, but I will bring down the third bird in the column with this arrow sticking in its head. If I miss I hope that you will not laugh at me." He fitted the arrow, and pulling the bow to its full limit released the arrow which flew overhead and brought down the third bird. A man was sent to bring the goose, and upon his return it was seen that the arrow had gone through its head. When they saw this Ch'ao Kai and the other leaders were deeply impressed, and called Hwa Jung "The general with an uncanny arm."

Wu Yung said, "After this we cannot call you Small Li Kwang, because even Yang Yu-chi was not as good as you. We really are very fortunate to have such a man as you here." There was not a man on Liang Shan Po who did not respect him after that.

The next day they had a celebration feast in the great hall, and elected Hwa Jung to the fifth position. Chin Ming was married to Hwa Jung's sister and was elected the sixth leader. The position of the other leaders were also arranged, Liu Tang the seventh, Huang Hsin, the eight, and so on. The bandits were detailed to build boats, make arms and ammunitions, erect buildings, etc. but we need not go into the many details.

Sung Chiang traveled through the night, and the day following his departure, he reached his native village about 4 a.m. in the afternoon. He stopped at an inn kept by Chang, the elder of the village, for a rest. Chang was on good terms with all the members of Sung Chiang's family. He saw that Sung Chiang had been crying so he asked, "You have been away from home for nearly a year and half, and it is good for you to return now. But how is it that you seem to be in trouble? What is the matter? Your crime has been mitigated."

"Old Uncle, what you say about my affairs is quite right, but as my father has died how can I rejoice?"

Chang laughed, and said, "Is this one of your jokes? Your father was here only a short time ago, drinking wine, and has just gone back home an hour ago. Why do you talk like this?"

"Uncle, please do not jest with me." Sung Chiang then produced the letter he had received. "You will see from this that my younger brother, Sung Ching, states that my father died in the first month of this year, and is waiting for me to return home for the funeral."

"Ah! But nothing of the kind has happened. Your father came here with a man to drink wine this morning. How could I talk lies about such a matter?"

Sung Chiang now doubted the letter, although the matter was not clear yet. He thought over the matter but found no explanation, and then at last decided to go home and clear the matter up. When he entered the gate of the homestead he saw no signs of mourning. When the servants recognized him they saluted, and he asked, "Where are my father and Sung Ching?"

"Your father has been expecting you every day. He will be much pleased to see you. He has just come back from drinking with a friend, and is asleep inside."

Sung Chiang was surprised at this, and throwing down his cudgel, he entered the house. His brother Sung Ching upon seeing him kotowed, and he was not wearing mourning. Sung Chiang was now angry, and abused his brother. "You undutiful beast! My father is at home, so why did you write me that letter saying that he was dead. I was so upset that besides crying I tried to kill myself. So unfilial you are!"

Sung Ching was on the point of replying to this when his father emerged from behind the screen in the room. "My son, do not get angry," he said. "That was not your brother's fault. I wanted very much to see you again, so I told your brother to write the letter stating that I was dead, and urging you to return home at once. I heard that you were at White Tiger Mountain where there are many brigands, and I was afraid that you might join them, and become both disloyal and unfilial. The letter was given to a man Shih Yung who had just come from Squire Ch'ai's place looking for you. The whole scheme was arranged by me so that you must not feel any resentment to your brother for carrying out my orders. I had just now returned from elder Chang's inn, and was going to sleep when I heard your voice."

Sung Chiang kotowed to his father, and was much pleased at this unlooked-for climax. He asked, "How about my affair here? I have heard that my crime has been pardoned."

"At first they troubled us a great deal," said Sire Sung, "but afterwards inspectors Chu Tung and Lei Hung used their influence so they made no more trouble here. On the coronation of the crown prince the emperor issued a decree reducing all sentences by one degree, and abolishing the sentence of death from a number of crimes. Even if your return home was known to the yamen, you would not receive the capital punishment but be banished to a distant district. So we can leave the matter alone."

"Do those two inspectors ever come here now?" asked Sung Chiang.

"I heard sometime ago," said Sung Ching, "that they had been transferred to some other places."

Sire Sung however insisted that his son must be tired, and they must all retire, and this was done.

It was now dusk, and the moon was rising in the east. About 9 p.m. as they were all asleep there was a big noise outside the front and back gates. They then saw that the premises were surrounded by men who held burning torches. They called out, "Don't let Sung Chiang escape!" On hearing this his father was upset.

    A crowded street; a compact throng,
        Loyalty and justice seen.
    A river's bank, the scene where strong
        Heroes meet and disagree.

CHAPTER 35

WU YUNG RECOMMENDS TAI TSUNG; SUNG CHIANG MEETS LI CHUN ON CHIEH YANG MOUNTAIN

SIRE SUNG put a ladder against the wall, and looking over saw about a hundred men in the light of torches. In front of them were the two inspectors who had been recently appointed at Yun Cheng Hsien. They were brothers, called Chao Neng and Chao Te, and they called out, "Sire Sung! You will know our business, and we hope that you will surrender your son Sung Chiang. We will treat him well. If he does not surrender we shall have to arrest you, his father."

"When did Sung Chiang return?" asked Sire Sung.

"Do not talk nonsense," said inspector Chao Neng. "A man saw him this afternoon at Mr. Chang's wine shop, and followed him here. You need not try to hide him."

Sung Chiang was standing at the foot of the ladder, and said, "Father, do not talk with them any further. I will surrender as I have many friends at the yamen, and I have already been pardoned. Why plead with these fellows? They are both wellknown to be rascals. They have suddenly been made inspectors, but what do they know about reason. There is no good feeling between them and me, so it is a waste of time to talk with them."

"I have brought you trouble," said Sire Sung to his son.

"Do not let that upset you. If they go into my case it cannot do any harm. If I escape now I should be arrested eventually, and should have no further chance of seeing you. If I am now arrested, and even banished to some other district I shall at least eventually return, and meet you again. I should be able to be with you at your last moments."

"As you look upon it like this," said Sire Sung, "I will myself bribe the officials concerned, and see that you have every advantage."

FLYING PRINCE RECOMMENDED

Sung Chiang now mounted the ladder, and called out, "Do not make such a noise. My crime has been pardoned so that I cannot be executed. Will you two inspectors come inside our petty farmhouse, and drink wine with me? To-morrow I will go with you to the yamen."

"You need not attempt to entice us into your trap," said inspector Chao Neng.

"Why should I implicate my father and brother by such a trick? You can come inside without any suspicion," said Sung Chiang. He then descended the ladder, opened the farmyard gate, and invited the two inspectors indoors. They were entertained to wine, chicken, and goose. The soldiers were provided with food, and also money. Sire Sung presented the two inspectors with twenty ounces of silver. That night they all slept at the farmhouse. At dawn the following day the party started out for the town. When they reached the yamen it was broad daylight, and the magistrate occupied the bench. He asked Sung Chiang to state his case, and listened to the following statement. "I did a great wrong to take Yen Po-hsi as my concubine, and once we quarreled after taking too much wine, and I happened to kill her quite unintentionally. I escaped but have now surrendered for justice, and will confess the crime as stated."

The magistrate ordered that the prisoner be detained in the jail. All the yamen employees were sorry to see Sung Chiang as a prisoner. Many of them spoke to the magistrate of the good things Sung Chiang had done in the past, and begged him to show mercy to the prisoner. The magistrate was inclined to be lenient, and he gave orders that the prisoner should have no cangue or be chained up in the prison. Sire Sung bribed all the officials concerned. Mrs. Yen had died about six months ago so that there was now no one to press the accusation of murder. As Yen Po-hsi was also dead her old lover Chang San had now no enmity against Sung Chiang. So after sixty days the case was referred to Chi Chou for a sentence. The governor considered the case as reported by dispatch, and in view of the emperor's decree he passed a light sentence. Sung Chiang was to receive twenty blows with a bamboo, be branded and transferred to a prison at Chiang Chou. But as the officials at Chi Chou had all been bribed, they reported that the sentence had been carried out although nothing was done to Sung Chiang.

But he was given a small cangue, and sent to Chiang Chou under the escort of two men—Chang Chien, and Li Wan. Sire Sung and his son Sung Ching were waiting outside the yamen for the escort, and invited them to take a final meal at an inn there. Money was presented to the escort, and Sung Chiang was given new clothes, new hempen shoes, and a bundle of useful articles. Sire Sung took Sung Chiang to one side and there said to him, "I know that at Chiang Chou there is plenty of rice and fish, and I will bribe the officials there to supply you with food. I shall send your brother there with money, and he will see you often. On your way you will pass close to Liang Shan Po, but if the brigands there capture you I hope that you will not join them as people would abuse your name and say that you were both disloyal and unfilial. This point you must not forget. Make no haste on the way. Heaven will watch over you, and you will soon return home, and be reunited to your father and younger brother."

Sung Chiang was much affected and burst into tears and thus took leave of his father. Sung Ching accompanied him for the first stage of the road. When they separated at last Sung Chiang said to his brother, "I am now a prisoner, and while I am away I want you to look after our father, and never mind coming to Chiang Chou to see me. I know a great many bandits, and they will help me. I can easily get all the money I want. If Heaven takes pity, I shall return home some day."

When they took leave of each other Sung Ching weeped bitterly. He returned home, and looked after his father in accordance with Sung Chiang's wish.

The escort and Sung Chiang continued their journey and because Sung Chiang had given them plenty of money, they treated him well. One evening when they were at an inn Sung Chiang said, "I will not deceive you. We shall pass quite close to Liang Shan Po, where there are many brave men, and when they hear that I am passing they will perhaps try to liberate me. So to-morrow it would be better for us to start early, and travel by small side roads even though they take us a little out of our way."

"Sir, if you do not tell us we should not know it. But we know the side roads, and shall not meet those men." They discussed their plans, and the next morning they got up about 4 a.m. After breakfast they set out, and went by a side road. They had traveled about ten miles when they saw a company of men coming round a mountain just in front. Sung Chiang said it meant trouble; as he recognized among them Liu Tang, the Red Haired Devil. The escort was afraid, and knelt down.

"Younger brother," said Sung Chiang, "whom do you want to kill?"

"Elder brother," replied Liu Tang, "had we not better kill those two fellows at once?"

"You need not soil your hands in that way," said Sung Chiang. "Give me your sword, and I will kill them myself."

Liu Tang handed him the sword, and Sung Chiang then asked, "Why do you wish to kill them?"

"I am acting according to the orders of our chieftain on the mountain who knew all about your case. We wanted to go to Yun Cheng Hsien and rescue you from prison, but we then heard that you were not in prison, and were being well treated. Afterwards we heard that you were to be escorted to Chiang Chou so we guarded all the roads so that we could take you to our mountain. Why not kill these two men?"

"This is the way you will disgrace me, as I shall thereby lose my reputation of loyalty. I would much rather die myself than suffer disgrace." So saying he took the sword to cut his own throat. Liu Tang sprang forward, and caught him by the arms saying, "Elder brother, do not be hasty. Let us discuss matters." He took the sword from Sung Chiang who said, "Younger brother, if you respect me please let me go to the prison at Chiang Chou, and when I have served my sentence I will certainly visit you, and discuss matters with you."

"I cannot take the responsibility for such a course," said Liu Tang. "On the main road there are Wu Yung and Hwa Jung whom I will ask to come here to decide this matter."

"I am quite determined whatever you do."

One of the brigands was dispatched, and in a short time Wu Yung and Hwa Jung came galloping up. They both dismounted, and after the usual salutations Hwa Jung asked, "Why has your cangue not been removed?"

"That is a legal procedure with prisoners. Who would dare to infringe the regulations?" asked Sung Chiang.

Wu Yung laughed and said, "I understand your idea. It is easy for us to let you proceed on your way, but our chief Ch'ao Kai has not met you for a long time, and he would like to have a confidential talk with you. So I request you to come with us up the mountain, and after the interview you can go your own way."

"You have grasped my idea," said Sung Chiang. "In case however I die I hope that you will not punish my escort. I want them to be at ease."

"Sir, we depend on you saving our lives," said the two men.

They all then set out, and soon came to the lake where they found a boat waiting for them. They crossed the lake, and found sedan chairs waiting and were carried up the mountain. Men were sent in all directions to summon all the leaders to the assembly hall for a conference. When they had assembled Sung Chiang was conducted to the hall where Ch'aoCed him. "Formerly you saved our lives at Yun Cheng Hsien, and we escaped to this place, and we have been thinking of your generosity ever since. Since we arrived here many gallant heroes have joined us on your esteemed recommendation. This has added luster to our straw sheds, but we have had no opportunity of repaying your benevolence."

"Since I left you," said Sung Chiang, "I killed a bad woman, and escaped to the wilds where I have been wandering for about six months. I have often wished to come here to pay my respects to you, and on the way here I met a man named Shih Yung in a village inn who had a letter for me stating that my father had died. But it was my father's desire that I should not enter your band, and when I received the letter I at once returned home. As to my case I was well treated by the officials, and was not punished severely. I was banished to Chiang Chou which is not a bad place. When I heard of your orders I dare not decline to come here, and now that I have met you I cannot stay here, but must proceed on my way as the time limit is nearly up."

"Why be in such a hurry?" said Ch'ao Kai. "Please take a seat."

So they all sat down, and Sung Chiang asked his escort to stand behind his chair. Ch'ao Kai asked all the leaders to approach and salute Sung Chiang, and after this they all took their seats. After they had been drinking wine for some time Sung Chiang at last arose and said, "It is obvious that you regard me with respect, but as I am a criminal I cannot stay here and must now take my leave of you."

"Why feel so estranged?" asked Ch'ao Kai. "As you do not wish your escort to be injured we will give the men money, and they can then return, and report that we bandits at Liang Shan Po have captured you, and so they will not be blamed."

"Do not talk like that," said Sung Chiang. "Such a procedure would not be to my credit, but would bring trouble. I must be filial, and respect my father's wishes, or otherwise he will be implicated. It was Heaven's will that I should meet Shih Yung and return home. If now I stay here I shall be opposing Heaven, and disobeying my father, and shall have a bad reputation. If you will not agree to let me depart it would be better if you kill me at once." He then burst into tears, and knelt down on the ground.

The leaders raised him up and said, "As you are determined to go to Chiang Chou, we ask you to stay here for the night only, and early to-morrow morning you can depart." They wanted to take off his cangue, but he would not let them do so. They all sat down to drink more wine.

The following morning when he was preparing to leave Wu Yung spoke to him, "Please listen to me now. I have a very good friend at Chiang Chou who is superintendent of the two prisons there. He is called Tai Tsung. He knows magics, and can travel about two hundred fifty miles in one day so that people call him the Flying Prince. He distributes wealth in good cause. Last night I wrote a letter to him which I am going to give you, and when you reach your destination you must make his acquaintance. Whatever happens you can make him your confident."

A feast had been prepared for Sung Chiang, and the leaders also presented him with money. They also gave the escort twenty ounces of silver. The leaders accompanied Sung Chiang down the mountain. Wu Yung and Hwa Jung crossed the lake, and went with him about eight miles along the road before they bade him good-by.

Sung Chiang and his escort continued on their way to Chiang Chow, and they had been traveling for about two weeks when they came to a place where there was a high mountain. The escort said that the mountain was called Chieh Yang and after crossing it they would come to the Hsun Yang River where they could get a boat to take them for the remainder of the journey to Chiang Chou.

"As the weather is fine just now," said Sung Chiang, "let us now cross the mountain and find a place to rest on the other side."

The escort agreed to this, and they all set out. It was almost noon when they reached the summit, and from there they saw an inn at the foot of the mountain. In front of the inn were several large trees, and many grass huts were around it. In the shade of the trees was a flag flying. Sung Chiang was much pleased and said, "We will stop at the inn for some refreshment, and then push on."

When they reached the inn they all entered, and the escort put their sticks against the wall. They all sat down at a table with Sung Chiang in the inferior seat. They waited for a long time, but nobody came to attend to their wants. So Sung Chiang called out, "Is there nobody in charge here?"

From an inner room a voice answered, "Coming! Coming!" and a very big man came out of a side room. He had a red complexion with bushy whiskers, and his eyes were bloodshot and as fierce as a tiger's. On his head was a tattered turban, and his gown was without sleeves. Around his waist was a large cummerbund. He called out, "How much wine do you want?"

"We are very hungry," said Sung Chiang. "What kind of meat have you got?"

"I have some beef and strong liquor."

"That is fine. Bring us four pounds of beef and a horn of liquor," ordered Sung Chiang.

"Do not think me strange, but I make it a rule to have the money paid in advance with the order."

"That is all right. I will pay you first. Wait a bit,

and I will get the money." Sung Chiang opened his bundle, and took out some money. The man stealthily looked at the bundle, and saw that it was very heavy at which he was much pleased as he knew there must be plenty of silver there. He took the silver from Sung Chiang, and went into another room, and soon returned with the beef and wine. The three men dined together, and their conversation was about the bandits abroad, who would sell drugged food and wine to travelers and rob them of all their wealth and make pies out of their flesh. One of them said he did not believe such tales.

The proprietor of the inn heard this and laughingly said, "You had better be careful because this food and wine may be drugged."

Sung Chiang laughed and said, "So you are ridiculing us for talking about drugged food."

"Elder brother, a cup of warm wine would be much better," said one of the escort.

"I will go and get some warmed wine for you." The man then went, and soon returned with three cups of hot liquor. The three guests were hungry, and when they saw the food and wine they only thought of eating and drinking same. They soon emptied their cups, and almost immediately the escort fell back with saliva running from their mouths. Upon seeing this Sung Chiang jumped up, and said, "What is the matter with you two? Are you drunk after drinking only two cups of wine?" He stepped forward to raise them up, but he was also feeling faint, and fell down. As they all lay there they all looked at each other, but not one of them could move or get up.

The inn proprietor said, "I am sorry. For many days I have found no business, but to-day Heaven has sent me these three." He first seized Sung Chiang and dragged him into a room at the back where he placed him on the block of wood where men were usually cut up. He then dragged the other two men to the same place. He also took their baggage, and put it in another room, where he opened it and found the silver. He said, "I have kept this inn for many years, but have never before seen a prisoner with so much money. What is the reason for this? It must be a gift from Heaven for me!" He then fastened up the baggage, and went to the door of the inn to look for his assistants. But although he glanced in all directions he could not see a single one anywhere. He however saw three travelers coming up the road towards the inn. He recognized them, and went forward to meet them. He asked, "Elder brothers, where are you going?"

One of the tall men replied, "We are going up the mountain to meet a certain person, and he ought to be here to-day. We have been waiting for several days, and cannot understand what has delayed him."

"Who is the man you are waiting for?"

"He is a certain famous man."

"What is his name?"

"I think you know him. He is Sung Chiang of Yun Cheng Hsien and is coming from Chi Chou Fu."

"I have heard of him, but what is he traveling this way for?"

"I did not know before, but to-day a friend of mine has arrived from Chi Chou Fu, and he said that Sung Chiang has been banished to the prison at Chiang Chou, but he did not know for what reason. I think he must come this way. I have often thought of going to Yun Cheng Hsien to make his acquaintance, but as he is passing this way now I must meet him. That is why I come here to-day with my two friends. How has business been with you this last month?"

"I will be frank with you," replied the inn proprietor. "During the last few months I have done no business, but to-day Heaven has sent me three men with many things."

"What kind of men?" hurriedly asked the man.

"Two men escorting a prisoner."

"Is the prisoner a little fat man with a dark complexion?"

"He is not very tall and has a swarthy complexion."

"Have you killed him?" hurriedly asked the visitor.

"I dragged him into the room, but have not cut him up as my assistants are absent."

"Let me have a look at him."

The four men went into the room, and there were the three men lying on the cutting-up-block. But they did not recognize Sung Chiang so the visitor said they would examine the baggage, and read the official dispatch. When this had been done the man reading the dispatch said, "Heaven has directed me to come here to-day. If I had been even a little late my elder brother would have been cut up." He gave orders for an anti-drug to be administered to revive Sung Chiang. This was quickly done, and he was carried into the other room and seated in a chair. Soon he opened his eyes, and looked around. The visitor saluted him, and Sung Chiang asked, "Who are you? Am I not still dreaming? What is this place? What is your name?"

The visitor replied, "I am Li Chun of Lu Chou, and I am captain of a boat that sails on the Yangtze River. I have a good knowledge of currents, etc., and so people call me the Muddy Water Dragon. This man is the innkeeper and he robs travelers who come this way. His name is Li Li, and his nickname is Murderous Angel.

They then explained how the event had happened, and Sung Chiang told them all about his adventures. They pressed Sung Chiang to stay there instead of going to prison, but again he stood firm and declined their offers. They administered restoratives to the escort, and they soon recovered. When they came round they said, "We are very unlucky as we got drunk so easily."

At this the others all laughed. That night they all slept at the inn. The next day they were invited to Li Chun's house where they stayed for a few days then Sung Chiang and his escort set out on their journey again.

The three men traveled until about 11 a.m. when they came to a market town. The street was very crowded, and they saw a crowd forming a ring round some object. Sung Chiang forced his way through the men, and saw in the ring a man with a stave who was selling medicine. He watched the man performing with his stick, and when that was finished Sung Chiang applauded his skill. The man took a tray, and addressed the crowd, "I come from a distant place, for certain business. I am perhaps not well skilled in military arts, but I hope that you will praise me to your friends so that they will buy my drugs. If you want the medicine you can buy some now, but if you do not care for the medicine then please contribute a small amount of money, and not let my tray be quite empty." He passed the tray round the crowd, but nobody gave money. "I hope you gentlemen will be generous in assisting me." He again walked round with the tray, but nobody contributed even a copper.

Sung Chiang seeing this asked his escort to let him have five ounces of silver, and offering it to the man said, "I am a criminal, and cannot give you much. This small amount will however indicate that I hold you in respect."

The man held the money aloft on the palm of his hand, and said, "It is strange that in this town of Chieh Yang Chen there is not one man who appreciates my skill. This benefactor in passing through the town however presents me with this money. In the words of the poet

> 'Men laughed at Chen Yuan Ho,
> Who lavishly spent his money;
> Such men are not always rich,
> Or dressed in the best of clothes.'

"This silver is equal to ten times the amount from a wealthy man. I salute you my benefactor, and request your name so that I can spread your fame abroad."

"Sir, do not talk about it, as my gift is so trifling," said Sung Chiang.

While this was happening a big man had pushed his way through the crowd, and he now said to Sung Chiang, "What fellow are you? Where do you come from? How dare you come here, and try to cast our town in the shade by offering money? He raised his fists to strike Sung Chiang.

> Dragons now were stirred to fury,
> But they found their destiny.

CHAPTER 36

THE INVULNERABLE ONE PURSUES SUNG CHIANG; THE BOATMAN MAKES A NIGHT ROW ON HSUN YANG RIVER

THE big man said, "I have ordered the people not to give any money to this man, so how dare you offer him money without my consent."

Sung Chiang replied, "I gave him money, but that is not your business."

The fellow took hold of Sung Chiang and said, "You banished thief! How dare you reply to me!"

"Why should I not answer you?" asked Sung Chiang.

The man raised his fist to strike Sung Chiang, but the latter stepped back to avoid the blow. The man however advanced a step, and was in the act of striking when the drug seller seized him, and lifting him up threw him to the ground. The big fellow was getting up when the drug seller knocked him down again with his foot. The escort with Sung Chiang now intervened to persuade the medicine man not to go any further.

The man had now got up, and spoke, "Wait a little. We will soon see who is who." He then went away.

Sung Chiang turned to the drug seller, and asked for his name.

"I am a Loyang man. My name is Hsueh Yung, and my grandfather was a military officer in the army, but owing to intrigues of his fellow officers he got no further promotion. My father and myself have had to sell medicine for a living. Abroad I have got the nickname of the Sick Tiger. I beg to ask your name."

"I am Sung Chiang of Yun Cheng Hsien."

The man knelt down when he heard this. Sung Chiang raised him up and said, "Let us find a place where we can drink wine together." He agreed, and gathering his things together went with Sung Chiang to an inn near by.

The innkeeper, however, said, "Although I have both wine and meat yet I dare not supply you with them."

"Why not?" asked Sung Chiang.

"Because you have had a row with that big man. He told the people that if anybody supply you with wine or food he would smash up our places. We dare not offer any resistance to him. He is the bully of this town, and we all have to do as he says."

"In that case we shall have to go," said Sung Chiang.

"I should like to go now to the inn where I live, and settle my bill," said Hsueh Yung. "I will come to Chiang Chou to see you in a few days."

Sung Chiang agreed to this, and gave him twenty ounces of silver. They then went their own ways.

Sung Chiang and his escort tried to get food at several inns, but they could not get refreshment anywhere. They at last left the town, and traveled until it was nightfall without being received by any inn. They discussed matters, and could not understand why they should have provoked the big fellow by giving the medicine vendor money. Just then however they happened to see a light in a forest in the distance and they decided to go and ask for a night's lodging.

It was not on the main road, but they agreed that it was the only place for a rest. When they had gone about half a mile off the road they came to a large farmhouse. They knocked at the gate, and the farm laborers asked, "Who are you, and why do you come after dark like this?"

"I am a prisoner on the way to Chiang Chou," said Sung Chiang. "We cannot find an inn to stop at, and I beg you to allow us to stay here for the night. We shall leave early to-morrow, and pay you for the lodging."

The servant asked them to wait there while he went, and reported the matter to his master. He soon returned and admitted them. The master gave orders that they were to have rooms and also food. When they had finished their meal, and the things had been cleared away the escort said that as there were no strangers in the room Sung Chiang could remove his cangue, and have a peaceful sleep that night.

He did this, and then they went outside to lavatory before retiring for the night. It was a clear starlit night, and looking round they saw that there was a footpath at the side of the wheat stacks leading behind the room in which they were housed. When they returned to their room Sung Chiang said that it was very fortunate for them to get such a place for the night. Just then they heard men light a torch, and come searching round the wheat stacks. Looking through a crack in the door Sung Chiang saw that it was the host with three laborers who bore torches. Sung Chiang said, "This farmer reminds me of my father who could never sleep until he had been all round the premises at night." Just then however they heard someone knocking at the farm gate. The farm laborer opened the gate, and about seven men came in the farmyard. The leader held a sword in his hand, and his men were armed with sticks. Sung Chiang recognized the leader in the light of the torches, as the bully of Chieh Yang Chen. The old host asked, "Where have you come from, and whom are you looking for?"

The leader replied, "You do not know, father. Is my elder brother at home?"

"Your brother became drunk, and is sleeping in the room at the back."

"I will go and call him," said the leader. "He will go with me to drive a fellow out of this district."

"With whom have you had a dispute? Your brother would not put up with the dispute. You had better tell me all about this matter."

The leader then recited all that had happened on the street that morning, and that he had given orders to all the innkeepers not to supply food or lodging to the prisoner who was passing. They had captured the drug seller and the following day they would take him to the river, bind him with ropes, and throw him into the water. "As regards the prisoner and his escort we have not been able to find them yet. I want my brother to go with me now and search everywhere for those three fellows."

"My son!" said the farmer. "This is not a creditable affair. If the prisoner gave some money what has that got to do with you? Why do you now wish to attack him? You listen to me, and let the matter drop. You must not speak to your elder brother about this. If he hears that you have been ill-treated he will certainly want to support you. I am afraid that you will kill someone. Listen to me now, and go to bed. Do not attempt to disturb other people's rest this night."

But the son would not listen to his father's advice, and entered the yard with a sword in his hands, followed by his father.

Sung Chiang had heard all this, and spoke to his escort, "This is an unfortunate position. What shall we do? We had better go on our way for if this man gets to know that we are here he will kill us. The farmer may not say anything about us, but how dare the servants conceal us from him?"

The escort agreed, and wanted to go at once. Sung Chiang said, "We cannot leave by the gate so we will get through a wall at the back of this building." They got their baggage, and having got through the wall they found a footpath leading into the forest, and they went that way. They had been walking about an hour when they came to a river bordered by reeds. It was the Hsun Yang River. Just then they heard behind them a great noise and many whistles being blown. It was a critical moment, and they all prayed to Heaven for assistance. They hid themselves in the reeds, and watched the flaming torches approach. They were all afraid, and went further into the depth of the reeds until they reached the edge of the reeds facing the swift running river.

Sung Chiang had given up all hope when he saw a small boat emerge from the reeds. He called out, "Sir, please come here, and save us three men. We will give you money."

"Who are you, and how did you get in such a place?"

"There are men pursuing us, and we came here just to escape from them. Bring your boat here at once, and you will be rewarded."

SUNG CHIANG IS PURSUED 509

The boatman forced his boat through the reeds, and the three men were soon on board. The baggage was thrown into the boat, and the boatman heard the noise it made and knew it contained silver, and was pleased. He sculled the boat out into the river. Looking back they saw about ten men standing on the bank of the river with lighted torches. The pursuers saw the boat, and there was much shouting for the boat to return. The three men lay down in the bottom of the boat, and the boat proceeded on its way. The pursuers called out, 'If you do not return we shall kill you later on." The boatman only laughed at this threat and replied, "My name is Chang, the boatman. You need not cry at me."

A voice from the bank said, "Chang, do you not recognize us?"

"I am not blind," replied Chang. "Of course I can see you."

"Then come here as I have something to say to you," the voice replied.

"You can speak to me to-morrow," replied Chang, the boatman. "My passengers are in great haste."

"But we want to arrest your passengers," said the voice.

"These three men are relatives of mine," said Chang, "and I depend on them for a living. I invited them to eat a bowl of 'Pan Tao Mien' (board, knife, and vermicelli) and when that is finished I will come back. Do you think I shall give you my livelihood for you to enjoy?"

"Chang! That is not our idea. We only want to arrest the criminal. Come here!"

"I have had no customer for several days so that I am not going to give you now what I have just got. Do not take this ill, and I will meet you again in a few days."

Sung Chiang was stupefied and though he had heard all this, but did not understand it at all. But he decided that they would always be beholden to this man for saving their lives. They had narrowly escaped a great danger.

As the boatman rowed he sang a Huchow song:

> Alone I live on the river's bank;
> Not a friend but money do I adore.
> Last night the moon helped me fine;
> I saw some gold and captured it.

Sung Chiang and his escort were terrified when they heard this song. But on second thoughts Sung Chiang considered that the boatman might be singing in a playful or jesting manner. They were discussing the question in the bottom of the boat, when the boatman lay down his scull and said, "You fellows! I know that you have cheated us people, and now I have you in my hands. Do you three fellows want to eat 'Pan Tao Mien,' (board, knife, and vermicelli), or would you prefer to eat 'soup pies.'

"Do not joke with us, sir," said Sung Chiang. "What do you mean by 'Pan Tao Mien' and 'soup pies'?"

The boatman glared and said, "I am not joking. If you want to eat 'Pan Tao Mien,' I have a sword here, and I can quickly mince your bodies, and throw the pieces into the water. If you prefer 'soup pies' then you quickly strip off your clothes, and jump into the river."

"We are in a tight corner," said Sung Chiang to his escort. "There is a saying, 'Blessings do not come in pairs; calamities never come singly.'"

"You three had better turn the matter over, and let me have your answer quickly," said the boatman.

"You do not understand," replied Sung Chiang. "We have no escape. I am a criminal and am being conducted to Chiang Chou by these two policemen. Please take pity on us, and spare our lives."

"This is nonsensical language," the boatman said. "Spare three of you! I will not let even one escape. I am sometimes known as 'Dog-faced Chang,' I do not make any difference even with my own father or mother. Do not say another word, but get into the water at once."

"We have much silver, gold, clothes, and other valuables in our baggage, and we will give them all to you. Please spare our lives," begged Sung Chiang.

The boatman picked up a bright sword with a very broad blade from the bottom of the boat, and shouted, "Now you three! Which is it to be?"

Sung heaved a sigh as he looked towards heaven. "Because I have failed in showing respect to Heaven, and have been unfilial to my parents, I have committed a crime, and implicated both of you two men."

The men took hold of Sung Chiang, "Sir, enough! We three will all die together."

The boatman called out, "Now you three, get your clothes off, and jump into the water."

The three men embraced each other, and gazed at the water. Just then they heard the sound of sculling on another boat, and the boatman turned his head to listen. A boat was quickly approaching from up river, and was soon alongside. There were three men in the boat, and one of them was a big man and was standing with a pitchfork in his hands. The other two were young men, and they were sculling. The big man called out, "Who are you and how dare you do business here? You will have to divide with us all that you have in your boat."

The boatman quickly replied, "Ah! Is that brother Li? I thought it might be someone else. Where are you going to do business? You have not got brothers with you this time?"

"Younger brother Chang, what is your game?" asked the tall man. "What things have you got in your boat? Have you any valuables?"

"If I told you, you would only laugh," said the boatman. "These last few days I have had no business—have lost all my money in gambling, and have not even a single cash. I was in a melancholy mood when these three men came to my boat with their baggage. Two were policemen and the other a small-sized criminal with a sallow complexion. I do not know who they are, but they are going to Chiang Chou. The prisoner however was not wearing a cangue. A number of men came to the river's bank with the two brothers Mu who wanted to capture the three men. As I judged that the escort had plenty of money I declined to hand them over."

"Ah! Can this be my brother Sung Chiang?" asked the tall man.

Sung Chiang seemed to recognize the voice and called out

from his hiding place. "Who are you? I request you to save Sung Chiang's life."

The tall man was startled at this and replied, "You really are my brother! Why not get up?"

Sung Chiang crept out. It was a bright starlit night, and he immediately recognized the man as Li Chun, the Muddy Water Dragon. Behind him he could make out the two men who were sculling as Tung Wei, the Cave Crocodile, and the other as Tung Meng, the Whirling Conch Shell.

Li Chun also recognized Sung Chiang, and jumped across to the other boat saying, "Brother, you have been frighted. Had I not just happened to arrive in the nick of time you would have been killed. To-day fate decided that I should be very fidgety at home, so that I got my boat to try to intercept some salt smugglers. I had not the slightest idea that I would save your life."

The boatman had listened to all this with great surprise, and now asked, "Can this man be Sung Chiang, Welcome Rain, of Shantung?"

"Of course it is."

The boatman knelt down, and kotowed saying, "My God! Why did you not mention your name before, and so stopped me from attempting your life? I was nearly to murder you."

"Who is this boatman?" asked Sung Chiang.

"He is my sworn brother," replied Li Chun. "He comes from the Little Orphan (a hill in the Yangtze River), and his name is Chang Heng. He is known as the Boatman, and he lives as a virtuous pirate on the river."

Sung Chiang and his escort laughed at this. The two boats were soon brought to the side of the river and moored.

Li Chun addressed the boatman Chang Heng, "To-day you are favored by Heaven to meet the greatest hero in the world, Sung Chiang, Welcome Rain. Take a good look at him, and never forget him." Chang Heng took a flint and steel and striking a light lit a lamp, and had a good look at Sung Chiang. He then knelt down, and said, "I hope that you will overlook my serious mistake. How did you come to be banished to the prison at Chiang Chou?"

Li Chun explained the whole situation, and then Chang Heng said to Sung Chiang, "Brother, I have something to say. I have a younger brother of the same mother. He is a big muscular fellow, can swim about fifteen miles, and can stay in the water for seven days at a time. In the water he swims in a straight line. He is also a skilled gymnast. Because of this he has received the nickname the White Fish. His name is Chang Shun. Previously we lived on the Yangtze River very peacefully and orderly, but the time came when we had no money, and then we took our boat to a quiet solitary place to do some illicit business. Those people who like to save money and at the same time get quick ferrying came to us. I arranged for my brother to pretend to be a traveler, and also to come to our boat with his baggage. When the boat was full I would push off, but would soon drop the anchor, and taking a sword demand the fares. The proper fare was five hundred cash, but I would demand three thousand cash. I would first ask my brother, and when he refused to pay I would take his head in one hand, and the seat of his trousers in the other and throw him overboard. The other passengers would then willingly pay the amount demanded without raising the least objection. I would then row them to a quiet part of the bank, and they would quickly disembark and disappear. My brother would swim underneath the water to the side of the river, and emerge when nobody was about. We would soon meet, and divide the money. We earned a good living by this means for some time."

"I suppose you had plenty of patrons who looked out for your boat," said Sung Chiang.

The men all laughed at this wit.

"We soon found another business," said Chang Heng. "I came here to help in salt smuggling whereas my brother started in business at Chiang Chou as a wholesale fishmonger. I should like to write a letter to him, but unfortunately I do not know characters."

"We will go into the village here, and find a man to write the letter for you," said Li Chun.

They set off to the village, but they had not gone half the

distance to that place when they saw many lighted torches on the river bank.

"I see that the brothers Mu have not yet gone back," said Chang Heng.

"Let us bring them here," said Li Chun.

"That will never do," said Sung Chiang, "as they want to arrest me."

"They are our friends," said Li Chun. He then whistled and the torches immediately approached. When they arrived they were surprised to see Sung Chiang with Li Chun and Chang Heng, and asked, "Do you know these three men? How is it you are with them?"

Li Chun laughed loudly and said, "Who do you think he is?"

"We do not know his name. But we saw him give money to a medicine vender in the market town, and so undermined our influence there. So we tried to arrest him."

"This is Sung Chiang, Welcome Rain, from Shantung, of whom I have spoken to you many times. Quickly pay your obeisance."

The two brothers kotowed and said, "We have heard of your fame for a long time, but we did not expect to meet you this day. We have treated you badly, and hope that you will forgive us."

Sung Chiang raised them up, and said, "I beg that you will give me your name."

Li Chun interposed, "These brothers are of a rich family in this town. This one is Mu Hung, and his nickname is the Invulnerable One and his younger brother is Mu Chun nicknamed Young Irresistible. They are the tyrants of Chieh Yang Chen. There are two other groups of tyrants whom you will have heard of. On the Chieh Yang Mountain I myself and Li Li are the tyrants. On the banks of this river are two tyrants, namely, Chang Heng and Chang Shun. These form the three groups of tyrants."

"I have not heard of these men before," said Sung Chiang, "but as we are all brothers I hope that you will now release Hsueh Yung."

"Do you refer to that medicine vender?" asked Mu Hung laughingly. "Do not worry about him. I will send my brother to release him, and bring him here. We now beg you to come to our home where we can offer suitable apologies for our blunder."

'They agreed to this, and messengers were dispatched with an order to prepare a feast for the coming guests. Two men were sent to summon the two boatmen to join them also at the feast.

It was about 4 a.m. when they all reached the farmhouse, and were welcomed by Sire Mu. It was almost dawn when Hsueh Yung arrived. They feasted together all that day. On the following day Sung Chiang wished to continue on his way but Mu Hung would not agree to this. They all went for a stroll viewing the sights in the town. Thus they stayed at Mu's house for three more days, and then Sung Chiang insisted upon departure as he was afraid that the time limit would be over.

At last they agreed to his departure. Upon his departure Chang Heng got a letter written introducing Sung Chiang to his brother at Chiang Chou. They all shed tears as he embarked on the boat. The boat had sails, and as the wind was favorable it soon reached Chiang Chou. They went straight to the yamen, and presented their dispatch to the governor.

The governor Ts'ai Te-chang, the ninth son of the premier Ts'ai Ching, was a proud man with an overbearing manner, and he was addicted to taking secret commissions. His father appointed him here because the prefecture was a very wealthy place. He saw that Sung Chiang did not look like an average man so he asked him, "How is it that there is no written statement on your cangue?"

The escort stated that on the journey there had been much rain which had washed the written statement away.

The escort was dismissed and Sung Chiang was sent to the prison where he was put in a small house separate from the main building.

Sung Chiang duly bribed the attendants and the warden with ten ounces of silver each, so that they were all pleased. When he was called to the inspection room the warden said, "Sung Chiang, listen to me. The founder of the Sung dynasty, Emperor Wu Te, made a law that criminals who had been transferred to a prison should receive one hundred blows with the bamboo. Now, those on my left and right, take the prisoner and inflict the usual punishment."

"On the journey here, sir," said Sung Chiang, "I caught a cold, and have not quite recovered from it."

"I can see that you are not quite well," replied the official, "so we will postpone the blows to-day. He was previously a clerk in a yamen so that we will use him in that capacity in this yamen." He thereupon wrote out an order to that effect.

Sung Chiang expressed his thanks, and returning to his quarters took his baggage to the office where he was to work as a writer. The prisoners realized that Sung Chiang was a man with influence. They bought wine, and invited him to drink with them, and he received their congratulations. The next day Sung Chiang invited the prisoners to wine in the same way. He also often asked the lower officials to dine with him, and sent presents to the warden. The result was that he had many friends. Within a fortnight they were all pleased to have made his acquaintance. An ancient says, "Human relations vary—sometimes friendship, sometimes the opposite. Some fawn upon the wealth and avoid the poor."

One day when Sung Chiang was entertaining one of the turnkeys the latter said, "The other day I told you that you must not overlook giving the head jailer some money, but how is it that you have not yet done so? It is now nearly ten days since you came here. He will certainly come to see you to-morrow, and then it will be too late to offer money."

"Never mind that," said Sung Chiang. "If he wants money I will not give him any. But if you turnkeys want money and ask me for it I will certainly supply the same. That superintendent shall not have a single cash. When he comes here I shall have something to say to him."

"Sir, but that man is a stern disciplinarian, and he is over us," said the turnkey. "If you have a disagreement with him he will certainly abuse you. In that case do not say that I did not warn you."

"Don't worry about that,". said Sung Chiang. "It may be of course that I shall give him something, and it may be that he does not want anything."

While they were talking about this a messenger came in, and reported that the head jailer was coming. He was evidently in a temper as he called out, "How is it that the newly arrived prisoner has not given me regular money?"

The turnkey said, "Did I not tell you so?"

Sung Chiang laughed and said, "I will go to meet him and will see you later." He did this.

> Seas of blood, and heaps of corpses,
> At the crossroads in the town;
> Mand'rin nets were spread on all sides,
> But the bandits broke them down.

CHAPTER 37

WELCOME RAIN MEETS THE FLYING PRINCE;
BLACK WHIRLWIND FIGHTS WITH
WHITE FISH

WHEN Sung Chiang reached the inspection room he saw the head jailer there sitting on a stool. The latter immediately called out, "Is this the prisoner who recently came here?"

A messenger standing there agreed to this.

"So you are the 'Black Dwarf' (a term of abuse), who deserves death. Upon whose influence are you relying that you disdain to give me any money?"

"Presents are made when people are on friendly footing," said Sung Chiang. "Why do you demand a present? You are a mean-souled fellow."

The men standing about perspired with fear when they heard this. The head jailer was very angry and replied, "Banished thief! You are very impudent. How dare you call me a mean-souled fellow? Now, executioners, seize this fellow, and give him a hundred blows with the bamboo."

But the men standing about were all on friendly terms with Sung Chiang, and when they heard this order they all sneaked out of the room. Seeing this movement the head jailer was very much annoyed, and taking a stick he advanced to beat Sung Chiang.

"Sir!" said Sung Chiang, "for what crime are you going to beat me?"

"You are a criminal, and are entirely in my hands. Even if you only cough in my presence that would be a crime."

"But even if I have a small fault I am not deserving of death."

"You say that you are not deserving of death," said the head jailer who was now very angry, "but if I decide to even kill you that can be easily done. I could kill you just like a fly."

BRIBERY IN PRISON

Sung Chiang, spoke in a sneering manner, "Because I have not given you money you think I am deserving of death, but what should a friend of Wu Yung at Liang Shan Po deserve?"

Upon hearing this the man hastily dropped his stick and asked, "What is that you say?"

"I said that Wu Yung may have a friend here."

The man was startled, and seizing hold of Sung Chiang asked, "Who are you? Why you talk like this?"

Sung Chiang laughed and said, "I am Sung Chiang of Yun Cheng Hsien, in Shantung."

The man was surprised and saluted saying, "So you are Sung Chiang, Welcome Rain. But this is not a good place for us to talk, and I cannot kotow to you here. I request you to accompany me to a place in the town where we can talk matters over."

Sung Chiang agreed to this and returned to his room. He took Wu Yung's letter and some silver. He then locked the door, and told a messenger to look after his room. They left the prison, and going into the town entered an inn, and sat down in an upper room.

"Sir, when did you last see Wu Yung?" asked the head jailer.

Sung Chiang took the letter and handed it to the man who after reading it placed it in his sleeve. He then knelt down and kotowed to Sung Chiang.

Sung Chiang also kotowed, and said, "What I said has upset you. Please forgive me."

The jailer said, "I was informed that a criminal named Sung was being sent to my prison, and I expected to get the usual five ounces of silver. But although I waited more than ten days no money was sent to me, so to-day as I had a little leisure I went to investigate the matter. I never suspected that you were the man. I am afraid that my manner was rather offensive, and I ask you to overlook it kindly."

"I heard of you through the jailer, and wished to meet you, but as I was not certain where you lived I thought it better to wait until you came to see me. So I had to wait a good few days. It was not that I did not intend to give you these five ounces of silver, but simply that I wished to meet you personally. I am much pleased that we have fortunately met here to-day."

Now who was this head jailer? He was no other than Tai Tsung. Now in that period of the Sung dynasty, head jailers at Chinling (Nanking) were called Chia-chang, whereas in Hunan they were called Yuan-chang. This Yuan-chang Tai Tsung had a very supernatural power. Whenever he had to travel on some extremely urgent matter he put mail armor over his legs. He then by magic could travel a hundred and sixty miles a day. If he doubled the mail armor then by magic he could travel two hundred seventy miles daily. That was why people called him the Flying Prince.

These two men talked matters over, and became much pleased with each other. They summoned the waiter to their private compartment, and ordered a big dinner to be prepared. Sung Chiang told Tai Tsung all that had occurred on the journey, and the latter laid bare his heart and told Sung Chiang all his intimate relations with Wu Yung. They had been drinking for some time, and were quite intimate when they heard a row down below.

The waiter rushed into their compartment, and said, "There is a man below making a row, and nobody but you, sir, can stop him."

"Who is the man," asked Tai Tsung.

"He is the man Li, the Iron Ox, who always accompanies you on your trips, and he wants to borrow money from our manager."

Tai Tsung laughed and said, "I know the fellow. He is very unruly. I request you, sir, to stay here, and I will go and bring him upstairs."

Tai Tsung went downstairs, and soon returned with a big wild-looking man.

Sung Chiang was surprised at seeing him, and asked, "Sir, who is this?"

"This is my assistant, Li K'wei, the Black Whirlwind, and he comes from I Shui Hsien, in I Chou, Shantung province. In his own village he is called Li, the Iron Ox. There he killed a man and escaped here. The government issued a pardon afterwards, but he then had not enough money to take him back home. He is a great drunkard, and when drunk he is a dangerous man. He is skilled in the use of the battle-ax and the cudgels. At present he occupies a minor post in this prison."

Li K'wei looking at Sung Chiang asked Tai Tsung, "Who is this black fellow?"

Tai Tsung laughed and remarked to Sung Chiang, "Sir, you will understand that this fellow is rather vulgar and has no manners."

"I only ask for his name," said Li K'wei, "so why do you say I am vulgar?"

"Younger brother," said Tai Tsung, "you ought to speak to me like this, 'Who is this gentleman?' But instead you asked, 'Who is this black fellow?' and that is not a nice expression. I will however tell you who he is. He is the hero whom you have often said you would try to meet."

"Can he be Dark Sung Chiang, Welcome Rain, of Shantung?"

Tai Tsung exclaimed, "Hei! How dare you refer to him in that coarse manner? And why don't you immediately kotow to him, instead of delaying so long?"

"If he is Sung Chiang I will of course kotow to him. But if he is some other fellow why should I kotow? Sir, do not deceive me or laugh at me about this matter."

"I am Dark Sung Chiang of Shantung," interposed Sung Chiang.

Li K'wei clapped his hands and said, "Master, why did you not say this before, and so enable the Iron Ox to have the pleasure a little sooner." He knelt on the floor and kotowed.

Sung Chiang raised him up and said, "Good fellow, please be seated."

Tai Tsung invited him to sit by his side, and drink wine with them.

"Very well," said Li K'wei, "but I shall want a large bowl of wine, and not one of these little cups."

"Brother," asked Sung Chiang, "what was that row about down below?"

"I had a big ingot of silver in a pawn shop on which they had advanced me ten ounces of silver, and to-day when I asked the innkeeper to loan me ten ounces of silver to redeem the pledge at the pawn shop he declined to advance any loan so I got angry, and broke up many of the things in the shop. Just then you summoned me up here."

"Was there any interest to be paid for the loan of the silver?" asked Sung Chiang.

"Yes, there was interest to be paid on the redemption of ingot."

Sung Chiang put his hand in his pocket and drew an ingot of ten ounces of silver. Handing this to Li K'wei he said, "Here is some silver which will enable you to redeem the ingot from the pawn shop."

Li K'wei took the silver, and said, "Thank you. Please wait here until I come back from the pawn shop. When I have redeemed my ingot of silver I can change it, and repay you. Then we will all go and drink wine outside the town."

"Please sit down, and drink wine with us now, and then go there afterwards," said Sung Chiang.

"I will go now, but be back very soon," said Li K'wei. He opened the curtains and departed.

"It would have been better if you had not lent him that money," said Tai Tsung.

"Why not?"

"Although he is straightforward yet he has a weakness for wine and gambling. When did he ever have an ingot of silver? He has cheated you to get the money. You noticed how quickly he left us when he had got the money. He has probably gone gambling, and if he wins he will return your loan. But if he loses how can he repay the loan? I shall then feel ashamed as he is my assistant."

Sung Chiang laughed, "But we are not strangers! Don't talk about such small things. If he wants to gamble then never mind. My opinion is that he is a loyal and straightforward man."

"He is a skilled athlete, and is very brave, but has a very coarse nature. In the prison when he is drunk he never hits the prisoners, but is always fighting with the brave jailers. I have had a lot of trouble with him. He always takes up the cudgels on behalf of the weaker brothers, and for this reason the people of this town are afraid of him."

"Let us have another drink," said Sung Chiang, "and then go for a stroll outside the town."

"I had forgotten," said Tai Tsung, "that I have not yet shown you the scenery round here."

BRIBERY IN PRISON

When Li K'wei had left with the silver he thought, "Sung Chiang is not a common man. We are not old friends, and yet he immediately advanced me this money. He is a hero who despises wealth and stands for justice—of that there is no shadow of doubt. These few days I have lost all my money in gambling so that I have not even a cash, and cannot invite him to dine with me. Now that I have the money I will gamble again, and when I have won I will then go and invite him to a feast." Li K'wei went outside the town, and entering the gambling den of Hsiao Chang-i, he took his seat at the table, and put down his money. He called out, "Give me the dice box. I will be banker this time."

The proprietor knew that Li K'wei had always been fair in his gambling, so he said, "Elder brother, let us just finish this round, and then you can have the dice box."

"But I want to gamble now."

"You had better watch us on one side, and do the guessing," said Hsiao Chang-i.

"I am not going to guess. I want to gamble, and here is my stake five ounces of silver." He took the dice box, and asked, "Now what is your stake?"

"I will stake five ounces also," said Hsiao Chang-i.

Li K'wei threw the dice, but only low numbers turned up. Hsiao Chang-i reached across for the money, but Li K'wei said, "I have ten ounces here."

"But you staked five ounces, and if you had won I would have paid you that amount."

Li K'wei did not answer, but threw the dice again, and again only low numbers turned up.

Hsiao Chang-i laughed and said, "Do not be in such a hurry. You have shaken twice with bad luck. You had better rest a bit now."

"But this money belongs to another man," said Li K'wei.

"That makes no difference. You will pay just the same. You have lost so we need not discuss anything else."

"Very well," said Li K'wei. "But please lend me some money, and I will repay you to-morrow."

"That is nonsensical talk," said Hsiao Chang-i. "There is an old saying, 'In gambling there are no duties (to parents or brothers) observed.' You have lost, so why wrangle about the money?"

"Will you give me the money or not?" asked Li K'wei.

"Li K'wei! You have always been straight in gambling, so how is it that to-day you wrangle about such a clear case?"

But Li K'wei did not reply. Instead he grabbed the money, and also all the other's silver on the table, and put it in his coat. He then said, "I have always been straight, but to-day I cannot observe the usual procedure."

Hsiao Chang-i now advanced to attempt to recover the money, but Li K'wei struck him a blow, and fell him on the ground, while all the other gamblers rushed forward to recover their money, but Li K'wei hit on every side, and kept them off. He then rushed away to escape. The gatekeeper tried to stop him saying, "Where are you going?" but Li K'wei pushed him on one side, opened the gate, and went out. The gamblers were following him and as they reached the gate they called out, "Li K'wei, you are quite unfair to take all our money." There was not one who was brave enough to pursue him, but as Li K'wei was running, a man took hold of him and called out, "Why do you take other people's money?"

"What has it got to do with you?" asked Li K'wei. Turning his head he saw that the man was Tai Tsung, and behind him was Sung Chiang. He was surprised at seeing them there, and said, "Brothers, please excuse me. Previously the Iron Ox has always been fair and square in gambling but to-day I have lost the money you gave me. I wished to invite you to a feast, but as I had no money I got annoyed, and grabbed other people's money."

Sung Chiang laughed at this. "If you are short of money you can always come and ask for it from me. As you have lost all your money to him to-day, you had better give him the money."

Li K'wei took all the money out of his coat, and placed it in Sung Chiang's hands. The latter summoned Hsiao Chang-i and handed him the money.

Hsiao Chang-i said, "Li K'wei lost ten ounces of silver to me, but although he took it by force I will not take it back from him. I have no desire to make him my enemy."

"You can take the money," said Sung Chiang, "without being afraid of him in the future."

Hsiao Chang-I was however still unwilling to take the money.

"Has he already injured any of you?" asked Sung Chiang.

"He struck the 'banker,' the other gamblers, and the gatekeeper," said Hsiao Chang-i.

"Then, take this ten ounces of silver from Li K'wei and distribute it among those men as compensation for their wounds. I will take Li K'wei away, and he will not trouble you again."

Hsiao Chang-I took the money, and after expressing his thanks went his way.

Sung Chiang asked the other two to go with him, and drink wine.

"On the riverside there is the Pi Pa Ting Inn. It is the ruins of a building of the Tang dynasty. We can drink wine there, and enjoy the view of the river."

"We can buy some eatables in the town, and take them there with us," suggested Sung Chiang.

"There is no need for that," said Tai Tsung. "We can get all we want at the inn."

"All right," said Sung Chiang. They all proceeded to the Pi Pa Ting Inn, and entering they found about ten tables arranged. They selected a clean one, and sat down according to the rules of propriety—Sung Chiang in the place of honor, Tai Tsung facing him, and Li K'wei at the side. They called for wine and food. The proprietor brought them large jars of the best wine, and Li K'wei said, "Let us have big bowls, as I do not like these small cups."

"What a rude fellow you are!" said Tai Tsung. "You just drink your wine and keep quiet."

"We two will have the small cups," said Sung Chiang to the proprietor, "but you can let this gentleman have a big bowl."

The proprietor did this, and Li K'wei laughingly said, "What a splendid fellow you are. People spoke well and truly of you. How well you have met my desires! The life will not be unworth to live when I have you as my sworn brother."

After they had drunk about six cups of wine, Sung Chiang saw that they were getting merry and he thought it would be nice to have some soup fish flavored with capsicum. He asked Tai Tsung whether they could get fresh fish at the inn.

Tai Tsung laughed, "Have you not noticed that all the boats on the river are fishing boats? This is just the place to get abundant fish."

"Well, how would it be if we had some fresh fish soup flavored with capsicum?"

Tai Tsung called the waiter and ordered fish for three. Very soon it was served, and when Sung Chiang saw it he said, "Excellent food served in a superb dish. Although the inn is small yet the dishes are extremely fine." He took up his chopsticks and invited the others to partake with him. He ate a little of the fish and tasted the soup. Li K'wei, however, did not use his chopsticks, but took the fish in his hand, and ate it including the bones. Sung Chiang could hardly suppress his laughter, and after taking a little more soup put down his chopsticks, and said:

"It is just a habit of mine to drink a little fish soup after drinking wine. This fish does not seem to be very nice."

"I also do not like it," said Tai Tsung, "salted fish does not suit my taste."

Li K'wei finished the fish in his own bowl, and then remarked, "As you two elder brothers do not like it I will eat it for you." So he reached across the table, and with his hand took the fish from Sung Chiang's bowl and ate it. He then did the same with Tai Tsung's bowl of fish. When he had finished the table was covered with the soup which had dripped from the fish.

Sung Chiang summoned the waiter and told him, "Our brother here is very hungry so please bring plenty of meat for him, and I will pay for it."

The waiter said they had only mutton,—no beef. Upon hearing this Li K'wei took the bowl of soup and threw it in the waiter's face and clothes.

"Why do you do that?" asked Tai Tsung.

"Because that fellow is so unreasonable," replied Li K'wei. "He insults me by saying that I can eat beef only."

"I just asked you what meat you would like," said the waiter.

"Go and bring what you have got," said Sung Chiang.

The waiter smothered his anger, and soon returned with a tray of mutton which he placed on the table. Li K'wei without saying a word reached out his hands, and took the mutton. He had very soon eaten the whole lot.

"What a robust fellow!" exclaimed Sung Chiang. "He is really a strong man."

"How well you understand my nature!" replied Li K'wei. "The mutton is much better than the fish."

Tai Tsung spoke to the waiter, "You have especially fine dishes, but the fish you served in them was not of the best. If you have any better fish please bring some for my friend here."

The waiter laughed and said, "I dare not deceive you, gentlemen. The fish was caught yesterday. The live fish caught to-day is still on the boats and we cannot buy it until the wholesale dealer begins to sell. For this reason we cannot supply you with fresh fish to-day."

Li K'wei jumped up, "I myself will go, and buy a pair of live fish for my elder brothers."

"You must not go," said Tai Tsung. "The waiter can go himself and ask for some fish."

"The fishermen will let me have the fish at once," said Li K'wei. "It is a small thing." He went off at once although Tai Tsung tried to stop him.

Tai Tsung spoke to Sung Chiang, "I hope that you will excuse me for introducing that kind of man to you. He is not a respectable man, and I am somewhat ashamed of his manners."

"That is his natural disposition, and how can you help it? I think he is a very sincere and honest man."

They stayed in the Pi Pa Ting joking and talking for some time.

Li K'wei arrived at the river bank, and there he saw about ten fishing boats all tied up in a line along the quay, under overhanging willow trees. Most of the fishermen were asleep on board, but there were a few repairing the nets, and some bathing in the river. That time was about the middle of June, and the sun was just setting in a red western sky. The wholesale merchant who sold the fish was not there.

Li K'wei shouted out, "Bring me two fresh fish."
A fisherman replied, "The wholesale merchant has not come, and we dare not sell any fish without him. You see that all the fish dealers are waiting for him over there."

"Why should I wait for any fish merchant?" said Li K'wei. "Let me have two fish at once."

"We have not yet burnt the joss paper, so how can we let you have any fish?" replied the fisherman.

Li K'wei saw that they would not give him the fish so he jumped on to the boat. The fish was in tanks in the holds and although Li K'wei did not understand the arrangements of the boat he removed a bamboo screen. The fishermen could not stop him, and the spectators on the bank were astounded. Li K'wei groped inside the water, but could not find a single fish. These boats had a hole at the stern which kept the tanks supplied with fresh water. There was a small bamboo screen which although admitting the water prevented the fish from leaving the tank. Because of this arrangement the fish was always fresh when sold at Chiang Chou (Kiukiang). When Li K'wei had removed the bamboo screen all the fish in the tank had escaped. As he could find no fish Li K'wei jumped on to another boat, and did the same thing again. About eighty fishermen now rushed at Li K'wei with bamboo poles to beat him. He seeing the advancing crowd immediately stripped off his coat and shirt, and seizing about six of the nearest bamboo poles in both hands he broke them into pieces at once. The fishermen were astonished at his strength, and immediately unloosened the moorings of the other boats and sculled them away from the wharf. Li K'wei was now very angry and taking one of the broken bamboo poles he leapt ashore, but the coolies there immediately put down their loads, and ran away. In the noise and confusion a man arrived on the scene, and the men called out, "Here comes the merchant. This black man has been trying to seize the fish, and so has frightened away all the fishing boats."

"Who has dared to do this crazy thing?" asked the merchant.

The men pointed to Li K'wei, "There he is. He threatens to beat us."

"You fellow with a leopard's heart and a tiger's gall,"

A FIGHT ON THE WHARF

said the merchant, "how dare you come here, and upset my affairs like this?"

Li K'wei saw that the merchant was big sized, and of about thirty-three years of age; he had a black moustache, and wore a blue turban with a red ribbon entwined in his hair; his shirt was of white cloth and he had a silk girdle; his hempen sandals were fastened with black and white strings; in his hand he carried a balance. He handed the balance to another man, and advancing shouted at Li K'wei, "Whom are you going to fight?"

Li K'wei did not answer, but lifted his bamboo pole to strike the man. The man stepped forward and seized hold of the pole. Li K'wei seized hold of the man's hair. The man raised his foot, and kicked Li K'wei who, however, still held on to his opponent's hair. The man struck several blows with his fist, but Li K'wei did not mind these at all, but when the man kicked him, he pulled the man down to the ground, and hit him with his fist—his blows were like iron mallets and sounded like the beating of a drum. The man had no means of escape, but a bystander seized hold of Li K'wei by the waist, and another man took hold of Li K'wei's hand, and they called out, "Stop this! Stop this!" Li K'wei turning his head saw that the men holding him were Sung Chiang and Tai Tsung. He at once released his hold, and the man immediately rushed away.

Tai Tsung complainingly said to Li K'wei, "I told you not to come here for fish, and now I find you fighting. If you had killed the man would you not have had to answer for it in prison?"

"You are afraid that I would implicate you. If I had killed a man I would answer the charge of murder, and not you."

"Brother, do not discuss the matter any further," said Sung Chiang. "Let us go and drink some more wine."

Li K'wei got his coat and shirt and throwing them over his arm he accompanied the other two. They had gone hardly ten steps when they heard a man behind cursing them. "You deserve death! I want to fight with you, and we will see who will win this time." Li K'wei turned round, and saw it was the very man he had just fought with. He was now stripped naked except for a small pair of drawers. His hair was bound up with red tapes on top of his head without a turban. He was by himself and carried a bamboo pole such as are used on boats. He was quickly approaching on a small boat and shouted, "You, rascal, deserving of hacking into a thousand pieces. If I were afraid of you I should not be brave. If you walk away, you are coward."

Li K'wei roared with rage at this, and throwing down his clothing he stepped forward. He and the man cursed each other and as Li K'wei was standing on the bank the man threatened to strike his leg with the bamboo pole. Li K'wei leapt on to the boat, and what happened occurred quicker than we can relate. The man had inveigled Li K'wei to come on the boat, for as soon as Li K'wei was on board he pushed the boat away from the wharf and it floated off into the current. Li K'wei could swim only a little, so this movement filled him with fear. The man put down his pole, and addressed Li K'wei, "Now we will fight and see who will win." He seized Li K'wei's arm. "But before we fight I am going to give you a drink of water." He was standing with both legs outstretched, and all at once he moved his weight on to one leg, turned the boat upside down and threw them both into the river.

Sung Chiang and Tai Tsung had watched all this from the bank, and were excited when both men fell into the river with a mighty splash. There was a big crowd of men also watching this, and one of them said, "That black man has now got his deserts. Even if he does not drown he will get a bellyful of water." Now they could see both men in the water, and the boatman caught hold of Li K'wei, and ducked him into the water again. They struggled together in the water, but there was not a single man on the wharf who did not applaud the spectacle. It was evident that Li K'wei was getting the worst as he was frequently pushed down underneath the water. Sung Chiang asked Tai Tsung to get some one to act as peace-maker.

Tai Tsung asked the crowd who the boatman was, and a man replied, "He is Chang Shun, and is the wholesale dealer in fish here."

Sung Chiang was startled upon hearing this. "Surely can he not be Chang Shun, the White Fish?"

"Yes, that is so."

"I have a letter from his brother Chang Heng in my quarters," said Sung Chiang.

Tai Tsung hearing this shouted at the top of his voice; "Brother Chang! Stop this fighting! Here is a letter from your elder brother. That man is one of us, and you can forgive him, and come here to talk matters over."

Chang Shun heard this, and also recognized Tai Tsung so he released Li K'wei and swam to the wharf. He saluted and said, "Sir, please excuse me."

"In my behalf I will ask you to go and save that man's life," said Tai Tsung. "When you return with him I will introduce you to somebody."

Chang Shun without a word dived into the river, and soon reached Li K'wei who was in difficulties. Chang Shun took hold of Li K'wei with one hand, and treading the water, and swimming with the other hand drew Li K'wei towards the wharf. Upon their landing all the crowd applauded. Sung Chiang was filled with admiration at this fine display by Chang Shun. Li K'wei was alternately vomiting water and taking in deep drafts of breath.

"Let us all go to the Pi Pa Inn and talk matters over there," suggested Tai Tsung.

Li K'wei and Chang Shun put on their clothes, and all four set off for the inn. When they had all taken their seats Tai Tsung spoke to Chang Shun, "Brother, do you know me?"

"Yes, I know you, but I have had no opportunity of meeting you before this," said Chang Shun.

Tai Tsung pointed at Li K'wei and said, "He has offended you to-day, but surely you also know him."

"Of course I know brother Li K'wei. Only we have never been at loggerheads previously."

"But you nearly drowned me to-day," interposed Li K'wei.

"You gave me a good beating too," responded Chang Shun.

"Well, I hope that you will both turn out to be good friends," said Tai Tsung. "Remember the saying, 'Friends are often made after a fight.'"

"You avoid meeting me on the road," said Li K'wei.

"Well, I prefer to meet you in the water," said Chang Shun.

They all laughed at this joke, and agreed not to talk about that affair again.

Tai Tsung pointing at Sung Chiang asked Chang Shun whether he knew who that was.

Chang Shun said he did not. He did not remember having met him before.

Li K'wei got up and said, "This elder brother is Sung Chiang."

"Can he be Welcome Rain of Shantung—Sung Chiang?"

"Yes, it is he," said Tai Tsung.

Chang Shun kotowed and said, "I have heard of your great fame for a long time, but have never expected to meet you. All travelers speak highly of you—your great generosity and your distribution of wealth in good cause."

"Do not mention my small affairs," said Sung Chiang. "A few days ago I was at Chieh Yang Mountain, and stayed with Li Chun, Muddy Water Dragon, and afterwards at Hsun Yang River I met your brother, Chang Heng, who gave me a letter to hand to you. It is in my baggage at my lodgings." He then explained how they had come to the Pi Pa Ting Inn to drink wine and how Li K'wei had gone to get some fresh fish against their wishes. How they had heard a row, and had come to see what had happened. He said he had been exceedingly fortunate in meeting three heroes in one day. He asked them all to drink three cups of wine with him to celebrate the auspicious occasion.

"If you wish fresh fish," said Chang Shun, "I myself will go and get some."

Li K'wei offered to go with him, but Tai Tsung objected, "Have you not had enough river water for to-day?"

Chang Shun laughed and taking Li K'wei by the hand said, "You come with me for the fish, and we will see how the fishermen will look upon us." So they both set off, and upon reaching the wharf Chang Shun whistled and all the fishing boats in the river came at once to the wharf. Chang Shun called out, "Which boat has caught golden carp to-day?"

Two men on different boats called out that they had the fish, and they soon brought about ten big carp to the wharf. Chang Shun selected four of the biggest, strung them on a willow twig, and handing them to Li K'wei told him to take them to the inn. He stayed behind to see the fish weighed and sold to the various dealers. When he got back to the Pi Pa Inn Sung Chiang said to him, "Why do you send so many fine fish? One would have been enough."

"These are only small things, and not worth mentioning," said Chang Shun; "you can take what you like, and any left over you can take along to your lodgings."

They all sat down in order of seniority. The waiter was told to boil the fish, and to steam another one in wine. While this was being done they drank wine and chatted together about their respective affairs. They then saw a girl about sixteen years of age, wearing crepe clothes who came to their table, gave them the usual woman's salutations, and commenced to sing. Now it happened that Li K'wei was just then in the midst of relating a story of his own exploits, and found it interrupted by the song, and that the other three were only listening to the music. He was annoyed and jumping up he flipped the girl's forehead with two fingers. The girl made an exclamation and fell down. She lay there without moving. The waiter was frightened and told the four guests that they must not attempt to leave until the matter had been investigated by the proper officials.

The unforeseen may sometimes end
Conditions which are perfect.

We will now relate how Sung Chiang and his friends escaped from the inn.

CHAPTER 38

SUNG CHIANG WRITES A SEDITIOUS POEM;
TAI TSUNG SENDS A FALSE REPORT
FROM LIANG SHAN PO

WHEN Li K'wei had knocked the girl down the innkeeper said, "Well, what are you four men going to do?" He also told the waiter to blow some water on the girl's face. This done the girl came out of her faint, and got up. They then saw that the skin on her forehead showed a scar. Her father and mother had now arrived on the scene, but when they knew that this had been done by Li K'wei the Black Whirlwind, they were afraid to say a word. The mother took a handkerchief and tied it round the girl's head. She picked up her hairpin which had fallen to the ground.

"What is your name?" asked Sung Chiang.

The mother replied, "I will tell you the truth, sir. Our name is Sung, and we come from the capital. We have no son, and only this daughter whose personal name is Jeweled Lotus. Her father taught her singing, and then told her to come to this inn to sing to the guests, and so earn a little money. She is quite untrained and sometimes sings when the guests are talking. To-day this occurred, and this gentleman's hand slipped so that she got hurt. But that is only a small affair, and is not worth bringing into court."

Sung Chiang saw that she was speaking in a conciliatory manner, and said, "If you will come with me to my lodging I will give you twenty ounces of silver as compensation. You can then find a husband for her so that she need not depend on her singing for a living."

"We did not expect so much," replied the parents.

"What I say is final," said Sung Chiang. "My words have not a double meaning. You tell your husband to come with us, and I will give him the money."

"Your succoring us in this way fills us with deep gratitude," replied the parents.

Tai Tsung spoke to Li K'wei, "You are always querulous and now you have caused our elder brother here to spend a lot of money."

"I did not use much force with my finger," said Li K'wei, "she tumbled down herself. You can see for yourself how delicate she is. If you hit me in the face with your fist a hundred times it would have no effect on me."

Sung Chiang and all the bystanders laughed at this. Chang Shun told the waiter that he would pay the bill for the wine, etc. supplied. "Never mind!" said the waiter. "That does not matter."

"But I asked you gentlemen to come here and dine with me," said Sung Chiang, "and I cannot agree to your paying the bill."

"It is seldom that we meet you," said Chang Shun. "When you lived in Shantung we often talked of going there to see you. To-day fortune has brought about this gathering, and if I pay, that will only be a very small part of what I think is due to you."

"Sir," said Tai Tsung, "as our brother, Chang Shun, appears to be determined I suggest that you give way to him in this case."

"If he pays to-day then I must invite him some other day to dine with me," said Sung Chiang.

Chang Shun was much pleased at this. Picking up two of the fresh carp he and the others and the old man Sung, accompanied Sung Chiang to his lodgings in the city where they all sat down. Sung Chiang took the twenty ounces of silver, and gave them to old man Sung who expressed his thanks and departed. Sung Chiang also took the letter out of his baggage, and handed it to Chang Shun who also then departed. He also took fifty ounces of silver and presented these to Li K'wei who then left with Tai Tsung.

Sung Chiang presented one of the carp to the warden, and had one cooked for himself. He found the fish nice eating and took a lot of it. In the night about 3 a.m. he had pains in the stomach, and was seized with violent purging and vomiting. He was soon rendered extremely weak. He had the sympathy of the jailers who came, and offered him bowls of rice congee.

The next day Chang Shun wished to show his gratitude to Sung Chiang for the letter he had received, so he got two more fresh carp to present to Sung Chiang. But when he reached the prison he found Sung Chiang lying on the bed unable to get up. He decided to go and fetch a doctor at once, but Sung Chiang said that it was only caused through eating too much fish, and said he would soon be better if Chang Shun would get for him some medicine called "Liu Ho Tang" (Six Harmonious Liquid). He asked him to take the fish away and present them to the warden and the head turnkey Tsao. Chang Shun did this, and, when he returned with the medicine he gave it to Sung Chiang and then left. In the prison was a man who knew how to make up medicines, and he administered the drugs.

The following day Tai Tsung and Li K'wei brought some meat to the prison for Sung Chiang who had recovered, but was not yet strong enough to take meat. They stayed with him till the evening, and then departed.

It took Sung Chiang about a week to recover his strength, and then as he felt quite better he decided to go into the town to see Tai Tsung.

For a whole day nobody had been to the prison to visit him. So, soon after breakfast he took some money, locked the door of his lodging, and left the prison sauntering slowly. Upon reaching the vicinity of the yamen he began to ask passers-by where Tai Tsung lived. One man told him that Tai Tsung had no home, but he often stayed at the Goddess of Mercy Nunnery near the God of the City Temple. Upon reaching that place however he found his door locked.

So he asked bystanders where Li K'wei, the Black Whirlwind, lived. They said that he also had no fixed residence, but sometimes could be found in the prison. He was often moving about—two days in the eastern side, and then for some time on the west side.

He then inquired for Chang Shun, the wholesale fish dealer, and they said that he lived in some village, and he only came to the wharf when there was fish to sell and only came into the town when he wanted to collect some accounts.

As Sung Chiang could not find anyone he knew he continued his walk, and went outside the town. He admired the views of the river, and he came at last to an inn on the river's bank, which had a blue flag flying from a pole with the characters, "Hsun Yang River View Point." Under the eaves was a board with three characters, "Hsun Yang Lou," written by the great poet Su Tung-po. Sung Chiang remembered that at home he had heard of this inn, but did not know that it was in such a place. As he was there by himself he decided to step inside, and have a look at it. When he got to the door he saw two white boards hanging from the red pillars with these inscriptions: "Nowhere is there wine equal to ours; our inn is famous everywhere." He went upstairs, and found a room overlooking the river. The view of the river from the veranda was very fine.

The waiter came and asked, "Will you wait for some other guest, or will you drink wine by yourself?"

Sung Chiang told him he would not wait, and that he could bring wine and food, but no fish. The waiter soon returned with Lan Chiao Superior Wine and food. Sung Chiang was highly pleased with the fine refreshments supplied. He was glad that he had found such a place in such ideal surroundings—it was worth being banished to such a spot for a few years. In Shantung they had fine old mountains, but nothing could equal to this. He drank and ate by himself, and was not aware that he was nearly drunk. He soliloquized, "I am from Yun Cheng Hsien in Shantung, and although a clerk I have met some fine men on my travels. Though I have a good name everywhere, yet now I am over thirty years of age and yet I have not made a glorious record. But branded as a criminal and banished here how can I meet my father and my younger brother who are now at home."

The wine now began to take effect, and he began to weep. The more he thought of his affairs the more he felt aggrieved. All at once he felt inclined to write an epic so he asked the waiter to bring a brush and ink slab. He looked round and saw that the whitewashed walls of the room were already well covered with inscriptions. He thought "Why should I not add my little quota? I will put the date down as well, and then when I come here again on some future occasion I shall realize what trouble I passed through at this moment." So he rubbed the ink on the slab, and wetting his brush he wrote on the white wall as follows:

> In youth I studied hard the classics old,
> As old I grew I fixed my mind intense,
> Now like a tiger bold I hide in hole,
> And lie with tooth and claw to wait my chance.
>
> My face was branded as a criminal,
> And then to Chiang Chou I was banished,
> But soon the tide will turn; I'll have revenge,
> And stain this spot with enemies blood galore.

When he had finished this and reread it, he was much pleased with the result, and laughed loudly. He was partly drunk, and gesticulated with his arms. He again picked up the brush, and added the following lines:

> My body is in Wu; but heart in Shantung;
> I float on sea and river like a weed;
> I laugh at rebels bold whose fame is unsung,
> For they just failed where I'll succeed.
> *Written by*
> SUNG CHIANG OF YUN CHENG HSIEN.

Placing the pen on the table he read aloud the whole thing. He drank more wine, and became quite drunk. He summoned the waiter, and paid the bill, and then staggered off downstairs. He reached his quarters in the prison, and throwing himself on the bed slept there until about 5 a.m. the next day. When he awoke from his drunken sleep he did not remember what he had written the previous day. He however felt the effects of his drunken carouse, and therefore did not go out that evening.

On the opposite bank to Chiang Chou (Kiukiang) was a wild and uncultivated country. In which there was a town called "nothing-to-do" army. In this town there lived an expectant magistrate named Huang Wen-ping who although a well-read man was a cringing fellow. He had a mean heart, and was envious of men who had got better official apointments. He tried to injure the successful ones, and treated with scorn the unfortunate ones. He acted in this way particularly in his own village.

He had heard that the prefect Ts'ai Chiu was a son of the

royal preceptor Ts'ai, and therefore he frequently crossed the river to visit the prefect, and made presents on the least pretext, in the hope that eventually he would be given a better official post. It was very unfortunate that Sung Chiang should have this mean fellow as an opponent. It happened that Huang Wen-ping had that day purchased a present for the prefect, and crossed the river with it. When he reached the yamen he found that the prefect was giving a feast to some officials so that he could not enter. He returned to his boat which was moored close to the Hsun Yang Lou. As it was a very hot day he went into the inn to rest a while. Going upstairs he went on the veranda to enjoy the view. Turning round he noticed the walls of the room covered with verses some of which were quite good, and some rather absurd which made him laugh. When, however, he happened to read the verses bearing the name of Sung Chiang he was startled and thought, "Is that not rebellious? Who has written it?" He then saw the name of the author, and sneered. "This fellow is very vain, and has also ambitious ideas. He is a low mean fellow, and is evidently also a criminal. Who can be his enemy on whom he wishes to have revenge? He evidently thinks of making trouble here although he is only a useless criminal. As he is evidently banished and away from home, he could accomplish nothing." But when he read the last two lines he put out his tongue (in disgust), wagged his head and said, "The fellow has no decency. Huang Chou killed many people, but this fellow wants to beat that record. He is evidently a rebel. But surely I have heard of that name Sung Chiang before this." He summoned the waiter and asked him who had written the verses.

The waiter informed him that they had been written by a man who came there yesterday, and drank some wine.

"What kind of man was he?"

"He was branded on the face," replied the waiter, "and evidently resides in the prison. He had a sallow complexion; was not tall, and was rather stout."

Huang Wen-ping asked for a brush and paper, and upon these being supplied he copied the verses down. He told the waiter that the verses must not be rubbed off the wall. He then went on his boat, and slept there for the night.

After breakfast the next day he got a man to carry his presents, and went to the prefect's yamen again. He was told by the servant to wait in a room, and very soon the prefect entered. After exchanging greetings, the prefect accepted the presents; and they both sat down.

Huang Wen-ping then explained how he had come to visit the prefect the previous day, but had retired on hearing that the prefect was giving a feast.

The prefect said this ought not to have stood in the way of Huang Wen-ping joining him seeing that they were friends. The prefect then said, "A letter has come from the capital stating that recently the imperial astrologer has examined the skies, and reports that the Dipper (the Great Bear) indicates that in the Kingdoms of Wu or Chu there is a man who is going to create a rebellion. It is important that a careful watch should be kept for the man. It has also been reported to me that little boys on the streets in this town are always repeating these sentences:

> "The country will be destroyed because in the home there is wood.[1]
> "The war was caused by drops of water beside the work.[2]
> "There will be thirty-six in both directions, and they will create disorder in Shantung."[3]

"Because of all this I have instructed all officials to be on their guard.'

Huang Wen-ping thought in silence a little time and then laughed, "Sir, there is nothing accidental in this." Taking the verses out of his sleeve he handed them to the prefect and said, "I did not expect to find the matter contained in these verses."

The prefect read the document and said, "These are seditious verses. Where did you get them?"

Huang Wen-ping explained how he had happened to notice them on the wall of the Hsun Yang Lou.

[1] It is hard to convey the hidden meaning in this. It is a riddle on the two characters Sung Chiang. "In the home there is wood" means under the character home = a roof there is wood, i.e., Sung.

[2] "Drops of water besides the work" = the two characters for water and work make Chiang.

[3] Three times 36 = 108 which was the number of bandits at Liang Shan Po.

"But what kind of man can have written them?"

"Sir, it is clearly stated that the verses were written by Sung Chiang of Yun Cheng Hsien."

"But who is Sung Chiang?" asked the prefect.

"In the verses he states that his face has been branded, and that he was banished to this place. So that he must be a prisoner here."

"In that case he cannot do any serious thing," said the prefect.

"Sir, you should not treat such man too lightly. In view of the letter received from the capital mentioning the strange rumors, it is clear that this man is the one referred to."

"Why do you think that he is the man?" asked prefect.

Huang Wen-ping then explained the meaning of the riddle as heard on the streets. "It is quite clear that he is the person referred to, and in the interests of peace and order he should be dealt with."

"Do you know that there is such a man here?"

"The waiter at the inn said that he was there two days ago," said Huang Wen-ping. "If you look through the register of the prison here you will soon know whether such a man is there or not."

"Your suggestion is very valuable and to the point," said the prefect. He sent a messenger at once to bring the register from the prison, and when it arrived he looked through it carefully. He soon found the entry that Sung Chiang had recently arrived.

"That is the man," said Huang Wen-ping, "and besides writing the seditious verse, he is the man also referred to the riddle. It is a serious matter. If you do not act at once the news may leak out, and so your plans may be defeated. You had better get this man arrested and imprisoned and meanwhile you can decide what to do."

"What you say is quite true," said the prefect. He then sent for the head jailer, and very soon Tai Tsung entered. He then ordered him to have Sung Chiang brought there immediately.

Tai Tsung was astonished at this order, and knew that it meant trouble. He went, and got soldiers armed and ordered them to assemble at his own quarters in the God of the City Temple. He then used his dodge of quick traveling, entered the prison, pushed open the door of the clerk office, and found Sung Chiang inside.

Sung Chiang said, "A few days ago I went into the city, but could not find you anywhere. So I went to the Hsun Yang Lou, and drank a bottle of wine all by myself. Since then I have stayed indoors to recover from the effects of the wine."

"Elder brother," asked Tai Tsung, "what did you write there?"

"How can I remember what I wrote when I was drunk?"

"I have just been summoned to the prefect who told me to bring to him the prisoner Sung Chiang who wrote those seditious verses in the Hsun Yang Lou. I was astonished to hear this. I summoned my soldiers to my own quarters, and then rushed here to warn you. Now what shall we do? What can I do to save your life?"

Sung Chiang scratched his head as he realized the danger. "This time I shall be killed."

"I will tell you a plan," said Tai Tsung. "I cannot stay here any longer, as men will soon come for you. So unloosen your hair, tumble about on the ground covered all over with night-soil, and pretend to be mad. When I come with the soldiers you can ramble in talk like a lunatic, and I will then leave you alone, and report to the prefect that you are in a mad fit."

"Many thanks for your good advice," said Sung Chiang. "I do hope that you will assist me in carrying it through."

Tai Tsung hurriedly took his leave, and upon arriving at the God of the City Temple he ordered the soldiers already assembled there to follow him to the prison. When they got there Tai Tsung with an assumed voice called out, "Where is that newly arrived prisoner Sung Chiang?" The jailer took them all to Sung Chiang's lodging where they found the latter lying on the floor with his hair all streaming loose. When he saw the soldiers he asked, "Who are you?"

Tai Tsung shouted at the top of his voice, "Seize that fellow!" Sung Chiang gazed upwards, and showed the white of his eyes. He struck out with his hand, and spoke in a confounded manner, "I am the son-in-law of the God Yü Wang

(Pearly Emperor), and he told me to lead a hundred thousand troops to Chiang Chou and kill all the people here. The god Yen Lo (Pluto) is my advance guard, and in my rear are the Five Great Generals. He gave me a golden seal weighing half a ton. I will kill the whole lot of you fellows."

The jailer said, "He is quite mad. What is the use of trying to arrest him?"

"That is so," said Tai Tsung. "I will go back and report the matter. If they insist upon seeing him then I will return here."

The soldiers accompanied Tai Tsung to the yamen where they found the prefect waiting for them. Tai Tsung reported to the prefect, "The prisoner Sung Chiang has gone quite mad. He rambles in his speech, and lies on the floor with his body and clothes covered all over with night-soil so I thought it better not to bring him here in that disgraceful condition."

The prefect was just on the point of cross-examining Tai Tsung when Huang Wen-ping emerged from a screen behind the prefect's seat where he had been hiding and listening. He said, "Sir, do not listen to this. The man who wrote those verses is by no means mad. There must be a subtle trick in this affair. Better have him brought here in whatever state he is. Even if he cannot walk he may get somebody to carry him along."

"What you say is quite sensible," said the prefect. He then told Tai Tsung that he must bring the man whether mad or otherwise.

When Tai Tsung received such definite orders he knew that it meant trouble. He took his men off to Sung Chiang's quarters where he spoke, "Brother, our plan has failed. You must come with me." A bamboo basket was brought in; Sung Chiang was lifted inside, and in this way was carried on the shoulders of the men into the hall where the prefect was waiting.

The prefect told them to produce the prisoner, and the men took him out of the basket, and placed him in front of the bench. They told Sung Chiang to kneel, but instead he stared at the prefect and asked, "Who are you, and what do you want to ask me about? I am the son-in-law of the Taoist God Yü Wang (the Pearly Emperor) and supporting me are the Five Great Generals. My father-in-law has sent me to take the lives of the people of Chiang Chou. The God of Hell is my advance guard. My seal weighs half a ton. You had better get out of my way as very soon I shall kill you all."

The prefect was nonplused at this, but Huang Wen-ping interposed, "Let us send for the jailer, and ask him whether this prisoner was mad when he arrived. If he was mad when he first came then it is genuine, but if he is only recently mad it must be pretended madness."

The prefect agreed to this, and sent for the jailer and also the turnkey. When they arrived he warned them to tell him the truth.

The jailer replied that when the prisoner arrived he was not mad, but he became mad that very day.

The prefect was angry at this, and told the soldiers to bind the prisoner, and give him fifty blows with the bamboo. This they did, and Sung Chiang's flesh was broken, and was covered with blood. Tai Tsung had to watch all this with a sore heart, but could do nothing to save his friend. Sung Chiang stood this for some time, but at last could no longer endure the pain. He confessed, "I ought not to have written those seditious verses when I was drunk."

The prefect wrote this confession down, and ordered that an extra large cangue should be fastened round the prisoner's neck, and that he be sent back to prison. This was done, and Tai Tsung had to give orders to the jailers to take special care of the prisoner.

The prefect retired from the bench, and was accompanied by Huang Wen-ping to his private quarters. There he said, "Had it not been for your valuable suggestion I should have been deceived by that fellow."

"Sir, this kind of case should be quickly settled," said Huang Wen-ping. "You should immediately write a report of the case, and send it forthwith to your father at the capital, so that they will see how well you handled the emperor's affairs. With that dispatch you can send a private note stating that if they wish to spare his life you can send him by cart to the capital. But as you are afraid that he might be rescued on the way you could have him executed here if they do not want to spare his life. That will put an end to the danger. When the emperor hears of how you have dealt with the case he will be extremely pleased."

"What you say is very reasonable," said the prefect. "In my dispatch I will mention what valuable assistance I got from you, and recommend you for a good post."

"I have to depend on your influence for this life," said Huang Wen-ping, "and in some future life I am willing to be a beast at your disposal in order to return your great favor. Huang Wen-ping stayed while the prefect wrote the dispatches and sealed them. He then asked the prefect, "Who is the confidential servant that will take this dispatch?"

"Here we have the best messenger Tai Tsung, the Flying Prince, who can travel about two hundred fifty miles a day, I will send him off early to-morrow morning, and he will be back in ten days."

"If he can go so quickly that will do very well," replied Huang Wen-ping.

They then adjourned to another room where the prefect entertained Huang Wen-ping to some wine. The following day the latter returned home.

Early the next day the prefect packed up a few presents, and sealed the package with labels of paper. He then summoned Tai Tsung and said, "I want you to take these dispatches and presents to my father, the royal tutor, at the Eastern Capital (Kaifeng), and convey my congratulations for his birthday on the fifteenth day of the sixth month. As that date is so near I want you to get there with all speed, and travel day and night. When my father writes his reply you must bring it here also as quickly as possible. I am aware of the rapidity of your flight, and I shall await your return with great expectation, so do not loiter on the way."

Tai Tsung dared not raise any objection to this, so he received the packages, saluted, and withdrew to his quarters. He then went to the prison, and saw Sung Chiang. "Elder brother, be at ease. The prefect is sending me to the Eastern Capital (Kaifeng), but I shall be back within ten days. When I am at the capital I will arrange some means of helping you. I will tell Li K'wei to bring you rice every day so that you will not be short of food. So please be patient for a few days more."

"I am much indebted to you for saving my life," said Sung Chiang.

Tai Tsung found Li K'wei, and told him, "Our elder brother wrote some seditious verses, and we do not yet know what the government judgment will be. I am now going to the Eastern Capital, and will soon be back. You must look after the rice for Sung Chiang, and take it to him yourself at all mealtimes."

"That is not a serious matter," said Li K'wei. "Many traitors have become officials. You go with an easy mind, as nobody in the prison here will make any trouble. If anybody attempts to create trouble for him I will deal with them by my ax."

When Tai Tsung was on the point of departing he said to Li K'wei, "Now, younger brother, take care. Keep off the wine, and avoid omissions of the rice. If you get drunk your elder brother will be hungry."

"You go with an unembarrassed mind," said Li K'wei. "If you doubt me then I will not touch a drop of wine till you come back. I will wait upon Sung Chiang in the prison from morning till night."

Tai Tsung was much pleased at this. "Younger brother, it is very good of you to say that." He then departed.

Li K'wei kept his word, and not only abstained from wine, but also waited closely upon Sung Chiang.

Tai Tsung put on his greaves, kneecaps, and hempen shoes. He wore also a yellow shirt and a cummerbund, and hid the dispatches in the latter. He changed his turban, and carrying the two wicker baskets of present on his shoulder he left the city. There he put on his charmed armor, and chanted the magical spell as he rushed off along the road at a great speed. That evening he stopped at an inn to rest, and offered some paper money to his god. He slept there that night. He started off again the next morning in the same way. He traveled at such a speed that a violent storm seemed to keep roaring in his ears. His feet scarce touched the ground. On the way he stopped occasionally to get a little food and wine at the inns. The second day was like the first. On the third day he had started very early, and had covered about a hundred miles by about 10 a.m. He felt hungry, but could not find an inn to rest. It was the month of July, and he was perspiring freely in the heat of the sun. All his clothing was wet with his perspiration, and he was afraid of getting a sunstroke. Just as he was feeling very hungry and tired he espied on the side of the road a small inn situated between a forest and a lake. Almost immediately, he arrived at the inn and saw that it was very clean, with about twenty tables all newly varnished, and windows wide open on all sides. He entered, took a seat at a table, took a cup of cold water, and rinsed out his mouth. He took off his gear, the wicker baskets from his shoulders, his cummerbund containing the dispatches, and placed them on the table. He took off his wet yellow shirt, and hung it in an open window.

When the waiter came he asked Tai Tsung how much wine and food he wanted.

"I don't want much wine," said Tai Tsung, "but enough rice for one person."

"We also have bread and vermicelli," said the waiter.

"I am a vegetarian. What kind of vegetable soup have you got?"

"We have some bean curd nicely flavored with capsicums."

"That will be fine," said Tai Tsung.

The waiter retired and very soon had the food and wine served and placed on the table. Tai Tsung soon finished what had been supplied as he was both hungry and thirsty. Soon after he felt very dizzy, lost consciousness, and fell to the ground.

The waiter seeing this called out, "He has fallen!" and a man came out of the room at the back. He was Chu Kwei, the Speedy Courier, of Liang Shan Po. He said, "Take the wicker baskets into the other room, and then search his clothing." Two men then appeared and searched Tai Tsung's clothing. They soon found the dispatches hidden in the cummerbund, and took these to Chu Kwei. He read the inscription, and found that it was written by the prefect to his father. He opened the envelope, and read the dispatch. "We have arrested Sung Chiang of Shantung who wrote seditious verses. We have him in prison awaiting your decision." On reading this he was so astonished that he could not speak. The men had now carried Tai Tsung into another room to be killed and there they found on him a wooden tablet warrant. Chu Kwei seized it and saw that the characters were in silver as follows: "Tai Tsung, head jailer of the Prison, at Chiang Chow."

When Chu Kwei read this he told the men to leave Tai Tsung alone. He remembered that the teacher Wu Hsiao-chiu of the bandits at Liang Shan Po had often said that he had a close friend at Chiang Chou named Tai Tsung. "Could this be the man? But how is it that he has this letter about Sung Chiang? I have been favored by Heaven in getting hold of this letter."

He called one of his men, and told him to administer an antidote to enable Tai Tsung to recover. This was done, and the mixture was poured down Tai Tsung's throat. In a short time he opened his eyes, and got up. When he saw the letter in Chu Kwei's hand he shouted angrily, "Who are you? What courage you have! You drugged my wine, and made me asleep. You opened the prefect's letter. Your crime is a serious one."

Chu Kwei laughed and said, "This letter is only a trifle. We at this place are outlaws already, and are planning to fight against the emperor."

Tai Tsung was startled at this bold remark, and asked, "Kind hero, who are you?"

"I am Chu Kwei, the Speedy Courier, of Liang Shan Po."

"As you are a leader of Liang Shan Po, you must know Wu Yung."

"He is our military councillor here. But how do you know him?"

"He is a personal friend of mine," said Tai Tsung.

"He often spoke of a friend of his at Chiang Chou called Tai Tsung—can you be that man?"

"Yes, I am that person."

"Sometime ago a man Sung Chiang was banished to Chiang Chou, and as he passed this place he met Wu Yung who gave him a letter for you. How is it that you are now carrying letters which concern the killing of Sung Chiang?"

"I am on very intimate terms with Sung Chiang," said Tai Tsung. "He wrote some seditious verses, and I could not see a way to save his life. I would not injure him in any way. I am now taking letters to the capital where I hope to find some means of saving his life. How can I intend to injure his life?"

"If you do not believe it," said Chu Kwei, "you had better read these letters yourself."

When Tai Tsung read them he was surprised. He then told all details of the affair to Chu Kwei.

"This being the case," said Chu Kwei, "you had better come with me to Liang Shan Po where we can deliberate and find some plan to liberate Sung Chiang."

After they had drunk some more wine Chu Kwei shot a whistling arrow across the lake, and very soon a boat issued from the reeds. They both embarked, and were conveyed across the lake to the Golden Sand Bank and were soon in the brigands' stronghold on the mountain. Their arrival had already been announced, and Wu Yung met them at the barrier. After salutations Wu Yung said, "I have not seen you for a long time. What wind has blown you here to-day? Please come into our stronghold." Tai Tsung was there introduced to all the other leaders, and Chu Kwei explained what had happened, and how Tai Tsung had been brought there.

As soon as Ch'ao Kai heard of Sung Chiang's misfortune he immediately went to give orders that horses and men should assemble, and advance at once to attack Chiang Chou.

Wu Yung remonstrated, "Elder brother, do not be so reckless. Chiang Chou is a long way from here, and I am afraid that our men might meet a calamity before they get there. 'Beat the grass and the snake will be startled.' In that case, the result would be only to drive our enemy into cover, and endanger Sung Chiang's life. So we must use strategy instead of force. I am not very clever, but I have a small plan which may save Sung Chiang if Tai Tsung will carry it through."

"Let us hear of your plan," said Ch'ao Kai.

"The prefect of Chiang Chou has written dispatches to his father, Ts'ai, royal tutor at Kaifeng. We can make a plot on this letter. We can write a forged reply, and ask Tai Tsung to take it to Chiang Chou. In the letter we will say that Sung Chiang must not be executed, but sent to Kaifeng for trial, and that after a close cross-examination he will be executed at the capital, which will put an end to all the rumors. When he passes close to this place on his way to Kaifeng, we can rescue him from his escort. What do you think of that?"

"And if he is not sent by this route then your plan will fail," said Ch'ao Kai.

"That will not matter," said Kung-sun Sheng. "We can send spies to find out which way the escort will travel, and we can have men in every place so that we shall be sure of rescuing him at one place or another. I am afraid, however, that the prefect will not send him to Kaifeng for trial."

"The plan will do," said Ch'ao Kai, "but we have no one who can imitate the handwriting of the royal tutor, Ts'ai."

"I have thought that over," said Wu Yung. "In the empire there are only four men whose penmanship is famous. They are Su Tung-po, Huang Lu-chih, Mi Yuan-chang, and the royal tutor, Ts'ai Ching. These four are all first class. I know a Hsiu Ts'ai (B. A.) at Chi Chou who is very good at imitating anybody's handwriting. His name is Hsiao Jang and he is called Skilled Calligraphist. He is also very good with the spear and sword. I know that he can imitate Ts'ai Ching's writing very closely. A good plan would be for Tai Tsung to go to his home and tell him a fancy tale that at the Sacred Mountain Temple, in Tai An Chou they want to erect a new stone tablet, and that they would be glad if he would go there and write the characters. For which service Tai Tsung is to offer fifty ounces of silver. When they have departed another man is to induce his family to come to our mountain. Then we can get them all to join our band here."

"It is a good plan to get the letter written," said Ch'ao Kai, "but how are we going to get a proper seal?"

"I know a man who can make an exact reproduction of the seal," said Wu Yung. "He is the best in China, and lives at Chi Chou. His name is Chin and he has a double personal name Ta-chien. He is a splendid engraver on jade stone, and he has the nickname the Jade Arm Engraver. We can offer him also fifty ounces of silver and pretend to go to Tai An Chou, and engrave the characters on the stone tablet there. On the way we can arrange to bring him to our stronghold here."

"A splendid plan!" said Ch'ao Kai.

The following morning Tai Tsung dressed himself as a lay temple assistant. He took with him about two hundred ounces of silver. He put on his charmed armor, and started off. He arrived at Chi Chou in less than four hours. Upon inquiring he soon found out that Hsiao Jang lived near the Confucius Temple on the east side of the yamen. He went to the house, and called out at the door, "Is Mr. Hsiao at home?"

A scholar soon appeared, but as he did not recognize Tai Tsung he asked, "Where are you from, and what do you want?"

After saluting, Tai Tsung said, "I come from the Sac ed Mountain Temple, at Tai An Chou where as a Tai Pao I look after the offerings made in the temple. Just now we wish to repair one of the towers, and a wealthy man offered fifty taels of silver which I have brought to present to you, and to ask you to go there, and write an inscription for a new stone tablet to be erected. I hope that you will come with me without delay as a lucky day has already been selected."

"I can only write essays or good penmanship," said Hsiao Jang. "If you want the characters on a stone tablet you must employ an engraver for that work."

"I have also got another fifty ounces of silver to engage Chin Ta-chien, the Jade Arm Engraver to do that work. I must ask you to introduce me to him so that we three can go together."

Hsiao Jang took the money, and then went with Tai Tsung to show him the way to Chin Ta-chien's house. They had just passed the Confucius Temple when Hsiao Jang pointed to a man approaching and said he was Chin Ta-chien. Hsiao Jang called Chin, and when he arrived presented him to the Tai Pao of the aforementioned temple, and explained what his business was.

Chin Ta-chien was much pleased to see the money. They invited the Tai Pao (Tai Tsung) to go with them into a wine shop where they entertained him to wine and food.

When Tai Tsung had given Hsiao Jang the money, he suggested that as a diviner had selected the day they should start on their journey that day.

"Just now the weather is hot," said Hsiao Jang, "and we cannot travel far even we set out to-day. Let us start to-morrow morning about 5 a.m."

This was agreed to, and Hsiao Jang took Tai Tsung to stay at his house that night.

The next morning they all started off about 5 a.m., and they had only gone a few miles when Tai Tsung said, "I will not press you two gentlemen to go any quicker, but if you like I can go in advance, and announce that you are coming to the temple." He then left them with his usual speed. The two men continued on their way slowly. By about 3 p.m. they had covered about three miles, when as they approached a hill they heard a whistle, and saw a big man with about fifty followers. The big man at the head was Wang Ying, Stunted Tiger, and he called out, "Who are you two men? Where are you going? Seize them! We will soon have their hearts to drink wine with."

"We are going to Tai An Chou," said Hsiao Jang, "to engrave an inscription on a new stone tablet there. We have only these clothes, and have no spare money."

"We do not want either your clothes or money," said Stunted Tiger. "We shall be satisfied if we drink the wine with your hearts."

But Hsiao Jang and Chin Ta-chien were very angry at this, and seizing their cudgels they advanced to attack Stunted Tiger.

Stunted Tiger defended himself with his sword and fought for about seven bouts when he withdrew. His two opponents pursued him when they heard gongs being sounded on the mountain, and on their left they saw Sung Wan, the Diamond in the Clouds, and on their right was Tu Chien, the Sky Feeler, and behind them was Cheng Tien-shou, the White Faced Squire. With each leader were about thirty men who rushed forward, seized the two men, and took them into the forest. The leaders said, "You need not be afraid. We have been ordered by Ch'ao Kai to arrest you, and take you up the mountain where he hopes you will join our band."

"What do you want us to do in your stronghold?" asked Hsiao Jang. "We are very weak, and shall only eat our rations."

"Our military leader, Wu Yung," said Tu Chien, "is your friend, and he knows that you have certain abilities. He intentionally sent Tai Tsung to induce you to come here."

Hsiao Jang and Chin Ta-chien looked at each other in surprise at this, but could not say a word more. They soon reached the roadside inn managed by Chu Kwei, Speedy Courier. There they were treated to a meal, and were then put on a boat and taken across the lake. Upon reaching the stronghold they were met by Ch'ao Kai, and Wu Yung who entertained them to a feast. Wu Yung explained how they proposed to forge a letter from the royal tutor Ts'ai, and asked them to join in "this righteous adventure."

Both men agreed to help in this plot, but pointed out that their families would be in danger as soon as the officials found out that they had joined the bandits.

"You two gentlemen need not fear that," said Wu Yung. "To-morrow you will understand how we have safeguarded them."

Early next morning one of the men reported, "They have all arrived." Wu Yung asked the two recruits to meet their families.

When Hsiao Jang and Chin Ta-chien heard this they could hardly believe it, but when they descended halfway down the mountain they saw many sedan chairs coming up the mountain carrying their families, old and young, and were very much surprised. When they asked their people for an explanation their wives said, "When you had just gone, these men came and said that you had stopped at an inn just outside the town. They added that there you were sick, and that you wanted us all to go there at once to look after you. When we got outside the town these men refused to allow us to get down, but brought us here without any stop."

Both Hsiao Jang and Chin Ta-chien upon hearing this were dumbfounded, and giving up any thought of an alternative they returned to the stronghold. When they had all been assigned quarters Wu Yung came and discussed with Hsiao Jang about the matter of writing the false reply from royal tutor Ts'ai.

Chin Ta-chien said that he had previously been employed to cut the seal for the royal tutor. The two men set to work accordingly, and had soon written the false dispatch which was duly sealed. This was handed to Tai Tsung with detailed instructions, and he took his departure with his mailed armor and soon he disappeared.

After Tai Tsung had departed the leaders sat down to another feast, when Wu Yung suddenly exclaimed, "Ai Ya! I have been confounded."

"Why, how is that?" asked the other leaders.

"That letter we sent is of no avail," said Wu Yung, "and will only result in the death of both Tai Tsung and Sung Chiang."

"What was the mistake?" asked the leaders in anxious tones.

"I have been careful at the beginning, but in the conclusion there is a serious oversight," said Wu Yung.

"I wrote exactly like Ts'ai, the royal tutor, would have written," said Hsiao Jang. "I made no mistake. I am not aware of anything being wrong."

"I am sure that there was not the slightest difference in the seal I engraved," said Chin Ta-chien.

Wung Yung then explained where the oversight was. This will lead to a bitter fight near the White Dragon Temple at Chiang Chou.

> Amidst arrows lives were saved,
> From throngs of swords heroes escaped.

CHAPTER 39

THE HEROES OF LIANG SHAN PO RESCUE MEN ON THE EXECUTION GROUND; THE HEROES HOLD A MEETING AT THE WHITE DRAGON TEMPLE

"WHAT oversight has been made in the letter?" asked Ch'ao Kai.

"In writing the letter I failed to exercise sufficient care," said Wu Yung. "I overlooked the four characters, 'Han. Lin Ts'ai Ching' on the seal. That is enough to result in the arrest of Tai Tsung."

"But I know," said Chin Ta-chien, "that Ts'ai Ching always uses such a seal on all his essays and letters. There is not the slightest error, so why do you say there has been an oversight?"

"You gentlemen overlook the fact that the prefect at Chiang Chou is the son of Ts'ai Ching, the royal tutor," said Wu Yung. "Is it likely that a father writing to his son would use such a seal? There is the mistake! I overlooked that. When Tai Tsung presents the dispatch at Chiang Chou they will suspect it and cross-examine him. If he tells the truth there will be serious consequences."

"Would it not be better to send a man after him, and bring the letter back?" asked Ch'ao Kai.

"How can we do that! Is he not the Flying Prince? He will now be nearly two hundred miles on his way. We must not however have the slightest delay in this matter, but must go at once to save those two men."

"How can we save them?" asked Ch'ao Kai. "Have you any plan?"

Wu Yung whispered in Ch'ao Kai's ear, and then said, "Sir, we must do this and issue an order to our men to start at once. It permits of no delay."

Ch'ao Kai issued the orders, and all the men went to get their arms, and very soon were on their way to Chiang Chou.

Tai Tsung arrived back at Chiang Chou within the scheduled time, and Ts'ai, the prefect, was very glad to see him back so quickly, and offered Tai Tsung three cups of wine as a reward. When the prefect received the dispatch he asked, "Did you see my father?"

"I stayed there for only one night, so I did not see the royal tutor," replied Tai Tsung.

The prefect read the letter which began with "I have duly received your presents." Then in the middle of the letter was this, "The emperor would like to see the rebel Sung Chiang, so you must send him here in a cart well guarded, and care must be taken that he does not escape on the way." The letter concluded with this, "As regards Huang Wen-ping, his case will soon be put before the emperor, and he will be appointed to a higher post."

The prefect was highly delighted, and gave Tai Tsung twenty-five ounces of silver. He then issued an order for a prisoner's cart to be got ready for Sung Chiang, and appointed an escort to go with it.

Tai Tsung after expressing his thanks went to his quarters, bought some food, and took it to Sung Chiang in the prison.

Ts'ai, the prefect, gave orders that the cart for the prisoner must start in a day or two. Just then the gatekeeper reported that Huang Wen-ping wished to see the prefect, and was told to bring the visitor into the private apartments. Huang had brought wine and fruit which he presented to the prefect who after thanking him said, "You give me so many presents that I hardly know how to recompense you."

"Don't mention it. They are only small things from the country."

"I shall congratulate you that you will soon be appointed to a good post."

"How do you know that?"

"Yesterday I got a reply from my father in the capital, and he orders me to send that seditious man Sung Chiang there. Your name will be mentioned to the emperor and you will be promoted very soon."

"Many thanks for your recommendation. Your messenger must have flown like a spirit."

"I will show you the reply which will convince you that I am telling you the truth."

"As it is a personal letter from your father I dare not presume to look at it. But as you have asked me to do so I will beg you to let me see it."

"You are a very intimate friend of mine," said the prefect, "so why should you not read my letter?" He sent a messenger to bring the letter, and handed it to Huang Wen-ping. The latter read the letter through, and looking carefully at the seal noticed that it looked quite like the impression from a new seal. He wagged his head, and said, "This letter is not genuine."

"You are mistaken," said the prefect; "I know it is my father's handwriting. Why do you think it is false?"

"Sir, please allow me to speak. Do the letters from your father always bear this seal?"

"Other letters from my father did not bear such a seal as this, as he always signs his name. But the seal must have been at his side so he just used it for this letter."

"Please pardon me if I am too loquacious, but I think that this letter is a forgery to deceive you. As you know the styles of writing of Ts'ai, Su, Huang, and Mi are well known everywhere so that many people have learned them. Only this seal is exactly like what your father (Ts'ai) used when he was a member of the Hanlin College. But as he is now the royal tutor why would he use this seal? Moreover, as he is writing to you, his son, why does he use a seal with his full name on? Your father is the most able and illustrious man in the empire, and would not make such a mistake as this. If, however, you do not believe me then you can cross-examine the messenger as to what people did he see in the royal tutor's residence. If his answers are wrong then the letter must be false. You have been very kind to me in the past so I presume to talk to you in this free manner. Please excuse me."

"Never mind," said prefect Ts'ai Chiu. "The messenger has not been to Kaifeng before so I shall soon find out if he did not go there this time." He asked Huang Wen-ping to sit behind the screen, and sent a messenger to summon Tai Tsung as he wanted to see him about some other matter.

Now when Tai Tsung arrived at Sung Chiang's cell in the prison he whispered to him all that had happened at Liang Shan Po. The next day Tai Tsung was invited by a friend to dine at a wine shop in the town, and while they were drinking a messenger came and told Tai Tsung that the prefect Ts'ai wanted to see him. When he reached the yamen the prefect spoke to him, "I think that I did not reward you sufficiently for the excellent service in which you carried out that commission to Kaifeng."

"I am your messenger so why dared I to be slow in executing your business."

"I have been very busy lately and have not had the opportunity of speaking to you about that matter again. When you visited the capital by which gate did you enter?"

"When I reached Kaifeng it was evening and almost dark so that I could not see the name of the gate."

"Whom did you speak to at the door of my father's residence? Where did you rest while you were there?"

"I gave your letter and presents to the doorkeeper, and he told me that I had better sleep in some inn for the night. I did so, and the next morning I went to your father's residence about 4 a.m., and received the reply. As I knew the matter was urgent I did not delay by talking to the doorkeeper, and started off immediately on my return journey."

"Could you tell me how old was the doorkeeper, was he lean or stout, tall or little, and had he a moustache or not?"

"It was dark in the evening when I was there, and the following morning it was not quite daybreak so that I could not get a clear view of the gatekeeper. He was not very tall, and had a little moustache."

The prefect became angry at this, and shouted out to his attendants, "Seize that man!" They did this, and bound him with ropes.

"I have committed no crime," said Tai Tsung.

"You deserve death," shouted the prefect Ts'ai Chiu. "The doorkeeper Wang Kung at my father's house died a number of years ago, and that work is now done by his son who is quite young so that he cannot have a moustache as you say. Moreover, young Wang could not go inside with the letter. When letters and dispatches arrive his duty is to call a servant named Chang who would take the letters to the steward Li who after delivering it and finding all in order, would come to the door to receive the presents. It takes two or three days before a reply can be got. Further, the presents would not be received in an irregular manner as it is usual for a confidential clerk to receive them, and he would ask many questions. Yesterday I was so busy, that I was almost deceived by you. Now you have a chance of speaking the truth, and you must tell me where you got this letter."

"When I was on this business I did everything with the greatest speed, and therefore did not notice clearly who handed me the letter."

"Nonsense! You thief will not speak the truth unless I beat it out of you," shouted the prefect Ts'ai Chiu. "You there! Beat this fellow severely!"

The attendants did not like to do this, but they knew that if they dealt only light blows the prefect would notice it, and only be more angry. So they took Tai Tsung, and dealt heavy blows so that blood was soon flowing from the wounds. Tai Tsung could not stand the pain any longer, so he confessed, "Certainly the letter is a false one."

"Where did you get it?" asked the prefect.

"When I was passing Liang Shan Po I was seized by some bandits who took me to their stronghold, and were going to cut me open, and take out my heart. They found your letter in my clothes, and so they released me. I knew that I could not return here, and attempted to commit suicide. But they wrote the reply and told me that that would save my life. I was afraid that if I told you the truth you would punish me so I deceived you in this way."

"That may be so, but there is still something in your statement that means deception. It is evident that you are in complot with the bandits on Liang Shan Po, and planned to take my letter there, and then make up this tale when you returned. Beat this fellow again!"

But Tai Tsung was now determined not to admit that the bandits were his friends. When prefect Ts'ai Chiu saw that the beating had no effect he said, "I will not ask him anything else. Put a cangue on this man, and lock him up in the prison."

This was done, and then prefect Ts'ai expressed his thanks to Huang Wen-ping. "If it had not been for your valuable suggestion I should have made a serious blunder."

"It is evident that this fellow is in close alliance with the bandits on Liang Shan Po, and that he has planned all this deception himself. If you do not have him executed at once you will live to regret it," said Huang Wen-ping.

"I am going to cross-examine these two prisoners, and after getting their confessions will have them executed before I report the case to the emperor."

"Your measures are excellent," said Huang Wen-ping. "I am sure that the emperor will appreciate very much your capable administration. If you do this it will prevent the brigands from trying to rescue their friends from jail."

"You have been of great assistance to me and I will report the case to the emperor, and strongly recommend you for promotion."

After dining together Huang Wen-ping returned to his own home.

The next day when prefect Ts'ai Chiu entered the court he summoned the recorder, and told him to quickly write out the case, and add to it the statements made by both Sung Chiang and Tai Tsung. He was also to write out a wooden tablet stating the crimes of both men who were to be executed at the crossroads the following day. Now it was a general rule that rebels were to be executed without delay. When they were executed there would be no further trouble.

Now the recorder, named Huang, was a personal friend of Tai Tsung, but although he would have liked to save him yet he saw no means of doing so. But he replied, "Tomorrow will be the anniversary of the late emperor's death, and the following day will be the 15th of the seventh month, the Festival of Departed Spirits, so that we cannot execute the prisoners on those days. Three days from now is also debarred as it is the anniversary of the emperor ascending the throne, but five days from now there will be no obstacle in the way." By saying this recorder Huang hoped to postpone the fatal day.

EXECUTION PREVENTED

Prefect Ts'ai Chin agreed to this, and early in the morning of the sixth day he gave orders for the execution ground to be prepared for the execution. On that day about five hundred soldiers were on parade in front of the prison about 10 a.m. with the executioner. The superintendent of the jail informed the prefect that everything was ready. Recorder Huang produced the boards with the names of the prisoners, and the prefect wrote opposite each name the character "Behead." The boards were attached to two reed mats to be suspended on the prisoners' backs. In the jail of Chiang Chou (modern Kiukiang) many jailers sympathized with the prisoners, but they could not save them. In the jail the prisoners' hands were bound; their hair was washed with glue so that it stood upright, and in it was stuck a goose quill, and a red silk flower. They were taken to the Green Faced Idol inside the prison where they partook of their final meal and wine. They then kotowed to the idol, and were conducted to the main entrance of the prison. Neither of the prisoners uttered even a word. Sung Chiang occasionally stamped with his foot, while Tai Tsung hung his head and sighed. There was a huge crowd of about two thousand civilians pressing forward to see the sight. Upon reaching the execution ground at the crossroads the soldiers formed a ring. The prisoners were placed in the center, and told to sit down—Sung Chiang facing the south, and Tai Tsung facing the north. It was about a quarter to one when the official in charge of the execution arrived.

The crowd witnessed that on Sung Chiang's back was a board with this announcement: "This criminal, Sung Chiang, purposely wrote a seditious poem, containing false and devilish sentiments. He was in complot with bandits of Liang Shan Po, in rebellious designs. According to law he is to be executed."

On Tai Tsung's back was a board bearing this statement: "This criminal, Tai Tsung, secretly conveyed a letter for Sung Chiang to Liang Shan Po concerning rebellious designs, and according to law he is to be executed."

Now, the prefect reined in his horse to await the report. He noticed that on the east side of the execution ground there was quite a crowd of beggars carrying snakes,[1] who were trying to get to the execution ground but they were being forced back by the armed guard.

He also heard a noise on the west side, and saw there a crowd of medicine sellers armed with sticks who were also being repulsed by the soldiers.

A soldier called out, "You fellows have no manners! This is an execution so why should you want to witness it?"

"What do you say? We travel in all parts so why should we be stopped here? We have seen men executed in many places. Even when the emperor at the capital orders an execution he allows anybody to witness it. But you fellows at this insignificant place, try to make it appear an important affair when you only kill a couple of men. If we go inside and look on what difference does it make?"

They still tried to force their way in, but the soldiers would not let them do so. In this tumult the superintendent of the execution shouted out, "Do not admit those fellows!"

While this row was still proceeding the prefect sitting on his horse saw a crowd of men on the south side carrying loads on bamboo poles over their shoulders. They were also trying to get to the execution ground. The soldiers called out, "This is an execution! What do you fellows come here for?"

"We are carrying these things to give to the prefect so why don't you let us proceed?"

"Even men 1 the prefect's yamen have to go some other way," replied the soldiers.

The men put down their loads, held the poles in their hands, and stood looking on.

The prefect now noticed on the north side a number of hawkers pushing carts who also were insisting upon seeing the execution. The soldiers blocked the way, and the hawkers said, "We are in a hurry. Let us go through."

"This is an execution. You cannot go this way!"

The hawkers laughed, "That sounds easy. But we come from the capital and do not know the byroads about here.

---

[1] The beggars who wanted food often carry snakes. They need not say a word, but just show the snake and that meaning is understood.

We only know the main road." The soldiers still would not allow them to pass, and the hawkers put down their carts and stood on them so that they could see over the heads of the soldiers.

By this time there was a general uproar on all sides and just then a messenger pressed his way out through the crowd, and coming to the prefect announced, "It is now a quarter to one." The prefect ordered that the execution was to take place.

Inside the ground were two executioners who held swords in their hands ready for the final moment. The word "Execute" had been called out when one of the hawkers standing on thier carts took a small gong out of his clothes, and struck it four times. Immediately the crowds on all the four sides pressed forward.

Overlooking the execution ground was a tea house, and standing on the veranda was a tall man with a sallow complexion. When he heard the gong he bellowed out like a clap of thunder, and with an ax in each hand he leapt from the veranda on to the ground. He rushed at the executioners and killed them on the spot. He then rushed at the superintendent of the execution, who was seated on his horse, and the numerous soldiers who were armed with spears could not impede him. Seeing this hopeless position the prefect Ts'ai Chiu took to flight with those soldiers. The sudden attack from all sides resulted in many soldiers being killed, and the remainder scattered about leaving the prisoners behind. The hawkers soon released the two prisoners and put them in their carts. Some of the attacking crowd used bows and arrows, others spears, others bamboo poles, while others simply threw stones at the soldiers. This huge crowd were bandits from Liang Shan Po led by seventeen of the leaders under Ch'ao Kai. But Ch'ao Kai was surprised to see the man with the two axes who was doing deadly work among the soldiers. He did not know the man, but Tai Tsung informed him that the man was Li K'wei, Black Whirlwind, a very rough character who however was a supporter of Sung Chiang.

Ch'ao Kai called out, "Are you not Black Whirlwind?" but the man did not reply as he was still busy brandishing his two axes. Ch'ao Kai therefore told the two bandits who carried Tai Tsung and Sung Chiang on their backs respectively to follow the big black fellow. All the bandits now moved towards the crossroads where many soldiers and people had been killed, and the ground was covered with streams of blood.

The bandits followed Li K'wei and they fought their way out of the town. The rear was brought up by four of the leaders with men armed with bows who discharged arrows rapidly at the crowd of soldiers and civilians who dared not approach them. The bandits at last reached the bank of the river. Ch'ao Kai saw that Li K'wei was covered with blood, and was still killing people who were in the way, so Ch'ao Kai called out to him, "We are not fighting civilians so do not kill any more people." But Li K'wei paid no attention to this, and continued killing people. Wherever he saw a man he killed him. When the bandits had gone about two miles along the bank of the Yangtze River they still could not find a way for further progress. Ch'ao Kai was much annoyed at this unexpected check, but Li K'wei called out, "Never mind! I will carry my brother Sung Chiang on my back to the temple." They then saw a large temple, but noticed that the doors were firmly closed. Li K'wei however took his ax, and soon cut the doors open.

Ch'ao Kai noticed that there were very old fir trees which cast deep shadows on both sides of the door, and that above the door was a board with four characters in gilt, "White Dragon's Spirit Temple."

The men carried Sung Chiang and Tai Tsung into the temple, and put them down there. Sung Chiang now opened his eyes, and seeing Ch'ao Kai and the other men he cried, saying, "Elder brother, am I not dreaming?"

"Sir, if you had only been at Liang Shan Po this trouble would not have arisen," said Ch'ao Kai. "But who is this sallow complexioned man who has been killing so many people?"

"He is Li K'wei, the Black Whirlwind. He tried to rescue me from prison but I was afraid and would not listen to his suggestions."

"He is a very rare kind of man," said Ch'ao Kai. "He is not afraid of either swords, axes, or arrows."

"I think we had better find new clothes for our these two brothers," interposed Hwa Jung.

Just then Li K'wei came out of the porch of the temple with two axes still in his hands.

"Where have you been?" called out Sung Chiang.

"I want to find the caretaker of this temple, and kill him," replied Li K'wei, "I do not know what spirits or devils have caused them to fasten the doors of the temple in broad daylight, so I thought it better to sacrifice to the door god with his head but so far I could not find him anywhere."

"Come here," said Sung Chiang, "and I will introduce you to my commanding officers."

Li K'wei threw his axes down and kneeling before Ch'ao Kai said, "Brother, please excuse my rough manners." He then saluted all the other men who were standing around, and among them was much pleased to recognize Chu Kwei who was a compatriot of his own village.

Here Hwa Jung interrupted, "Elder brother, as you said that it would be better if we all followed this man, Li K'wei, who will guide us to a better spot, but now we are all in an awkward position, because we are surrounded by water, and have no means of escape should troops be dispatched from the town to capture us."

"Do not get excited," said Li K'wei, "I will go with you into the town, and kill some more men even including the prefect Ts'ai Chiu so as to enjoy ourselves."

Tai Tsung had now regained consciousness, and after listening to this said, "Younger brother, you must not do such a stupid thing. There are about seven thousand cavalry in the town, and against them you would stand no chance."

Yuan the Seventh, said, "On the other side of the river there are many boats. I and my two brothers will swim across, and get the boats to come here so that you can all embark."

Ch'ao Kai thought this a good plan, and the three brothers Yuan stripped off their clothes, armed themselves with a dagger each, and plunged into the water. They had not swam more than a third of a mile when the men on shore saw three boats coming down the river. The men on the boats were sculling energetically, and a whistle was being blown. There were about ten men on each boat who were well armed and this filled the brigands with great anxiety. Sung Chiang who was inside the temple heard the noise, and said, "In my life there is nothing but trouble." He got up and went outside to see what was happening. He saw a big man standing on one boat armed with a five-pronged spear. On his head he wore a red turban, and was dressed in white silk. He was blowing the whistle. Sung Chiang at once recognized him as Chang Shun and signaled to him with his hand shouting out, "Younger brother, save me!"

Chang Shun at once recognized Sung Chiang, and called out that he was coming. The boats almost flew to the bank of the river. The brothers Yuan who were swimming saw the three boats, and at once turned back to the bank they had left. Sung Chiang knew the men on the boats. On the first boat was Chang Shun with about ten followers. The second boat carried Chang Heng, Mu Hung, Mu Chun, and Hsueh Yung with about fifteen other men. On the third boat were Li Chun, Li Li, Tung Wei, and Tung Meng and about ten other men. They were all armed and disembarked.

When Chang Shun met Sung Chiang he was much pleased and wept saying, "From the time of your imprisonment I have felt uneasy, but could see no way of setting you free. Then I heard of the arrest of Tai Tsung, and in addition I did not meet Li K'wei so I had to find my elder brother (Chang Heng) and we both went to Sire Mu's farmhouse and summoned many of our friends to assemble at that place. To-day we intended to go to Chiang Chou (Kiukiang) to rescue you from the prison, but did not think that other men would precede us with that object. We dare not venture to make acquaintance of such great heroes as these—are they not all chivalrous men under Ch'ao Kai from Liang Shan Po?"

Sung Chiang pointed with his finger and said, "This is my elder brother, Ch'ao Kai. Please come inside the temple, and I will introduce all of you to each other."

They then all went into the temple, altogether twenty-nine leaders, and there occurred what we have called, "The Meeting at the White Dragon Temple."

They had just finished their general introduction to each other, when one of the bandits rushed into the temple in an agitated manner and said, "In the town there is great noise of gongs and drums assembling the troops, and many soldiers are already passing the gates to arrest us. There are myriads of flags enough to conceal the sun, and swords as numerous as a field of hemp. Cavalry was in front and officers with so many big swords and big axes in the rear; they are now rushing upon this temple."

Li K'wei upon hearing this shouted, "Kill them!" and seizing his two axes he rushed out of the temple.

Ch'ao Kai called out, "If you don't do it at once, it can never be done. All you gentlemen must now assist me in defeating these soldiers, before we go back to Liang Shan Po."

His followers all cried out with one voice, "We will obey your orders."

> Waves were stained with blood so rare,
> Dragons came forth from their lair;
> During storm that raged then,
> Tigers leapt from mountain den.

CHAPTER 40

SUNG CHIANG ATTACKS THE NOTHING-TO-DO ARMY; CHANG SHUN ARRESTS HUANG WEN-PING

IN the White Dragon Temple there were seventeen leaders including Ch'ao Kai, and ninety brigands. To these were added nine leaders under Chang Shun, and their forty followers. The latter were all experienced smugglers on the river (Yangtze Chiang) and they arrived in three junks. When they heard that troops were leaving the town to capture them they all followed the lead of Li K'wei and left the temple fully armed, a body of over one hundred and fifty men. Sung Chiang and Tai Tsung were first placed in safety on a junk. Li Chun, Chang Shun, and the three brothers Yuan remained with the boats, and got everything ready for a rapid flight.

The brigands saw that there were about seven thousand soldiers advancing towards the temple from the town. They all wore helmets, and coats of mail, and were fully armed.

Li K'wei stripped himself of all clothing for the fight, and was rushing forward with two axes in his hands in front of the men. Just behind him were Hwa Jung, Huang Hsin, Lu Fang, and Kuo Sheng acting as his bodyguard. Hwa Jung saw that all the mounted troops were armed with spears, so he took his bow and shot an arrow at the commanding officer who fell off his horse wounded. The troops seeing this, realized their danger, turned their horses round, and retreated, scattering the infantry about who had been supporting them. The bandits seized the opportunity, and running forward attacked the confused mass. They killed right and left, and soon blood was flowing in all directions. They pursued the troops up to the town gates where the soldiers on the walls threw bowlders and logs of wood on Ch'ao Kai's brigands. The troops had retreated into the town, and closed the gates behind them. They were too afraid to even open the gates for several days afterwards.

The men under Ch'ao Kai returned to the White Dragon Temple, and embarked on the junks near there. Ch'ao Kai superintended the embarkation, dividing his men equally on the three boats. Sails were hoisted, and as there was a favorable wind, they set out for Sire Mu's village. They soon reached their destination and disembarked. The son of Sire Mu met them, and took them all to the guest hall where his father received them.

The bandits all found a good resting place for that night. A great feast was prepared and they all partook of same. When the wine was handed round they chatted about their recent exploit. Ch'ao Kai said, "We should have been captured had it not been for the timely arrival of our brothers with their junks."

"But why did you take that road?" asked Sire Mu.

"I myself preferred the most crowded road, where I could kill a great number. They followed me. I did not ask them to do so," said Li K'wei.

The whole party laughed, and thereupon Sung Chiang arose, and addressed them, "If you gentlemen had not arrived both Tai Tsung and myself would have been executed. To-day your favors are as deep as the sea, so that I can never recompense you. There is only one man I hate, this is Huang Wen-ping, because he searched minutely for my smallest fault, and several times tried to put me to death. I must be revenged. May I request you, gentlemen, to do one more act of great kindness and accompany me to the Nothing-to-do Army to kill Huang Wen-ping, and so appease my enmity?"

"We rescued you from the execution ground," said Ch'ao Kai, "but how can we do this second thing? They will now be ready and prepared for us. We had better return to Liang Shan Po, and come here again with more men including our leaders Lin Ch'ung, Chin Ming, and others."

"If you go to the mountain you will not be able to get back here," said Sung Chiang. "First, because it is a long way there, and secondly, the officials will have time to get reënforcements from all quarters. We must not indulge in false hopes, but seize the present opportunity and do the deed before they can get ready for us."

"What you say, elder brother, is quite true," said Hwa Jung, "but nobody knows the road or the lay of the land about there. We must first send a spy to the village of the Nothing-to-do Army, and discover the best way of procedure, and find out where Huang Wen-ping lives. Then we shall have no difficulties to begin our work."

Hsueh Yung now stood up and addressed them, "I have been there for several times and know the village of the Nothing-to-do Army very well. Shall I go as your spy and report on the position there?"

"That will be an excellent plan," said Sung Chiang.

So Hsueh Yung bid adieu and left that night.

Sung Chiang and the leaders at Sire Mu's house discussed their plans for the attack on the Nothing-to-do Army and got all implements of warfare ready. After two days Hsueh Yung returned accompanied by another man.

"Who is this man?" asked Sung Chiang.

"He is Hou Chien of Hung Tu" (the modern Nanchang, Kiangsi prov.), replied Hsueh Yung. "He is an excellent tailor and can use the needle with great speed. He is a pupil of mine in the use of military weapon, and can use the stave and spear with skill. He is thin and also very light and therefore he has got the nickname Nimble Monkey. He works at the home of Huang Wen-ping. I asked him to come here."

Sung Chiang was much pleased at this, and asked him to be seated for a conference. This Hou Chien was also a baleful star and could easily be induced to help them. Sung Chiang asked him many questions about the roads to the village of the Nothing-to-do Army and the latest news about Chiang Chou.

Hsueh Yung said that prefect Ts'ai Chiu had had a roll call of the army and the people and found that over five hundred had been killed. He did not know how many had been wounded. An urgent messenger had been dispatched to the capital to report the matter. The town gates were now open only in the morning, and all men passing in or out were very closely interrogated. Everybody knew that the prefect Ts'ai Chiu did not wish to injure elder brother but had been egged on by Huang Wen-ping to put you and Tai

Tsung to death. Since you two had been rescued from the execution ground the whole town was in a nervous state, and everybody was expecting further trouble. "I (Hsueh Yung) went to the village of Nothing-to-do Army to spy where I happened to see this man (Hou Chien) and when I talked matters over with him I knew all the particulars."

"Well, Hou Chien, how do you know these?" asked Sung Chiang.

"From my youth I have had lessons in the military arts from Hsueh Yung," said Hou Chien, "and cannot forget his kindness to me. A few days ago Huang Wen-ping sent for me to go to his house and make some clothes. I met Hsueh Yung on the street, and from him I knew your plans. I wanted to come here and report matters in detail. Now, Huang Wen-ping has an elder brother, named Huang Wen-hwa, and they are both of the same mother. Huang Wen-hwa is a philanthropist, and is always repairing bridges and roads, redecorating the idols and providing food for the priests, and helping poor people in distress. The people in the town always call him Huang, the Buddha. On the other hand, Huang Wen-ping has a bad disposition, and is always trying to injure people. He has the nickname Stinging Bee. These two brothers live in two detached houses in a small alley near the North Gate. I had work to do at Huang Wen-ping's house and one day I heard him say that the prefect Ts'ai Chiu had been cheated, but he (Huang) had pointed out the deception, and had recommended the prefect to kill the persons concerned. Huang Wen-hwa then scolded his brother, saying, "You are again doing something that will injure other people. It is not your affair so why do you wish to interfere and injure these people? Heaven will see that your 'crows will come home to roost' very soon." The other day we heard of the affair at the execution ground, and Huang Wen-ping went off to Chiang Chou to discuss measures with the prefect, and so far he has not returned."

"How do their houses stand?" asked Sung Chiang.

"They are close together," said Hou Chien, "with only a vegetable garden between them."

"How many people are there in Huang Wen-ping's household?" asked Sung Chiang.

"Altogether there are about fifty people," replied Hou Chien.

"Heaven tells me to take revenge," said Sung Chiang, "and has sent this man to help me. I therefore appeal to all you brothers for your assistance."

"We will all go," the leaders replied. "We will kill these wicked people and assist in your revenge."

"I will deal with Huang Wen-ping himself," said Sung Chiang, "and I do not want you to injure any of the people at the village as they are not at fault. His brother (Huang Wen-hwa) is benevolent so under no circumstances must he be injured for otherwise people would rightly abuse me. I have a certain plan and I hope that you will assist me in carrying it out."

All the brigand leaders said, "We will follow your orders."

"Then I will ask Sire Mu to prepare for us about ninety sacks," said Sung Chiang, "about one hundred bundles of faggot, five junks, and two small boats. I want Chang Shun and Li Chun to row the two small boats, while Chang Heng, the Brothers Yuan, and Tung Wei will manage the five junks and take with them good sailors. That is part of my plan."

"All the things you require are ready now," said Mu Heng, "and the people of this village are all good sailors. May I ask for further details of the plan?"

"Well, I want Hou Chien, Hsueh Yung and Pai Sheng to go to the Nothing-to-do Army village, and hide there secretly. About 2 a.m. to-morrow we will all reach the village and then release a pigeon with a whistle on its tail. When Pai Sheng hears that whistle he must ascend the wall, and display a piece of white silk to indicate the position of Huang Wen-ping's house. Shih Yung and Tu Chien will disguise themselves in the village as beggars, and when they hear the signal they must set fire to some house, and then run to the village gate and kill the gatekeepers. Li Chun and Chang Shun must cruise about on the river in their boats, and wait there for further developments." When Sung Chiang had explained his plans all the men concerned left at once to carry out their various duties. The cloth sacks were filled with sand, bundle of reeds and oil were got ready and placed on the junks. The brigands then armed themselves, and took their positions in the bottoms of the boats. The leaders were then divided up, and allocated to their seven junks. Chu Kwei and Sung Wan were to stay behind, and got information as to anything that might occur in Chiang Chou. Tung Meng went in advance in a quick boat as a scout. That night all the boats reached the village without any difficulty.

It was the end of September and the nights were cold. It was a bright moonlight night and the river was calm. The hills were reflected in the river, and even their green color was clearly shown in the water. The boats reached Nothing-to-do Army village about 10 p.m. where the bank of the river was covered with thick reeds. Tung Meng, the scout, soon came and reported that all was quiet in the village. Sung Chiang ordered that the sand bags, the bundles of reeds, and some firewood should be taken near the village gate. Just then they heard the watchman in the village beating his drum indicating the end of the second watch. The leaders and men all moved near the village leaving only six men on the boats. When they were all assembled near the North Gate Sung Chiang gave an order, and the pigeon was released. Soon they saw a bamboo pole on the wall with a white flag fluttering in the breeze. Sung Chiang ordered that the sand bags be piled against the wall near the flag, and that the men climb over the wall. Pai Sheng was waiting for them on the wall and pointed out the house where Huang Wen-ping lived.

Sung Chiang inquired for Hsueh Yung, Hou Chien and Pai Sheng said that they were already in the house. He was also informed that Shih Yung and Tu Chien were waiting near the village gate. Sung Chiang then led his men down from the wall to the entrance of Huang Wen-ping's house where he found Hou Chien hiding inside the gate. He summoned Hou Chien, and whispered to him, "Go and open the garden gate. Tell the men there to bring all the reeds, oil, and firewood inside. Hsueh Yung is to set fire to the whole pile and Hou Chien to knock at the door of the house and shout 'Your brother's house is on fire! We want to bring the boxes, etc. here.'" Sung Chiang then divided his men into two parts, one to watch the front gate and the other guard the back door.

Hou Chien carried out his instructions. The servants inside Huang Wen-ping's house saw the flames, and at once opened the door. Sung Chiang and his followers thereupon rushed forward shouting "Kill." They killed every person they met, and very soon there were over fifty dead men, but so far they had not seen Huang Wen-ping. In the house were large stores of wealth which had been extorted from people from time to time, and these were now seized by the brigands and taken away.

When the fire broke out Shih Yung and Tu Chien had attacked the gatekeepers and killed them. The neighbors seeing the flames were running with ladders and buckets of water to put out the fire. Shih Yung called out to them, "You people must go back. We are bandits from Liang Shan Po, and have only come here to help Sung Chiang to take his revenge and kill Huang Wen-ping. This does not concern you, and you must not interfere. All go back home!" Many people did not believe this, and stopped to look on. But when they saw Li K'wei, the Black Whirlwind, approaching with an ax in each hand, they quickly retreated with their buckets of water and ladders with a shrill outcry.

In a street at the back were some soldiers who now came to help to put out the fire. Hwa Jung shot an arrow at them, and Li K'wei shouted, "Let those who want to die come forward." But without any hesitation the soldiers retreated.

Hsueh Yung was now inside the house, setting fire to all the rooms. Li K'wei returned to the village gates and hacked them with his axes. The brigands all made their escape, and carried all the loot to the junks.

The people in the village had heard of the fight at Chiang Chou and dared not pursue the bandits.

Sung Chiang followed his men to the boats, and was disappointed that he had not met Huang Wen-ping.

The fire at the Nothing-to-do Army village illuminated the sky all red, and this could be seen in Chiang Chou where the prefectural yamen was soon informed of the incident. Huang Wen-ping was staying in the yamen and when he heard the report he hurried to see the prefect. "My village is in flames! I will go there, and see the remains." The prefect gave an order for the town gate to be opened, and that an official boat be got ready. Huang Wen-ping expressed his thanks and embarked at once. The red flames were reflected in the water. One of the boatmen said that the fire was near the North Gate. Huang Wen-ping saw that this was true, and became much more afraid. When the boat was in the middle of the river he saw a smaller boat passing by, and another came towards the official boat. When quite close a big man on the smaller boat held a pole with a double-pronged hook, and called out, "We are going to Chiang Chou to report about the fire."

Huang Wen-ping emerged from the cabin, and asked where the fire was.

The man replied that the fire was near the North Gate and that all the people in Huang Wen-ping's house had been killed by bandits from Liang Shan Po who had escaped with all the loot.

Huang Wen-ping unvoluntarily heaved a deep sigh, and was almost frightened out of his senses. When the man heard this he drew the boats together with his hooked pole, and jumped on board the official boat. Huang was crafty, and knew at once that they were arresting him so he retreated through the cabin to the stern where he dived into the river. But he was face to face with a man who had dived from the other boat, and who seized him by the waist. He was brought to the side of the boat and was hauled on board and bound with a rope. The man who had captured Huang Wen-ping in the water was Chang Shun, the White Fish, and the man who had used the hooked pole was Li Chun, the Muddy Water Dragon.

The boatmen on the official boat all kotowed and Li Chun told them that they were quite safe as he only wanted Huang Wen-ping that they could go and report to the prefect Ts'ai Chiu what had happened and tell him that at present the bandits would not trouble him any further. The men were awfully afraid, and went off at once with their boat. Huang Wen-ping was on the smaller boat and was taken at once to Sire Mu's village. The junks with the loot had arrived there already, and the loot had been unloaded on the bank. Sung Chiang and the leaders were pleased to hear of the arrest of Huang Wen-ping who was taken to the village. All the leaders assembled near the guest hall where there was a willow tree. Sung Chiang stripped the clothes off Huang Wen-ping and bound him to the tree trunk. Sung Chiang ordered a servant to bring a large pot of wine and offer a drink to all the leaders. This having been done Sung Chiang cursed the prisoner.

"Huang Wen-ping, you rotter! I had no enmity towards you so why did you try to harm me, and incite the prefect several times to kill both me and Tai Tsung? You have studied books of the sage so why did you do this vile thing? I had not killed your father so why you insisted on putting me to death? You have the same mother as your brother Huang Wen-hwa and yet he always acts benevolently, and is called Huang, the Buddha. Therefore last night I saw to it that he be quite free from any harm. You have a bad reputation; you fawn on the rich and influential, and make presents to them; you oppress good people. No wonder that the people call you the Stinging Bee. But to-day I am going to take away your sting."

"I know that I am at fault," said Huang Wen-ping, "and request a quick dispatch."

"You donkey!" shouted Ch'ao Kai. "You will soon be dead! If you had only known beforehand what will happen to-day you would have repented of your crimes before this."

"Who will help me to execute him?" asked Sung Chiang. Li K'wei jumped up and said, "I will cut him to pieces. He is very fat, and I think it is better to roast his flesh over the fire."

"Splendid!" said Ch'ao Kai. "Bring a sword and cut him up into small pieces. Get a fire ready for the roast and we will also have some wine to appease the enmity of our worthy brother."

"You want a quick death," said Li K'wei, "but I will kill you by slow degrees." Taking the sword he cut Huang Wen-ping's leg and then cut slices off other parts and placed them over the fire to roast. At last he cut open the breast and taking out the heart placed it in boiling water to provide a restorative for drunkenness. When the leaders and brigands saw this they all saluted Sung Chiang who knelt down to them and then they all did likewise. They then asked whether he had anything to say.

"I was only a clerk, and had no ability," said Sung Chiang,

"but I have always been trying to make the acquaintance of heroes. I remained poor and uninfluential and therefore could not do much entertaining of friends. I was branded and banished to Chiang Chou and when passing Liang Shan Po declined the offer of Ch'ao Kai to join you heroes there, because my father had given me definite orders to the contrary. But Heaven favored me and on my journey I happened to meet many fine heroes at Hsun Yang River. While drunk I wrote some extravagant poetry, which endangered the life of Tai Tsung. You gentlemen were not afraid of 'entering the tiger's den and the dragon's pool' in order to save our lives. You all united to help me to get revenge. But we have now committed a great crime, and made rows in two cities, and it will certainly be reported to the emperor. I cannot help, therefore, but seek refuge with you at Liang Shan Po, but I do not know whether you would now allow me to do so. If you are willing we will depart to-day, but if anyone is unwilling let him follow his own desires. If you are afraid of the consequences of what we have done then any delay will only make matters worse."

Interrupting him Li K'wei jumped up and shouted, "We must all go! If there is anyone who will not go I will chop him in two with my ax."

"You talk wildly," said Sung Chiang, "our brothers here must go willingly or not at all."

Many of the leaders said, "We have killed many soldiers, and have upset the whole district so that it will undoubtedly be reported to the capital. Troops will be dispatched immediately to attack us. If we do not go with you to Liang Shan Po where else can we go for safety?"

Sung Chiang was much pleased and thanked them all for their decision.

That day Chu Kwei and Sung Wan were dispatched to Liang Shan Po to report their plans. All the rest of the bandits were divided into five companies for the march and the loot was distributed equally for each company. Sire Mu and all his family and servants loaded up their things to go with the brigands, and then set fire to all the buildings. We need not follow all the five bands of brigands but the leading band under Ch'ao Kai had traveled about seven miles on the third day when they came to the Yellow Gate Mountain.

While riding on horseback Sung Chiang remarked to Ch'ao Kai, "This mountain looks queer and hideous and I think there are large bands of highwaymen among it. We had better halt a little, and allow those behind us to catch up to us." Before Ch'ao Kai could reply to this they heard the noise of gongs and drums being beaten at the foot of the mountain where the road passed.

"What do you think of that?" asked Sung Chiang. "We must stop here and fight them when those behind arrive here."

Hwa Jung took his bow and fitted an arrow to it. Ch'ao Kai and Tai Tsung unsheathed their swords while Li K'wei got both his axes ready to protect Sung Chiang. They all galloped in front of their men. About five hundred brigands came into view with four leaders in front, one of whom shouted, "You made trouble at Chiang Chou, killed many soldiers there, looted Nothing-to-do Army village, and are now on your way to Liang Shan Po. We have waited for you for a long time, and now if you will hand over Sung Chiang to us we will leave you alone."

Sung Chiang upon hearing this rode forward, dismounted, knelt down, and said, "I was wronged, and had no means for redress. But heroes came from all parts to save my life. I am not aware how I have offended you four heroes so I hope that you will forgive me."

The four men immediately dismounted, threw aside their weapons, ran forward, and kneeling before Sung Chiang said, "We have heard of the fame of Sung Chiang, the Welcome Rain, of Shantung, and have long expected to meet him. We heard of your imprisonment at Chiang Chou and after talking it over we decided to go there to rescue you from the prison. We first sent a spy to Chiang Chou and he returned and reported that you had already been rescued by a number of bandits who had taken you to Sire Mu's home. Afterwards we heard that you had destroyed Huang Wen-ping's house and looted all his things. We anticipated that you would pass this way, and have been waiting here for several days to meet you. We were afraid that our reports might not be reliable so we decided to challenge your men so as to make sure of seeing you. We hope that you will overlook our rough manner. We have been lucky in meeting you to-day. We have prepared a feast for you in our stronghold, and invite you all to come and stay with us for a few days."

Sung Chiang was overjoyed and raised up the four men asking for their names in turn. The head man was O Peng, a Hupeh men. Previously he had been a soldier, but finding his superior officer very unfair he had left, and become a brigand and had gained the nickname of the Golden Winged Hawk.

The second was Chiang Chin of Tan Chou in Hunan. He had failed in the government examinations and had then studied military exercises and strategy. He was also very good at calculations on the abacus, and with the most intricate calculation he never made the slightest mistake. Because of this he was known as the Marvelous Mathematician.

The third was Ma Lin, a Nanking man. He had been a man of leisure and could play on two metal flutes at the same time. He was so swift with the sword that over a hundred men could not get near him, and for this he had got the nickname Iron Flute Jinn.

The fourth man was T'ao Tsung-wang, and he was a Kuan Chow (Honan) man. He had been a farmer and defended himself quite well with a hoe. He had got the nickname of Nine Tailed Tortoise.

After the introductions the brigand servants offered a big jug of wine and two plates of meat. This refreshment was also offered to the men, and it took nearly two hours before they had all partaken when the second detachment of men arrived. They also took the feast of welcome and then they all proceeded up the mountain. Men were left behind to conduct the third, fourth, and fifth detachments of Ch'ao Kai's men to the stronghold, and it was about half day before they all arrived. A great feast had been prepared for all the men, and during the feast Sung Chiang spoke, "I am on my way to take refuge at Liang Shan Po where I shall throw in my lot with Ch'ao Kai. I do not know whether you four heroes are quite satisfied with this place or whether you would prefer to join our band at Liang Shan Po."

"If you two gentlemen would accept our small services," said all the four leaders, "we should be delighted to join you."

Ch'ao Kai was much pleased at this. and said that they would be heartily welcomed.

They stayed on the mountain for one day and the new recruits got all their things in order. On the following day Sung Chiang and Ch'ao Kai started off in charge of the first detachment as before, and the whole columns covered a distance of about seven miles. The four new leaders formed the rear, and altogether they had about five hundred men in their detachment.

On the road Sung Chiang spoke to Ch'ao Kai, "I have in my life traveled far and wide, and met a great many dangers, but never have I been in the company of so many heroes. I now give up all my other thoughts in thinking but will follow you until death does separate us."

The band duly reached Liang Shan Po. After several days of arranging matters a general meeting was held, at which Ch'ao Kai requested Sung Chiang to accept the position of chieftain.

"How can it be?" said Sung Chiang. "You overlook that you have faced great risks in saving my life. Why should you ask me to take your position as chieftain? If you press me any further I should think of committing suicide."

"Why talk like that?" said Ch'ao Kai. "If, in the first place, had you not faced great risk of death in order to save the lives of us seven men we should all of us have been dead long ago. You are our great benefactor. Who could accept the position if you do not?"

"My elder brother," said Sung Chiang, "I should be ashamed to occupy the position as you are ten years my senior." He again and again urged Ch'ao Kai to keep the chieftainship, and at last the latter took his seat with Sung Chiang the second, Wu Yung the third, Kung-Sun Sheng the fourth.

Sung Chiang now addressed the men, "We must not now make any distinction of meritorious service, so I will ask all the old leaders of Liang Shan Po to take their seats on the left, and all the new leaders on the right. When future services are rendered, we will decide the position of each leader."

They all agreed to this and took their seats accordingly. There were altogether nine leaders on the right, and twenty-seven on the left.

During the feast Sung Chiang explained in detail how the children's ballad at the eastern capital had been interpreted by Huang Wen-ping so as to complicate Sung Chiang himself. How the false letter conveyed by Tai Tsung had been explained by Huang Wen-ping who had strongly urged the prefect to have both Sung and Tai executed. "How could we escape death if you gentlemen did not rescue us?"

Li K'wei jumped up and said, "My good elder brother! You justly answer the will of Heaven as announced by the boys in the street of the capital. You suffered from Huang Wen-ping's ill favor, but he suffered from the slashes of my sword. We are a strong band here so what have we to be afraid of? Our elder brother Ch'ao Kai can now be made the Big emperor of Sung dynasty, and our elder brother Sung Chiang can be the Small emperor of Sung dynasty. Wu Yung can be Minister of State, Kung-Sun Sheng can be Minister of Education. We will form an army, attack the capital, and seize the throne. There we shall enjoy ourselves. Would it not be better than living on this mountain surrounded by water?"

"Iron Ox!" replied Tai Tsung, "you are talking nonsense. You cannot talk wildly here as you used to do at Chiang Chou. Here you should listen to our leaders and await their orders. You are not allowed to talk nonsense and interfere with the affairs. If you are still meddlesome, your head will be cut off as an example to the rest of our band."

"Ai Ya! Ai Ya!" exclaimed Li K'wei, "if you cut off my head, how long will it be before another head grows there? But I will now confine myself to filling the neck with wine."

All the assembled leaders laughed at this.

During the next few days all the loot from Huang Wen-ping's house and the presents sent by the prefect Ts'ai Chiu to his father Ts'ai Chin were distributed equally among the brigands. On the third day Sung Chiang at a feast told the leaders that he wanted to ask leave to go to a certain place.

> Spears and swords in forest dim,
>   Our hero will escape;
> Excellent, service was prescribed,
>   By the mountain side.

We will now relate how Sung Chiang went to a certain place.

CHAPTER 41

DIVINE BOOKS RECEIVED AT HUAN TAO VILLAGE; SUNG CHIANG MEETS THE MYSTICAL GODDESS OF PARADISE

WHILE dining one day Sung Chiang addressed the bandit leaders as follows: "I am greatly indebted to you for saving my life and receiving me on your mountain. We have been feasting merrily here now for several days, but I do not know how my father is feeling at home. As a result of the affair at Chiang Chou, I expect that instructions have been sent to Yun Cheng Hsien for the arrest of my father and family. In that case the worst may happen to him, but I have no information here about it. I think I had better bring my father here, and then I shall no longer be anxious about him. Would you gentlemen allow me to go on that important business?"

"This is an important matter relating to the affection between son and father," said Ch'ao Kai. "We are all enjoying ourselves here so how could we allow your father to be in misery at home? Of course we must allow you to go home. But we have recently had a busy time, and we have not yet quite fixed up our quarters here. Within two days, however, we can summon a band of soldiers to go to bring your father here."

"It sounds all right to wait for a few days," said Sung Chiang, "but I am afraid that a summon has already been dispatched from Chiang Chou for the arrest of my father. The sooner I go the better it will be. There is no need for many men to go with me, because I can go secretly, and bring my father here without a single person getting to know about it. If I took many men on such an expedition the people would be startled, and afraid, and it would be difficult to do the business."

"Brother, if you travel alone you would have no assistance in case of trouble," said Ch'ao Kai.

"Shall I die for my father's sake I would not regret it," said Sung Chiang.

They would not agree to let him go that day, but as Sung Chiang was determined they at last gave him a felt hat, a sword, and a stick, and accompanied him down the mountain where he departed by himself.

He crossed the lake, and started on the road to Yun Cheng Hsien, and when not far from that place he stayed one night at an inn. The next morning he arose early, and arrived at the village quite early. But as it was daylight he hid in a wood for the nightfall when he went to his village. When he knocked at the door of his father's home the door was opened by his brother Sung Ching who was startled to see him and hurriedly spoke, "Elder brother, why have you returned?"

"I have come to take both you and my father away," replied Sung Chiang.

"Everybody here knows of your affair at Chiang Chou," said Sung Ching. "The magistrate sends two inspectors here every day to see that we do not leave, and as soon as a dispatch arrives from Chiang Chou we shall be arrested, and locked up in prison. We shall wait there until you are arrested. Both day and night there are about two hundred soldiers patrolling near our house. You must go at once to Liang Shan Po, and ask the brigands to come here immediately to rescue our father."

When Sung Chiang heard this he was startled, and had a cold sweat all over his body. He dared not enter the house, but at once departed on the road to Liang Shan Po. That night the moon gave a dim light, and it was not easy to see the footpath. He decided to travel by small bypaths on his way back. He had only been walking for about two hours when he heard behind him the noise of many men. He turned round, and saw many torch-lights about half a mile away, and even heard one man shout, "Don't let Sung Chiang escape." He went on his way and thought, "I am in trouble now because I did not listen to Ch'ao Kai's advice. May Heaven have pity on me and rescue me." Just then the wind blew the clouds away, and there was bright moonlight. He recognized the place which he was approaching.

It was a small village called Huan Tao, and was surrounded by high mountains which made it difficult in traveling. Below the mountain there was a stream, and a footpath which was the only way, wherever one approached the village. He wanted to avoid this place, and turned to find another way, but the men close behind prevented him from returning as near them the fields were well illuminated by the torchlights. He therefore went forward, now looking for a spot where he could hide. He came to a wood in which he noticed a temple, so he went there pushed open the door, and looked round inside for a hiding place. He could not find a suitable place in the buildings either at the front or the rear of the temple, and he was getting quite anxious. Just then he heard a man outside call out, "We must all go inside this temple," and he recognized the voice of inspector Chao Neng. In the room where he happened to be was a shrine so he raised the curtain and went inside the niche. There he crouched, trembling with fear. The men were now inside the temple, and were searching in the rooms with their torchlights. Sung Chiang thought, "I am evidently in a tight corner, and must pray to the gods for protection." He did this and the men went away one after the other, without looking in his hiding place. "Heaven has had pity on me!" he thought, but inspector Chao Te had not yet left the room, and he now raised the curtain, and looked inside the niche. Sung Chiang was terrified. However there was so much smoke from the torchlights and dust on the curtain that Chao Te got some in his eyes, and he could not see clearly. He threw his torch on the ground, stamped out the flame, and then going outside said to his men, "The fellow is not in the temple. But where can he have got to as there is no other path?"

"He must be hiding in the wood," said a soldier. "He cannot escape from this place, and he cannot go up the mountain. We had better guard the road, and even he can fly he cannot get away. We can wait until daybreak, and then make a thorough search."

Inspector Chao Te agreed to this, and led his soldiers out of the temple.

"The gods have protected me. If they save my life this time I will certainly rebuild the temple and images,"

DIVINE BOOKS RECEIVED

said Sung Chiang to himself. He heard a soldier outside said, "He must be here." Chao Neng, Chao Te, and the soldiers again entered the temple. Sung Chiang was again trembling with fear.

"Where is he?" asked inspector Chao Neng to the soldier.

"Inspector," replied the soldier, "look at these marks of hands on the door. They were made by somebody who pushed open the door to get into the temple."

"That is so," said inspector Chao Neng. "We must make another careful search."

The soldiers again went all over the temple looking carefully, but without any result. The men then made a search in the room where Sung Chiang was, but when they lifted the curtain in front of the niche there arose a big wind which blew out their torches, and made everything as black as night.

"What a strange thing!" exclaimed inspector Chao Neng. "The spirit of the Goddess must be here, and she rebukes us in this way for searching in her temple. We must go away at once. We will guard the road till daybreak and then come back."

"But that is the only place in the whole temple that has not been properly searched," said inspector Chao Te. He took a spear, and was stepping forward when there was a great gust of wind outside the temple which shook the building, and hurled stones about. A dark cloud now filled the room. It was very cold, and hair stood on end. They were horror-stricken. Inspector Chao Neng gave the order for all to leave as the Goddess was offended. The men all left hurriedly, and when outside the temple they ran for their lives.

Sung Chiang, although still afraid, could not avoid laughing at this. But he realized his position. "Those fellows have failed to find me, but they still guard the path." While he was still thinking he heard the steps of people approaching from behind. "Further trouble!" he thought. "I cannot get away!" Looking round the curtain he saw two little figures dressed in blue clothes who said, "We have been commissioned by the Goddess to invite you." Sung Chiang dared not speak, and the figures continued, "You may now proceed." Sung Chiang dared not move, and the figures repeated,

"Master Sung, you need have no further suspicion. The Goddess has waited a long time for you."

Sung Chiang knew by the tender tone of the voices that these must not be males so he emerged from under the chair of the idol, and looking out he was astonished to see that they were two young maids with blue clothing, resembling the two images made of mud. He heard a voice outside say, "Master Sung, the Goddess calls for you." He pulled the curtain to one side, and then saw that the two figures had hair twisted round on the tops of their head; they were standing in a proper, respectful attitude, and had their hands raised in saluting position. He asked, "Where are you two fairies from?"

"We have been sent here by the Mother Goddess to invite you angel to come to the heavenly palace," said Little Blue Clothes.

"There must be some mistake. My name is Sung Chiang, I am not an angel."

Little Blue Clothes replied, "Why mistake? You may now go. The Goddess has waited for you a long time."

"What Goddess?" asked Sung Chiang. "I have not worshiped and known before so how dare I go now?"

"If you go there you will soon know her. You need not inquire any further about her," said Little Blue Clothes.

"Where does the Goddess live?" asked Sung Chiang.

"In a palace at the back of this temple," replied Little Blue Clothes. The two figures moved off, and Sung Chiang followed them. They left the temple, and turning a corner they came to a door in a wall. "Master Sung, you may enter through this door," said Little Blue Clothes. They entered, and Sung Chiang looked round. The sky was studded with stars, and the breeze was fragrant. There were many trees and bamboos on all sides. He thought, "If I had known of this place before I would have come here to hide, and not have faced all those dangers in the temple." As he advanced he noticed that there were fragrant flowers on both sides of the path, with fir trees of huge dimensions. The path was very smooth, and bore markings like those on the back of a tortoise. He thought, "I did not expect to find such a delightful place behind the old temple." They had not gone very far when he heard the sound of flowing water, and soon came to a bridge made of blue stone, with red balustrades. They crossed this, and on both banks of the stream were numerous strange flowers and grasses; deep green firs; luxuriant bamboos; weeping willows; peach trees with red flowers. The water below was as pure as silver and snow, and evidently flowed from a cave in the rocks. Across the bridge was a long avenue of strange trees leading to a vermilion red starred gate. Upon entering that Sung Chiang looked upward, and saw a palace. He thought, "I was born and brought up at Yun Cheng Hsien, but I never heard of this place." He was rather afraid, and dared not go any further. Little Blue Clothes urged him to go forward, and they entered the gate. There was a path, now, with dragons carved on the stones, and this led to the hall with large vermilion red pillars on the veranda and richly embroidered curtains hanging between the pillars. In the hall were many lanterns which gave a very brilliant light. Little Blue Clothes went up the dragon carved stone slope, on to the veranda where there were many other Little Blue Clothes who said, "The Goddess requests the angel to enter." Sung Chiang was now trembling with fear, and his hair was standing on end. The flags of the floor bore imperial designs of dragons and phœnixes.

Little Blue Clothes went inside the curtain and announced, "Angel Sung Chiang has arrived, and is waiting outside." Sung Chiang bowed his head and saluting said, "I am only a mortal from the earth and have not made the acquaintance of the gods. I pray for your pity, and that you will bestow grace upon me."

A voice inside the screen called out, "Request Sung Chiang to be seated." He dared not raise his head. The four little blue-clothed maids brought an embroidered cushion, and he had to sit down quite uneasily. The voice inside again called out, "Roll up the curtain." The Little Blue Clothes did this, and hooked the curtain up.

The Goddess spoke, "Angel, have you been well since we parted?"

Sung Chiang replied, "I am only a mortal, and dare not even look at your divine person."

"As you are here you need not stand on any ceremony," said the Goddess. So Sung Chiang raised his head, and saw a large hall filled with glittering articles of gold and jade, with lanterns of dragon and phœnix designs (i.e., imperial symbols). On both sides were Little Blue Clothes with audience tablets in their hands, and holding aloft banners, umbrellas, and fans. In the center of the hall was a couch ornamented with dragon designs and precious stones, and there sat the Goddess. She wore a dark crimson silk robe embroidered with golden threads, and was holding a jade scepter. She had admirable eyes, and a general fairy-like appearance. She said, "Angel, you are here by my invitation." She then gave an order for wine to be served, and Little Blue Clothes at once brought it in a precious porcelain vase ornamented with lotus flowers. The chief of the Little Blue Clothes offered a cup of wine to Sung Chiang, who dared not refuse it. He arose, took the cup, and facing the Mother Goddess he drank the wine. The wine was very fragrant, and he had the sensation of his heart being sprinkled with pure dew. Another Little Blue Clothes came forward with a tray of dates, and offered them to him. He was afraid of committing a breach of etiquette, so he tremblingly took just one single date off the tray, munched it slowly, and kept the stone in his hand when finished. Another cup of wine was now offered to him, and he again drank. The Mother Goddess ordered that more wine be offered, and he drank the third cup. He also partook of two more dates in the same way as before. He now felt slightly intoxicated, and being more afraid of committing a breach of etiquette, he kotowed, and said, "I do not drink much wine usually, and I request that you do not press me further with your delicious fragrant nectar."

The Mother Goddess issued an order, "As the angel does not want any more wine, do not offer it. Let the three Divine Books be bestowed on him."

A Little Blue Clothes went behind a screen, and returned with a tray on which was a bundle made of imperial yellow silk containing the three divine books which were offered to Sung Chiang. The bundle was about five by three inches, and Sung Chiang bowed in accepting it, and placed it in his sleeve.

The Mother Goddess said, "Angel Sung, I have given you three volumes of the Divine Books, and in future you can act as the agent of Heaven. In all affairs be honest and upright. In official affairs support the emperor and tranquilize the people. When affairs are wrong rectify them. Do not forget this, but do not disclose the source of it to anyone."

Sung Chiang bowed, and signified his obedience to these orders. The Mother Goddess continued, "Because your mind is still depraved, and you have not yet completed the journey fit for your soul, the Supreme God has decreed that you must continue your life on the earth. Now live there a good life, and in a short time you will go to Heaven. If you do evil things you will go to Hell, and I cannot save you from that. Read, mark, and inwardly digest the truths contained in those three Divine Volumes. Nobody but an angel like yourself must ever see those books. When you have completed your meritorious duties then burn the books so that those who come after you may not get them. Heaven and earth are wide apart, and as you cannot stay here long you had better return to earth at once." She then ordered the Little Blue Clothes to conduct him back to the earth. Her last sentence was: "We shall meet again at the Imperial Palace in Heaven some other day."

Sung Chiang thanked her, and then followed two Little Blue Clothes out of the star gate of the Palace. When they reached the blue stone bridge the Little Blue Clothes said, "You have had a shocking experience, but you were protected by the Mother Goddess so that you were not arrested by the soldiers. It will soon be daybreak when all the danger will have passed with the darkness. Angel, look over the balustrades, and watch the two dragons playing in the water."

Sung Chiang did this, and saw the dragons. While he was doing so the two Little Blue Clothes pushed him over the balustrades into the water and he suddenly awakened as though from a dream.

Looking round he saw that he was back in the temple and from the position of the moon that it was after midnight. He noticed that he had three date stones in his hand, and feeling inside his sleeve found the three Divine Books there. He had a distinct flavor in his mouth of the fragrant wine. He thought, "What a strange dream! But was it a dream, or the real thing? If it was a dream, how about these books, dates' stones, and the flavour of wine? I remember so clearly all that she said, and can never forget it. But if I have been asleep all this time in the temple this idol must have great spiritual powers. What is the name of this idol, I wonder?" He raised the curtain, and looked at the idol. It was the image of a beautiful woman just like the Mother Goddess he had seen. "As the Mother Goddess called me 'Angel,' it is evident that in my former life I was a very important person. I must make use of these Divine Books, and not forget what I was told so clearly. The Little Blue Clothes said there would be no danger after daybreak, and as it is quite daylight now, I will go and look round." He stretched his hand into the niche, and took his short stick. He brushed the dust off his clothes, and then slowly walked on to the veranda of the temple. Looking upwards he saw a board over the door with four characters: "Taoist Mother Goddess Temple." He saluted with both hands raised, and exclaimed, "What a pity! But as the Mother Goddess has saved my life and presented me with these Divine Books, I will certainly return here when I have made my fortune and will put all things in good condition. I hope that the Goddess will condescend to protect me in the future." This done he cautiously left the temple and made his way towards the entrance to the village. He had not gone far when he heard a great noise in the distance. He thought, "Another calamity! I will stay here. If I go forward they will arrest me. I had better hide in these bushes at the side of the road." He did this, and then saw a great many soldiers hurrying into the wood along the road out of breath, and calling out, "May the Gods spare our lives!" Hiding behind the trunk of a tree, he thought this was very strange. "Why have they come here to arrest me instead of waiting at the entrance to the village as they said they would?" Looking again, he saw inspector Chao Neng who was also exclaiming, "Ye Gods! Ye Gods! Save me!" Sung Chiang thought, "But why are they hurrying along and making such a noise?" Just then he noticed a big man in the rear who was evidently chasing the soldiers. His breast was bare, and he carried an ax in each hand. He called out, "Wherever you go I shall catch you!" As he came nearer, Sung Chiang recognized him as Li K'wei, Black Whirlwind. Sung Chiang thought,

"Is not this another dream? I cannot leave this spot however." Just then he saw that inspector Chao Neng had tripped over the root of a fir tree, and had fallen to the ground. Li K'wei rushed forward, and planted his foot on inspector Chao Neng. He raised his ax to deal the death blow. Just at that moment he saw two men after him—O Peng and T'ao Tsung-wang—who were armed with swords, and being afraid that they were coming to get credit for killing his prisoner he at once brought his ax down and chopped inspector Chao Neng in half. The soldiers seeing this scattered in all directions. Yet Sung Chiang did not dare to leave his hiding place. He saw three other big men coming along, and when they were closer he recognized Liu Tang, Shih Yung, and Li Li. One of them said, "We have scattered the troops, but where is Sung Chiang? What shall we do now?"

Shih Yung exclaimed, "Look! There is a man hiding behind that tree."

Sung Chiang came out, and said, "I am much obliged to you brothers for again saving my life. How can I ever repay you?"

They were all much pleased at seeing him, and immediately Li Li and Shih Yung went off to inform Ch'ao Kai.

"How did you know that I had come this way?" asked Sung Chiang.

Liu Tang replied, "When you had left the mountain Ch'ao Kai and Wu Yung were much worried about you and dispatched Tai Tsung to find out what way you had gone. But even then Ch'ao Kai was still anxious, and dispatched us to support Tai Tsung in case you were in any danger. On the way we met Tai Tsung who said that there were two inspectors who were trying to arrest you. When Ch'ao Kai heard this he was very angry and sent Tai Tsung to Liang Shan Po to get a large body of men to come and rescue you. When near here a man on the road told us that you had gone to this village. So we came here, and met the soldiers whom we attacked, and killed many of them. Li K'wei chased many soldiers in this direction and we followed him. We had no idea that you were here."

Just then Shih Yung returned with about seven of the leaders and Ch'ao Kai who were all pleased to see Sung Chiang.

Ch'ao Kai said, "You would not listen to my advice, but left the mountain unattended. If we had not arrived you would have been in a dangerous position."

"As I was anxious about my father's safety," said Sung Chiang, "I could not stay."

"I will tell you now some good news," said Ch'ao Kai. "I gave orders for Tai Tsung and other leaders to get your father and brother, and they have escorted them to Liang Shan Po."

Sung Chiang was exceedingly pleased at hearing this, and saluted Ch'ao Kai, "Sir, you have done me a great favor, and I shall never forget it in my life."

They then all mounted their horses, and returned from the Huan Tao Village. Sung Chiang rode with his hands in a praying position as he was expressing thanks to the gods for his marvelous escape, and promising that he would make sacrifice later as a thank offering. They all duly reached Liang Shan Po without any further incident. Upon reaching the stronghold Sung Chiang met his father and brother at the main hall, and was exceedingly pleased to see them again. He said, "Father, I have been an unfilial son and caused so much trouble to you."

"That hateful fellow Chao Neng came every day to see that we did not escape," said Sire Sung. "He was only waiting for a letter to arrive from Chiang Chou then he would have arrested us and taken us to prison. When I heard you knocking at the back door I knew that there were about nine soldiers in front of the house. But they disappeared afterwards. In the midnight there came about a hundred men who forced open the gate of our farmyard. They forced me to enter a sedan chair, and told your brother to take with us some things. They then set the farmyard on fire. They took us here without allowing me to inquire who they were or where they were going."

"To-day we are all united together again," said Sung Chiang, "owing to the exertions of our brothers at this place." He then told his younger brother to salute and thank Ch'ao Kai and the other leaders for their timely action. After this, Ch'ao Kai and the leaders all paid their respects to Sire Sung. They then all sat down to a great feast to celebrate the union of the father and the son.

On the third day of this feasting Kung-Sun Sheng recollected that his mother was still at Chichow in Chihli province, and that he had not heard from her for a long time. During a feast Kung-Sun Sheng stood up, and addressed the assembly, "I am grateful to you heroes for your kind treatment to me. Since my arrival here we have had many glorious feasts and much pleasure, but all this time I have never once been home to see my mother. I am afraid that my old Taoist teacher will be anxiously thinking of me so I request that you will allow me to leave you for five months so that I can go and see how things are at home."

"I have heard you say before that your mother was in the North," said Ch'ao Kai, "but as you mention this matter to-day we cannot stand in your way. If you will wait till to-morrow we will arrange matters for your departure."

Kung-Sun Sheng thanked Ch'ao Kai for granting leave. The next day a special farewell meal was arranged in honor of him. He wore his old Taoist priest robe, with a coir palm hat. On his back were two swords, and in his hand he carried a fly brush. All the leaders were assembled, and they all drank him toast.

Ch'ao Kai finally spoke to him, "Do not break your promise about returning to us. We would rather not allow you go and we are only allowing you to go because of your anxiety about your mother. After a hundred days we shall be looking forward to your return."

"How dare I break my promise to you when you have treated me so liberally?" said Kung-Sun Sheng. "When I have visited my Taoist teacher and made proper arrangement for my mother I will return here at once."

"Would it not be better if you took some men with you so that you could bring your mother to our mountain here?" asked Sung Chiang.

"My mother likes to live in a quiet life," said Kung-Sun Sheng, "and hates any bustle. She won't agree to come here. We have fields and houses, and my mother prefers to stay and attend to those matters. I will just visit them, and then rejoin you here."

"In that case we will do as you wish," said Sung Chiang. "We hope that it will not be long before we see you again."

Ch'ao Kai presented Kung-Sun Sheng with a quantity of gold and silver to cover his traveling expenses, and the latter said, "I do not want so much." He only took half, and placed it in his belt. He then took his leave and departed.

He had just left when Li K'wei, the Black Whirlwind, entered the main gate crying loudly. "What is the trouble about?" asked Sung Chiang.

"I am very angry," said Li K'wei. "People bring their fathers here, while others go to see their mothers. Only I was come out from under the earth without father and mother."

"Well, what is your idea?" asked Ch'ao Kai.

"I have a mother at home," said Li K'wei. "My elder brother works as a servant at another house, and cannot do much to support my mother. If I bring her here to enjoy her life I should feel much more contented."

"You are right," said Ch'ao Kai, "I will let you have some men to go with you and bring your mother here."

"That won't do," said Sung Chiang. "Li K'wei has a bad temper, and should he return to his native village it would cause some trouble. If you sent men with Li K'wei that would also not do as he has a fiery disposition, and would make some disturbance on the way. He killed many men at Chiang Chou, and everybody knows that he is the Black Whirlwind. There will be a warrant out for his arrest. To look at his face would be enough to arouse suspicions anywhere. He would have a long way to go, and in case of danger how could we help him? You had better stay here until matters have settled down a bit, and then perhaps you could go in safety."

Li K'wei was vexed at this, and said, "Elder brother, you are most unfair. You got your father to come here for safety, while my mother is to remain at home in misery. It makes me so angry that my stomach is quite upset."

"Younger brother, do not get vexed," said Sung Chiang. "You can go if you will comply with three conditions."

The hand that shook mountains
Fought tigers with boldness.

CHAPTER 42

THE FALSE LI K'WEI COMMITS HIGHWAY ROB-
BERY; THE BLACK WHIRLWIND KILLS
FOUR TIGERS ON I LING

LI K'WEI had asked for the three conditions, and Sung Chiang replied, "When you go to I Shui Hsien, in I Chou, Shantung province to bring your mother here you must not drink wine on the way. That is the first condition. Secondly, you must go by yourself, because you have a hasty disposition and I am afraid that nobody wants to go with you. Thirdly, you must not take those axes with you, and on the way you must be discreet, and quickly get back here."

"I can easily comply with those conditions," said Li K'wei. "You need not worry. I should like to leave to-day." On that day he got his baggage ready, armed himself with two swords. He took one large ingot, and about five small pieces of silver. He drank a few cups of wine, took leave of his companions, and then went down the hill and across the lake.

After his departure the leaders were assembled in the main hall when Sung Chiang spoke, "I am afraid that our younger brother Li K'wei will get into trouble. I do not know whether there is any man here from his village. If so he might follow him, and report to us what happens on the way."

"Chu Kwei comes from the same village as Li K'wei," said Tu Chien.

"I had forgotten that," said Sung Chiang. "Of course they recognized each other as such at the White Dragon Temple near Chiang Chou." He immediately sent a man to summon Chu Kwei, and soon the latter arrived from his inn.

"Our brother, Li K'wei, has just gone to I Shui Hsien to bring his mother here. No man was sent to accompany him on account of his bad temper, when drunk. I understand that you are from his native district, and therefore I should be glad if you would follow him, and watch what might happen to him."

"I am a I Shui Hsien man," said Chu Kwei. "I have a younger brother who keeps a wine shop in that town just outside the West Gate. This man Li K'wei lived near a village called Po Chang in that district. He has an elder brother named Li Ta who is in regular employment. Li K'wei is a fierce and stupid man. Some time ago he committed murder at his village, and had to leave home, and dared not return. I have no objection to follow him, and look after him, but who will look after my inn while I am away? I have not been home for a long time, and should very much like to meet my brother again."

"You need not worry about your inn as I will send Hou Chien and Shih Yung to look after it during your absence," said Sung Chiang.

This was all arranged, and Chu Kwei started off on his way to I Shui Hsien.

Li K'wei traveled by himself, and duly reached his destination. He had stuck to the conditions laid down by Sung Chiang, and had not taken any wine on the way. At the West Gate he saw a big crowd of men reading a proclamation posted on the wall. He entered the crowd and listened to a man who was reading the proclamation for the information of the illiterate crowd. It read as follows: "(1) There is a thief called Sung Chiang of Yun Cheng Hsien; (2) Also a jailer named Tai Tsung, from the prison at Chiang Chou; (3) Also another thief named Li K'wei, of I Shui Hsien." As soon as he heard his own name Li K'wei got excited, and did not know what to do when a man embraced him saying, "Elder brother Chang, what are you doing here?" Upon looking at the man he recognized him as Chu Kwei, the Speedy Courier, and asked, "And what are you doing here?"

"Come with me and we will discuss matters," said Chu Kwei. They went together outside the town, and stopped at an inn in a small hamlet, where they entered a small room at the back of the premises.

Chu Kwei pointed at Li K'wei, "What a nerve you have! That proclamation was offering a reward of ten thousand strings of cash for the arrest of Sung Chiang; five thousand strings for Tai Tsung, and three thousand strings of cash for your arrest. Why did you stop there looking at such a notice? Should any man recognize you you would be arrested at once. Sung Chiang was afraid that you would get into trouble, and sent me here to watch over you. I left the mountain a day after your departure, and arrived here a day before you. What has delayed you?"

"It is due to Sung Chiang ordering me not to drink wine," said Li K'wei. "I walked slowly because of that. Do you know anyone at this inn? Where is your home in this place?"

"This inn belongs to my younger brother, Chu Fu, and I used to live here. I was once a merchant, but lost all my capital, and so went to Liang Shan Po. I have not been here since that time." He called for his brother, and introduced Li K'wei to him. Chu Fu then brought in some wine and invited them to partake of same.

"Our elder brother gave me an order not to drink wine," said Li K'wei. "But as I am no longer on the road and have reached my destination, I may drink two cups of wine now."

Chu Kwei raised no objection to this, and they stayed eating and drinking there until nearly 2 a.m. It was a bright moonlight night and Li K'wei wished to go, but Chu Kwei said, "You had better avoid the byroad, but turn round to the east when you come to a clump of trees and that will bring you to your home at Po Chang Village. You must bring your mother here, without delay, and we will set off at once for Liang Shan Po."

"I will go along the byroads, and will lose no time," replied Li K'wei.

"By that unfrequented road there are tigers and also bandits," said Chu Kwei.

"What am I afraid of?" asked Li K'wei. He then armed himself with his two swords, and left the two brothers. When he had gone about three miles it was getting daylight, he saw a hare leap out of the grass at the side of the path, and race off along the road. He pursued his way, and in about two miles came to the clump of trees, with leaves of red autumn tints. As he turned round the trees he met a big man who shouted, "You will be aware that if you pay us money we will not interfere with your baggage."

The man wore a coat of rough cloth and had a red silk turban. His face was sallow, and he held an ax in each hand.

Li K'wei shouted, "Who are you that dare commit highway robbery here?"

"If I told you my name you would be frightened. I am called the Black Whirlwind. If you pay our toll we will spare your life."

Li K'wei laughed loudly, "How dare you use my own name in this way? Who are you, and where do you come from, you barefaced rascal?" He took his sword and advanced towards the man.

The man saw that he had a very strong opponent and tried to retreat, but Li K'wei struck him with his sword so that he fell to the ground. Li K'wei put his foot on the man's breast and asked, "Do you know me now?"

The man on the ground said, "Please forgive me, sir."

"I am Li K'wei, the Black Whirlwind. Why do you use my name in this way?"

The man replied, "My name is Li, but I am not the Black Whirlwind. You have a great name, and if I use it people are afraid of me. It was because I found out the power of your name that I became a highwayman. I only stop single individuals, and as soon as they hear your name they drop their baggage and run away. I do not kill people, and yet I make a little profit. My name is Li, the Devil, and I live at the village a little up the road."

Li K'wei said, "You are a rowdy fellow. You seize traveler's baggage, and also carry axes in both hands like me, so that you injure my reputation. You can taste one of my axes," so saying he seized an ax out of the man's hand.

Li, the Devil, called out, "Sir, if you kill me you will kill two persons."

"How do you make that out?" asked Li K'wei, staying the blow.

"At home I support my mother who is ninety years of age, and this is my only means of helping her in her old age," said Li, the Devil. "I never injure people, but only make them afraid. If you kill me, my old mother will die of starvation."

This man (Li K'wei) who never twinkled his eyes in chopping off people's heads, paused and thought when he heard this. "Here am I trying to succour my old mother, and yet killing a man who supports his old mother. Heaven will not allow me to live if I do this. No! No! I will forgive this man." He took his foot off Li, the Devil, who saluted him. "I will let you off," said Li K'wei, "but in future you must not make use of my name."

"As you have spared my life," said Li the Devil, "I will give up this kind of life and earn an honest living in some other way."

"You are a filial son," said Li K'wei, "so I will give you ten ounces of silver to enable you to start a business." He did this, and then went on his way.

Li K'wei could not help laughing. "That fellow was quite in my hands, and yet I have started him on a fresh life." He walked on, and about 10 a.m. he was both thirsty and hungry. The footpath was quite isolated without a single house within sight. But after going some distance he saw two small straw huts a long way off. He went towards the huts, and when near he saw a woman come from behind the hut. She had a flower in her hair, and was well rouged. He spoke to her, "Sister, I am a traveler, and cannot come across an inn. I am very hungry. If you can supply me with food and wine I will pay you well."

The woman dared not refuse this when she saw the build of Li K'wei. "I have no wine, but can find you a little food."

"That will do," said Li K'wei. "Let me have a good meal as I am very hungry."

"Will a peck of rice be enough?" she asked.

"Three pecks would be better."

The woman took the rice, washed it in the stream, and then boiled it. While she was doing this Li K'wei went to the back of the house to relieve his bowels and there saw a man trudging along. Just then the woman came out of the back door to get some vegetables, and she asked the man, "What is the trouble with your leg?"

"I very nearly cannot see you again," replied the man. "I was very unlucky. I went to that place, and waited nearly a fortnight for a traveler to pass, but there was nothing doing. To-day, however, a traveler arrived, but do you think who it was? It was Li K'wei, the Black Whirlwind! It was a strange occurrence that I should meet him on such a quiet byroad. He knocked me down with a blow of his sword, and intended to kill me. But I deceived him by saying, 'If you kill me, you will kill two.' He asked me for an explanation, and I told him falsely that I had an old mother at home who depended on my support. If I was killed she would die of hunger. The fool believed me, and spared my life. He even gave me money to turn over a new leaf. So when he let me go I did not come straight here as he might have found me out, but instead I went up the hills and made a long detour."

"Don't talk so loudly!" the woman said. "A man came here, and asked for some food and it may be the same man. He is sitting outside the front door. You go and have a look at him. If he is the same man then go and get some drug to put in his food, and when it takes effect we can kill him. We can then get his money, which will enable us to live in the town and enter into trade—much better than being mere highwayman here."

Li K'wei thought, "What a rascal! I spared his life, and even gave him money, and yet he plans to kill me. Heaven cannot allow such man to live!" He went round the corner to the back door where they were talking. As soon as Li the Devil saw Li K'wei he tried to escape, but Li K'wei seized hold of him. The woman saw this, and went through the house to the front door. Li K'wei knocked Li the Devil on the ground, and then taking his sword cut off the man's head. He then went inside the house to seize the woman, but she had disappeared. He however searched in the rooms, found the place where they kept the money and woman's ornaments, and he took these. He noticed that the rice was well boiled, but there were no vegetables. When he had eaten enough, he placed the corpse in the house and set the whole place on fire. He then continued on his way, and reached his village of Tung Tien Tung about 5 p.m. He soon found his home, pushed open the door and entered. His mother called out from her bed, "Who is that?" Li K'wei saw that his mother was blind, and was sitting on the bed reciting her prayers. He called out, "Mother! Your Iron Ox has returned!"

"My boy, you have been absent for a long time. Where have you been employed? Your elder brother works as a servant, but the wages he gets are hardly enough to support us. I have often thought of you, and have weeped so much that I have become blind in both eyes. What are you doing now?"

Li K'wei thought, "If I tell her that I am a brigand from Liang Shan Po she will not go with me. I must tell her some fibs." So he said, "Mother, I am in government employment, and have come to take you away with me."

"Splendid! But how can I go?"

"I will carry you on my back to the road where we can find a cart."

"Well, wait until your elder brother comes, and then we will discuss the matter."

"Why wait?" asked Li K'wei. "I am going with you."

Just then it happened that his elder brother Li Ta entered the room carrying an earthenware jar containing rice for his mother. When Li K'wei saw his brother he kotowed and said, "Brother, I have not seen you for years."

Li Ta spoke abusively, "Why have you returned? Much trouble you will bring here again?"

His mother answered, "Your brother is now in government employment, and has specially come to take me away with him."

"Mother! Don't believe his nonsense," said Li Ta. "Some time ago he killed a man, and I was arrested, and wore a cangue for it. I have had much suffering for him. I have heard that he has joined the brigands at Liang Shan Po, and recently rescued some of them from an execution ground at Chiang Chou. A warrant is out for his arrest, and as they have not found him they wanted to arrest me. My master pleaded for me at the yamen, and said that my brother Li K'wei left home ten years ago, and we have not heard anything of him since then. He thought that perhaps the bandits were using the name of Li K'wei falsely. My master gave money to the officials at the yamen, and that is why they have not arrested me. A proclamation has been issued offering a reward of three thousand strings of cash for the arrest of my brother, Li K'wei. Now, he returns home, and talks nonsense to you."

"Do not worry," replied Li K'wei. "How would it be if we all went to Liang Shan Po, and had a good time there?"

Li Ta was angry at this, and tried to strike his brother, but was aware that he could not overcome him. He then threw the earthenware jar on the floor, and ran out of the room.

"He has gone to report my arrival," said Li K'wei to himself, "so I must leave at once before they arrive to arrest me. My brother has never seen much money so I will leave fifty ounces of silver on the bed for him. When he sees it he will not be so keen to witness my arrest." He did this and said, "Mother! I will now carry you on my back."

"Where are you going to?" she asked.

"You need not ask, anyhow it is a much better place than this," said Li K'wei. He then lifted his mother on his back, and left the house with her.

Now Li Ta had run and informed his master of the return of his brother, and soon came back with about ten farm laborers. When he entered the room he found nothing but a piece of silver on the bed. He then considered, "My brother has left this money for me. Where can he hide now? He may come with other men from Liang Shan Po. If I try to overtake him I shall only get into trouble."

As the laborers could not find Li K'wei they did not know what to do, but Li Ta told them, "My brother has evidently gone, and carried off my mother. There are many byroads about here, but how can we find which way he has gone." The men saw that Li Ta did not know what to do so after a rest they all returned to the farm.

Li K'wei, carrying his mother on his back, chose the quietest paths, and towards evening arrived at the foot of a range of mountains. He recognized the place as I Ling, and knew that if he crossed the range there were farmhouses on the other side. The moonlight was bright, and he had no difficulty in slowly ascending the mountain path. His mother asked him to find some water as she was quite thirsty, and Li K'wei assured her that as soon as they had crossed the mountain he would find a house where they could rest and get food. His mother replied that at the last meal she had had only dry rice without any liquid, and so was very thirsty. He replied, "My throat also burns like a fire, and my breath is like smoke issuing from my mouth. You wait until I get to the summit when I will have a look around for some water."

"I feel as though I must die. I am so thirsty," said his mother.

"I am getting very tired, mother," replied Li K'wei.

When he reached the summit he put his mother down by the side of a big green bowlder, and left his sword there, and went off to look for water. He soon heard the sound of running water, and after a few turns he came to a small stream. He had a good drink, using his hands as a cup, and then thought, "How can I carry some water to my mother?" He looked around on all sides, and at last espied a temple in the distance. He made his way there through the dense bushes. At last he reached the temple, and saw that it was called, "The Ta Shen Temple of Ssu Chou." In front of it was a stone incense urn, and he seized hold of it with the idea of using it to carry the water. But the stone urn was one solid piece with the base, and he could not move it. At this he got angry and using his full strength at last rooted the stone out of the ground. He then lifted it, and broke the top part from the base on the stone steps leading up to it.

He carried the stone urn off to the stream where he thoroughly washed it, and cleaned it out with grass. He then half filled it with water, and carried it off in both hands. He followed the same way back, but had great difficulties in making his way with such an awkward load. When he reached the big green bowlder, however, he was astounded not to see his mother although his sword was still there. He called out aloud for her, but there was no response. He became very anxious, as although he looked all around carefully he could find no traces or clue of her departure. But when he had gone a distance of about thirty steps he found the grass covered with blood. He trembled with fear now, but followed the marks. These at last brought him to a cave where he saw two tiger cubs inside eating a human leg. Shaking with anger he thought, "I came from Liang Shan Po to take my mother, and carried her here on my back, but it seems that she has been eaten by the tigers." His mind was inflamed with passion, and his face glared with a fierce look—his moustaches standing out like porcupine's quills. Seizing his sword he slashed at the tiger cubs. They growled, showed their teeth and claws as they reared on their hind legs, and rushed at him. He killed one with a single cut of his sword, and the other cub retreated to the cave. Li K'wei followed with sword in hand and killed the second cub. He then turned round and saw the tigress outside racing towards the cave. He said, "So you are the beast who has devoured my mother." He threw down his long sword, and took the dagger from his waist. The tigress stopped at the entrance, lashing its tail from side to side, and not having seen Li K'wei, turned round facing outside. Li K'wei jumped forward, and stabbed the beast in the hind-quarters—a mighty lunge typical of the rage that he felt. The tigress roared, and leapt away with the dagger sticking in her body, and galloped away. Li K'wei picked up his sword and left the cave. As the tigress had galloped off wounded a strong wind sprung up, shook the trees as in a big storm. There is an ancient saying, "Clouds originate with dragons, whereas winds originate with tigers." At that spot the moonlight was quite bright, and suddenly there was a tremendous roar, and a tiger leapt forth. It rushed at Li K'wei, who deliberately and without fear, slashed with his sword, and cut its throat as it sprang at him. The tiger feeling the pain, and finding breathing difficult, retreated a few steps, and then as it expired gave forth its last roar which sounded something like a landslide of half a mountain. Li K'wei had now killed four tigers, and he now entered the tigers' den in the cave, looking carefully to see whether there was still another one. Having found nothing there and being tired, he made his way back to the temple, and slept there that night. The next day he collected the remains and torn clothing of his mother, and buried them behind the temple. He could not avoid crying while doing this. He felt very hungry now, and continued his way across the range of mountains. He soon met five hunters armed with crossbows and arrows. Li K'wei's clothes were all covered with blood, and this sight startled the hunters. They asked, "Are you a guardian spirit of this mountain? How otherwise dare you cross the range?"

Li K'wei thought, "I cannot tell them who I am because there is a reward offered for my arrest." So he replied, "I am a traveler, and last night I was crossing the mountain with my mother. While I went to get some water for her a tiger attacked and ate her. So I found the tiger's den, and there killed two cubs, and afterwards two fully grown tigers. I slept last night in the Ta Shen Temple and have just come from there."

"We don't believe that," cried the hunters. "How could one man kill four tigers? We might believe you killing two cubs, but to kill two fully grown tigers is really a big achievement. We have been beaten by the officials for not killing those two tigers. Those tigers have been on the mountains for a long time, and during the last five months nobody has dared go that way. We do not believe what you say! You need not try to humbug us."

"I do not belong to this district," said Li K'wei. "Why should I humbug you? If you don't believe me then I will go and show you the dead tigers, and you can get them carried down the mountain."

"If this is true we shall be much indebted to you," said the hunters. They blew whistles, and soon about fifty men had assembled at that spot. They got poles and ropes, and then all accompanied Li K'wei up the mountain. There sure enough they found the bodies of the four tigers, and carried them down the mountain. The hunters reported the matter to the head of the first village they came to, and they then all adjourned to the big house of the local wealthy man—Mr. Ts'ao. This man was a clerk in the district yamen, and had made his wealth by extortion in his own village. He was disliked and also feared by his own neighbors. Yet he was always talking of loyalty and filial piety so that he was well known as a hypocrite. As soon as he heard what had happened he invited Li K'wei into the hall where he asked for full details of the remarkable event. Aftert his had all been recited he asked for the name and home address of Li K'wei.

"My name is Chang," replied Li K'wei, "but people generally call me 'Courageous Chang.'"

"You are certainly courageous," said Mr. Ts'ao, "if you had not a large gall you could not have killed four tigers." He then gave orders for a big feast to be provided in honor to the "Courageous Chang."

It was soon known in the villages around that four tigers had been killed by one man and in no time the people were crowding into the village, and into Mr. Ts'ao's house to see the tigers. There they gazed at the great hero who was being entertained in the hall by Mr. Ts'ao. Among the people was the wife of Li the Devil, whose husband Li K'wei had killed a few days ago. She had run away to her parents' home and when she heard the news about the tigers she followed the crowd. She recognized Li K'wei and immediately returned home and reported the matter to her parents. They went at once to the local Ti Pao who was given to know that Li K'wei was the criminal for whose arrest a reward had been offered. He secretly sent a messenger asking Mr. Ts'ao to come and discuss a very urgent matter. When Mr. Ts'ao received the message he decided not to tell Li K'wei, but merely said that he wished to retire and change his clothes, but when outside the room he hurried straight off to the other village.

"This man who has killed the tigers," said the Ti Pao, "is Li K'wei, the Black Whirlwind of Po Chang Village, and there is a summon out for his arrest."

"In that case you must make careful inquiries among the people, and make sure of the matter before we act. It will be an easy matter to arrest him when we are sure about his identity. If he is not the man then we should only make trouble by arresting him."

"There is a woman here, Mrs. Li, who recognizes him," said Ti Pao. "He came to her house and later he killed her husband."

"As that appears to be conclusive," said Mr. Ts'ao, "we had better entertain him at the feast, and then ask him whether he prefers to go to the magistrate and ask for a reward for killing the tigers, or whether he prefers to receive the reward in our village. If he objects to go to the magistrate for the reward we can assume that he is guilty. Then we must press him to take plenty of wine and get him drunk when we can easily tie him up. Then we can go to the magistrate yamen and ask them to send a police inspector to arrest him and so there can be no failure."

The Ti Pao agreed to this and made arrangements accordingly with his men. Mr. Ts'ao returned home and there resumed his seat at the table with Li K'wei. He said, "I hope you are not offended at my leaving you. Please make yourself quite at home. Loosen your dress and put your dagger at one side."

"I left my dagger in the belly of one of the tigers," said Li K'wei, "and only have the scabbard here. When they cut the tiger open I hope they will find my dagger and return it to me."

"Never mind that!" said Mr. Ts'ao. "I have a very good sword here which I will present to you."

Li K'wei thereupon took off the scabbard, and belt and handed them to a servant. Mr. Ts'ao ordered a fresh supply of food and wine. The Ti Pao, the hunters and several other men were present at the feast, and they each in turn toasted Li K'wei. During the feast Mr. Ts'ao asked Li K'wei whether he would prefer to receive the reward for killing the tigers at the magistrate yamen or in that village.

"I am only a traveler," said Li K'wei, "and have hardly time to go to the magistrate. I just happened to kill the tigers on my way, and do not care to go to the magistrate. I will receive the reward here, but even if there is no reward I can leave without it."

"We do not care to treat you disrespectfully," said Mr. Ts'ao, "so you must at least wait until we have collected the money to present you. We will send the tigers to the magistrate yamen."

"Could you first give me a change of clothing," asked Li K'wei, "as these clothes are rather soiled."

Mr. Ts'ao agreed to this and ordered a servant to bring a suit of blue cloth. Li K'wei took the new clothes, and when he had changed he was met outside the door of the hall by many men who also wished to drink a cup of wine with him. One cup of wine was warm, another was cold, and so on. Li K'wei did not suspect any plot, and drank freely with great joviality. He had now quite forgotten Sung Chiang's order that he was not to drink wine. It was not very long before he was dead drunk. The men then removed him to a small empty room at the back where they stretched him on a bench, and then bound him to the bench with ropes. The Ti Pao then sent urgent messengers to report the matter to the magistrate yamen. He also had an accusation drawn up for Mrs. Li who accompanied the messenger to the yamen.

When the magistrate heard the report he was startled and asked, "Where has the Black Whirlwind been arrested? We must not allow this rebel to escape!"

The messenger and the hunters told him that Li K'wei was imprisoned in Mr. Ts'ao's house in their village. They were afraid that he might escape, and did not dare to try to bring him to the yamen. The magistrate summoned inspector Li Yun to the court, and instructed him to take a large body of policemen to Mr. Ts'ao's house and arrest the prisoner Li K'wei, the Black Whirlwind. He was to exercise great care, and be sure that the prisoner did not escape.

Inspector Li Yun got together about thirty of his most trusted men, armed them and departed for the village. The Hsien was only a small place so that everybody knew what was happening. Now the news soon reached the village on the east side of the town where Chu Kwei was living with his brother. Chu Kwei spoke to his brother, "That fellow Li K'wei is evidently in trouble. What shall we do to save him? I was specially deputed by Sung Chiang to come here, and watch the proceedings, Li K'wei will be arrested, but if I do not save his life how can I go back and face our elder brother Sung Chiang? What shall we do?"

"Do not get excited," said Chu Fu. "This inspector Li Yun is a skilled military man, and fifty men cannot rival him. You and I are no match against him although we worked together on the same plan. We must use strategy and not force. Now inspector Li Yun is a close personal friend of mine, and every day he has been training me in the use of military weapons. I have a plan, but it will prevent our living in this place any more. We must boil about twenty pounds of meat and cut it up into large pieces and prepare about ten jars of wine. In both of these we must mix some sleeping drug. About 4 a.m. we must start off with our assistants carrying the food and wine and wait in a quiet spot on the road for Li Yun. When he arrives we must offer him and his men the food and wine as a gift, and get them all senseless. Then we can release Li K'wei and escape."

"That is a splendid plan," said Chu Kwei, "and we will get things ready at once."

"Inspector Li Yun does not drink wine," said Chu Fu, "and as he will only take the drugged meat he will probably recover consciousness before the others. As soon as he finds out how we have deceived him it will not be safe for any of us to stay here."

"You are an innkeeper here," said Chu Kwei, "but you do not make much money. It would be better if you can go with me to Liang Shan Po and join the brigands there, and get much money and new clothing and enjoy life generally, We can tell two of your servants to get a cart, load up your valuables with your wife, and send them on in advance to wait for us at a village called Shih Li Pai."

"Brother, that is a good idea," replied Chu Fu. He arranged matters accordingly, and it was not long before the cart had started on its way.

That evening the two brothers boiled the meat and mixed the drug in same. They also prepared the wine in the same way. The whole supply was made up into two loads, and they also took about thirty cups with them. The two servants and the two brothers divided the loads. They got away about 4 a.m. and halted when they came to a quiet desolate spot on the road. It was just dawn when they heard the sound of gongs approaching, and Chu Kwei went forward by himself to meet the party. It was inspector Li Yun with his men escorting the prisoner Li K'wei, the Black Whirlwind, to the town. Inspector Li Yun was riding a horse in the rear of his party. As they came up to Chu Fu he called out, "Sir, I request you to stop, and accept a little refreshment." He at once offered Li Yun wine while Chu Kwei passed round the meat. Upon seeing this inspector Li Yun quickly dismounted and hurrying to the front spoke to Chu Fu, "Friend, why have you come so far as this to entertain us?"

"I wish to give you a little comfort," replied Chu Fu. He saw that inspector Li Yun was not drinking the wine so he continued, "I am aware that you are a teetotaler but I particularly request you to take a little liquor this time."

Inspector Li Yun did not like to refuse this pressing offer so he took a few sips. Chu Fu then pressed him to take a little meat, but inspector Li Yun declined this as he said he had had a big dinner last night.

"But you have a long way to go," replied Chu Fu, "and you will be hungry before you reach your destination. Please take a little at least and so save my face with your men."

Here again inspector Li Yun did not like to cause annoyance by declining the offer, so he ate some of the meat. All the policemen also partook of the wine and the meat, and Chu Kwei even offered it to all the villagers who were following the party. Without making inquiries as to whether it was hot or cold they all set to and had a good feed. They all took it in a happy-go-lucky style and no questions were raised.

Li K'wei seeing Chu Kwei and his brother knew that this was some trick so he said, "Are you not going to give me some of this stuff?"

"Why should we? You are only a mere criminal," replied Chu Kwei. "You had better shut your mouth as you have not long to live."

Just then inspector Li Yun saw that his men were looking at each other stupidly and could not move so he exclaimed, "We have been fooled by a ruse." He tried to move, but instead he also fell down and was soon asleep.

Chu Kwei and Chu Fu seizing their swords now shouted out, "Let no man depart!" Some men however tried to get away, but they were soon caught and killed on the spot. Li K'wei seeing this burst asunder the ropes and taking a sword went up to inspector Li Yun to kill him. But Chu Fu stopped him, "Do not kill him! He is my teacher, and is an extremely good man."

"Then let me at least kill that ass, Mr. Ts'ao," said Li K'wei. He went forward and found Mr. Ts'ao and the wife of Li the Devil, he killed both of them. He also killed the hunters, the Ti Pao, and all the soldiers. He then stripped a soldier of his uniform and put it on himself. The three men then left the scene by a small side path. But Chu Fu soon stopped and said, "How can I leave like this? Inspector Li Yun was my teacher, but how can he face the magistrate alone when all his men have been slaughtered? He must come to pursue us when he recovers consciousness, and I will wait for him and suggest to him to escape with me and join the bandits at Liang Shan Po."

Chu Kwei said, "Younger brother, what you say is quite

true. I will go forward and join the cart. Li K'wei will stop here with you and wait for him. But if inspector Li Yun will not come with you then you must not insist on waiting for him."

"I agree," said Chu Fu. Chu Kwei then departed.

Chu Fu and Li K'wei sat down and after about two hours they saw inspector Li Yun rushing towards them with a sword in his hand and shouting, "You brigands shall not escape." Li K'wei saw that inspector Li Yun was furious and fearing that he might strike Chu Fu, stood up, with his sword to fight with inspector Li Yun.

> Liang Shan Po gains two tigers,
> And welcomes and fêtes four men.

CHAPTER 43

THE GAY LEOPARD MEETS TAI TSUNG ON A NARROW ROAD; THE SICK KWAN SO MEETS SHIH HSIU ON A BIG STREET

LI K'WEI and inspector Li Yun fought for about seven bouts, without either gaining an advantage. Chu Fu at last also took a sword and rushing between the two stopped the fighting. "No more fighting!" he said, "listen to me! Teacher! I am much obliged to you for your instructions, and shall always think of repaying you for favors received. My brother Chu Kwei received orders from Sung Chiang, the commander in chief, at Liang Shan Po to come here to help Li K'wei. If you should arrest Li K'wei and send him to prison how could my brother face Sung Chiang if he had not helped Li K'wei to escape? I am responsible for the plan to get you to drink the drugged wine. Our elder brother wanted to kill you, but I interposed and saved your life. We thought that you would pursue us as you would not care to return to the yamen without obtaining your revenge. But when I remembered what favors you had bestowed on me in the past I decided to stay here and speak to you. Teacher, you are an intelligent man and will know how difficult it will be for you to explain to the magistrate how your policemen were killed and the prisoner escaped. You will undoubtedly be tried and nobody will help you. Would it not be better if you come with us to Liang Shan Po and there join our band? What do you think of that?"

Inspector Li Yun thought the matter over for some time and at last said, "I am afraid that they will not allow me to join their band."

Chu Fu laughed at this question. "Teacher, have you not heard the reputation of Sung Chiang who is famous for welcoming and receiving heroes from all quarters?"

Inspector Li Yun sighed, "I am homeless and without a place of refuge. I, however, have neither wife nor child to be arrested I will go with you."

Li K'wei laughed. "But, elder brother, why didn't you say this before?" He then exchanged salutations. All three men then pursued the cart of Chu Kwei, which they met halfway. They journeyed to Liang Shan Po, and upon arriving there Li Yun and Chu Fu were introduced to the leaders by Chu Kwei who mentioned their nicknames, "Blue Eyed Tiger" and "Laughing Tiger." Li K'wei then told them of his adventures and of the death of his mother and Sung Chiang laughing said, "You are a wonderful fellow. You killed four tigers and have now brought two living tigers to our stronghold." Everybody was pleased at the news, and a feast was arranged to celebrate the occasion.

Wu Yung spoke, "Our affairs have recently been very prosperous and we must have a great reputation everywhere. Great heroes have come here from all quarters because of the great virtue of our two chieftains, Ch'ao Kai and Sung Chiang, and also because they have heard of our great happiness. I propose that we establish three more inns in the surrounding country so that we can spy on travelers, and also look out for any more heroes who may pass this way. They can also inform us of any movement of troops so that we shall not be taken by surprise. On the west side there is a very wide area where we can well have an inn in charge of Tung Wei and Tung Meng with about ten men. An inn can be established on the road to the south, in charge of Li Li, with about ten men. Shih Yung and ten more men can start an inn on the north road. We must arrange boats and signaling arrows. We must also establish three barriers on those roads for our outposts, and we can place Tu Chien in charge of them. We must also place a number of men under T'ao Tsung-wang to deepen the creeks and waterways, and repair the roads in the surrounding area. He knows how to undertake that kind of works. Our granaries and storerooms must be kept in order by Chiang Chin. Hsiao Jang can have charge of all our means of communication between the various units. All engraving work on tablets etc. shall be in charge of Chin Ta-chien. All clothing armor, flags, etc shall be under the control of Hou Chien. Li Yun shall have charge of all building constrnctions. Ma Lin in charge of all boats, Sung Wan and Pai Sheng to be stationed at our main entrance, the Golden Sand Bund, while Wang Ying and Cheng Tien-shou be stationed at our outpost at Duck's Bill Beach, Mu Chun and Chu Fu to be in charge of the treasury, Lu Fang and Kuo Sheng to be in charge of the assembly hall; Sung Ching to be in charge of all rations." These appointments were agreed to, and arranging the details of all these staff matters took fully three days. Everything went smoothly at Liang Shan Po and the men were drilled every day.

One day Sung Chiang spoke to Ch'ao Kai, Wu Yung, and other leaders, "Just now we are all assembled at this place in the cause of justice, but our Kung-Sen Sheng is absent. He went to Chi Chou, Chihli province, to visit his mother and teacher and said that he would return in a hundred days. He has now been absent for a long time and yet no tidings has arrived concerning him. We had better send Tai Tsung to make inquiries, and then we shall know what has happened."

Tai Tsung agreed to do this and early the following day he departed for Chi Chou. On the way he took only tea and simple food without meat. On the third day he arrived at I Shui Hsien, and there happened to hear a man say that Li K'wei had escaped a few days ago after killing many policemen and that inspector Li Yun had disappeared, and nobody knew where he had gone to.

Tai Tsung was amused at this. He had left the town, and was proceeding on his way when he saw a man in the distance approaching who was armed with a spear. The man seeing Tai Tsung traveling at such a great speed called out, "Flying Prince" (which was Tai Tsung's nickname). Upon hearing this Tai Tsung turned his head to look at the man. He saw a big man with a straight nose, and a big mouth, a handsome countenance, a slender waist but broad shoulders. Tai Tsung retraced his steps and said to the man, "I do not seem to remember you and yet you have called my name."

The man quickly replied, "You are the Flying Prince," and he thereupon kotowed. Tai Tsung returned the compliment and then asked, "What is your esteemed name?"

"I am Yang Lin of Chang Te Fu, Honan province. I am a highwayman and people call me Gay Leopard. A few months ago I met Kung-Sun Sheng at an inn on the road, and he told me that at Liang Shan Po there are many heroes who are keen for justice. He gave me a written introduction for Liang Shan Po and urged me to join your band. I did not dare to go there straightway. He also informed me about the inn kept by Chu Kwei who was always looking out for suitable men. He also told me about you. I did not expect that Heaven would favor me and enable me to meet you like this to-day."

"I have orders from Sung Chiang to proceed to Chi Chou, and find out what has become of Kung-Sun Sheng," said Tai Tsung, "and I never expected to meet you."

"I know the Chi Chou district very well," replied Yang Lin, "and if you like I will accompany you to that place."

"That will suit me very well," said Tai Tsung. "After I have found Kung-Sun Sheng we can proceed to Liang Shan Po together."

Yang Lin was much pleased at this. Tai Tsung now took off his charmed puttees and they both traveled along the road at an ordinary pace. They stopped that evening at an inn, and there Tai Tsung told Yang Lin that he was a vegetarian. Yang Lin agreed to eat the same food. The following morning when they had started off Yang Lin said, "I am afraid that I am only holding you back, because I cannot travel at your speed. Would it not be better if we each went our own way?"

"I can fasten two of my charmed puttees on your legs," said Tai Tsung, "and then we can both travel quickly."

"I am only a common person," said Yang Lin, "and am afraid that I could not equal your skill in rapid locomotion."

"Never mind!" said Tai Tsung, "I have a means whereby any man can travel with me. I myself am a vegetarian but that will not be any obstacle to the other people." He then took two of his charmed greaves and put them on Yang Lin's legs. He had two on his own legs also. He then recited a spell breathed on the greaves, and they both started off. Tai Tsung controlled the speed at which they traveled whether slow or fast. They conversed as they traveled and did not notice how far they had gone.

About 10 a.m. they came to a post station which was surrounded by hills. Yang Lin knew the place as Yin Ma Chuan, and told Tai Tsung that the hill in front was generally infested with brigands, but he did not know whether there were any there now. The hills had a fine appearance with many pointed peaks, and streams winding in all directions. Just as they reached the foot of the mountain they heard gongs and drums being beaten and saw their way obstructed by a body of about one hundred men. In front were two big men armed with swords, who called out, "Halt! Who are you and where are you going? If you pay our road toll we will spare your lives."

Yang Lin laughed and said to Tai Tsung, "Elder brother, you can now watch me kill those men." Seizing his spear he advanced. The two men noticed the fierce look of Yang Lin and one called out, "No need for fighting! Are you not Yang Lin?"

Yang Lin stood still as he recognized them. The men now advanced and saluted. Yang Lin beckoned Tai Tsung to approach and introduced them to each other. "This is Teng Fei, of Hsiang Yang Fu, who is nicknamed Bloodshot-eyed Demon. He is skilled in the use of a chain, and in fight nobody can get near him. We used to be in the same band but I have not seen him for five years. I never expected to meet him in this place."

Teng Fei asked Yang Lin who his friend was as he was evidently no ordinary person.

Yang Lin introduced Tai Tsung, and after the usual compliments he then introduced the second man. "This is Meng Kang of Chen Ting Chou, Chihli province, and he is a boat builder. Once a commander-in-chief was worrying him about the work and he (Meng Kang) killed the man and then sought refuge in the mountains, and lived as a bandit. Because of his great size people call him Flagstaff."

Tai Tsung was much pleased and asked, "How long have you two gentlemen been doing business at this delightful spot?"

"I will tell you the truth," replied Teng Fei,"We have been here for more than a year. About six months ago we met on the west side of this place a man named Pei Hsuan, a Ching Chao Fu man, who had been an official clerk and used to write out excellent official indictments in this division. He was well known as an upright official and could not be tampered with, and so he gained the nickname of Iron Faced Clerk. He was both wise and brave. A very covetous governor was however appointed to this fu and made false accusations and banished Pei Hsuan to Sha Men Tao. On the way the escort passed this place, and we attacked them, killed most of the men and rescued Pei Hsuan. We now have about three hundred men here. Pei Hsuan is now our leader, and he is very skillful with two swords, one in each hand. We request you two gentlemen to come with us to our stronghold where we will introduce you to our leader." He then ordered horses for Tai Tsung and Yang Lin and the party soon reached the stronghold. Pei Hsuan had already been informed by messenger of the newcomers and he met them at the entrance. He was a fine type of man and had a very dignified appearance. After the usual introductions and salutations he invited them to come into the main hall where he asked Tai Tsung to take his seat facing him with Yang Lin and the others at the sides. A feast was arranged for that evening and during same Tai Tsung gave free accounts of the power of the bandits at Liang Shan Po, and eventually suggested that they should join them.

"Here we have about five hundred men, and three hundred horses, plenty of food and treasures. But if you do not disdain our humble establishment you might introduce us to your leaders and we might be of some use to you," said Pei Hsuan.

"Our two leaders, Ch'ao Kai and Sung Chiang, would treat you well, as they are keen on having heroes like you in their band," replied Tai Tsung. "If you go it will add brilliance to our present splendor. At present I am on my way to Chi Chou Fu to find one of our leaders Kung-Sun Sheng, and upon my return journey I will call here, and if you will be ready we can all depart together to Liang Shan Po."

They were all pleased with this proposal, and continued with their feasting and drinking.

The next day Tai Tsung and Yang Lin went on their way, and the bandits began to make preparations for their early departure to Liang Shan Po.

Tai Tsung and Yang Lin soon reached Chi Chou Fu and upon entering an inn there Yang Lin said, "As Kung-Sun Sheng is a keen Taoist moralist it is very probable that he is staying in some secluded spot in the mountains or forests and not in this town."

Tai Tsung agreed and they left the inn, and went outside the town. They traveled in the surrounding country and continually inquired for Kung-Sun Sheng, but nobody had heard of him. The next day they extended their journey, but again without any result.

On the third day of their wanderings Tai Tsung said, "Perhaps there will be somebody in the town who knows him. Let us go there." They made inquiries in the town that day, but without success. As they were going along the main street, however, they saw a procession with music. In front were two jailers carrying presents and rolls of silks and at the rear was a large umbrella of blue silk under which walked an execution supervisor. The latter was well dressed in blue silk. His eyebrows were long and his beautiful eyes were tilted upwards. His skin was light brown and his mustache was scanty.

He was a Honanfu man, named Yang Hsiung, and his cousin had been governor of Chi Chou Fu. The new governor knew Yang Hsiung and had appointed him superintendent of two prisons and also execution supervisor. He was skilled in military exercises, and because he had a yellow skin people called him Sick Kwan So (Kwan So being the name of a strong man of Tang dynasty). Behind Yang Hsiung in the procession was the executioner carrying a sword. An execution had just been carried out in the town at the crossroad, and on his way back to his home many people had congratulated him. He had to stop in many places on the street and drink wine with his numerous friends. Just as the procession reached them Yang Lin and Tai Tsung saw a band of about eight men emerge from a side street under the leadership of a man called Chang Pao whose nickname was the Goat Kicker. This man was in command of the city guard, but the men with him were a gang of rowdies who lived by demanding money from all classes of people both in the town and outside. The officials had failed to suppress their depredations. Many people were afraid of Yang

Hsiung, but Chang Pao was not of the number. Knowing that Yang Hsiung would have received many rolls of silk on way Chang Pao had got these rowdies together in order to create a disturbance on the street. Yang Hsiung had stopped to drink wine, and Chang Pao pressed his way through the crowd and said to him, "Congratulations!"

Yang Hsiung returned the salute and replied, "Brother, please join me with wine."

"I did not come for a drink," said Chang Pao, "but to borrow a hundred strings of cash from you."

"Although I know you," replied Yang Hsiung, "I do not remember having been very intimate with you so why should I lend you money?"

"To-day you have fraudulently taken valuables from a great many people so why should you not lend me some money?" asked Chang Pao.

"These things were duly presented to me as gifts by my admirers," said Yang Hsiung. "So why do you say they were fraudulently taken from people? You are a military man whereas I am in charge of the prisons so that we have nothing to do with each other, and you have no claim on me."

Chang Pao did not attempt to reply to this, but turning round told the rowdies to seize the rolls of silk. Yang Hsiung protested, saying "You have no manners." He was going to strike the rowdise but was seized hold of by Chang Pao, but two of the rowdies grabbed hold of his arms. Several men advanced in threatening attitudes, and Yang Hsiung's men bolted upon seeing that Yang Hsiung could not move, and also had to submit to the indignities. A man in the crowd carrying a load of firewood, however, jumped forward to assist Yang Hsiung. He called out, "Why do you beat this official like this?"

Chang Pao stared at the interrupter and said, "Beggars should mind their own business. This has nothing to do with you." The man was enraged at this insult, and seizing hold of Chang Pao's hair threw him to the ground. The rowdies came to the rescue of Chang Pao, but the man fought them with his fists—striking on all sides. This had taken men from holding Yang Hsiung, and he, freeing himself, also joined in the fight. The rowdies were soon knocked down, and Chang Pao seeing the position made his escape. Yang

Hsiung was now very angry, and pursued Chang Pao. The men with the booty were in front, and when they turned into an alley Chang Pao followed them with Yang Hsiung running after him.

The man who had changed the position kept on fighting the rowdies who were left behind. Tai Tsung nodded to Yang Lin and said, "What a fine man! He draws his sword to help another in trouble on the road." The two advanced and spoke to the man, "Listen to us! There has now been enough fighting." They conducted the man into an alley close by, where they found an inn. Yang Lin had carried in the man's load of firewood.

After the usual salutations Tai Tsung said, "We are quite strangers here, but we witnessed your chivalrous action, and being afraid that you might kill one of the men we intervened. Please drink wine with us, and let us become intimate friends."

"I am much obliged to you, gentlemen, for amicably settling that affair," replied the man, "and many thanks for your invitation."

They all sat down. Yang Lin summoned the waiter, and giving him an ounce of silver told him to serve whatever food was available. This was soon placed on the table with wine, and answering a question the guest stated, "My name is Shih Hsiu, and I am a Nanking man. I have had some training in military exercises, and I love to help people on the road who are in difficulties. Because of this people call me Desperado. I went with my uncle on a business trip, but he died on the way. I went on with the business, but lost all the money so that I could not go back. Therefore I stayed here, and eke out a livelihood by selling firewood. I tell you all this because of your helping me in that matter on the street."

"We are on business here," said Tai Tsung, "and are pleased to meet such a chivalrous hero as you. You merely sell firewood here so how can you hope to become wealthy? Would it not be better if you became a brigand and enjoyed life a little?"

"I am only skilled in the use of stick," said Shih Hsiu, "but as I have no other ability how can I improve my position and enjoy life?"

"You need not say you have no other ability," said Tai Tsung. "It is only too true that the government is corrupt and the officials are traitorous. I had a friend who through temper got into trouble, but he joined the bandits at Liang Shan Po where he now has good clothing and plenty of money. When government affairs are put in order he will undoubtedly be recalled and receive a good post."

Shih Hsiu sighed, "I would like to go, but I do not see how it could be done."

"If you want to go I could introduce you to the bandits."

"I dare not ask the names of you two gentlemen," said Shih Hsiu.

Tai Tsung disclosed their names, and offered Shih Hsiu ten ounces of silver which however the latter accepted only after much pressing. Just then they heard men outside and looking round they saw Yang Hsiung with about twenty policemen. Tai Tsung and Yang Lin were afraid of the police, and made their escape.

Shih Hsiu went forward, and asked Yang Hsiung where he was going. The latter said, "Brother, I have been looking for you everywhere. Why did you come in here to drink wine? When I was held up by Chang Pao and his gang, I could not have got free had you not intervened for which I am much obliged to you. I went to arrest Chang Pao, and get my presents back and so had to abandon you for the nonce. These men all came to my assistance, and when I had recovered all the stolen things I came to look for you, but could not find you. I however heard that you had come here with two men so I came here to look for you."

"I just came in here with two strangers to drink wine, and I did not think you would be looking for me."

Yang Hsiung asked for his name, etc. and Shih Hsiu gave him the information, and also his life's short history which we have just read.

Yang Hsiung then invited all the men to drink three cups of wine, and this having been done they all departed.

"I think that you have no relatives in this town," said Yang Hsiung, "and I therefore suggest that we become sworn brothers."

Shih Hsiu asked for his honorable age and upon learning that he was twenty-nine, he said, "Well, I am only twenty-eight, so I must ask you to be seated, and receive my kotow and salutations." This was done—Shih Hsiu giving four kotows. Yang Hsiung was much pleased at this and ordered the waiter to bring more wine. He said, "Younger brother, we will celebrate this by getting drunk."

While they were drinking wine Yang Hsiung's father-in-law named Pan came in with about five men, "What do you want, sir?" asked Yang Hsiung.

"I heard that you had had a fight on the street," said Mr. Pan, "and therefore I came to find you and help you."

"My younger brother here came to my assistance," said Yang Hsiung, "and we beat our assailant (Chang Pao) so that he would run away upon seeing our shadows. Just now I have become the sworn brother of this gentleman, Shih Hsiu."

"That is splendid," said Mr. Pan, "when my men have had a drink they will depart." The men were served with three cups of wine each, and then left. Mr. Pan then took his seat between the two friends.

"I am much pleased that you have become a sworn brother of my son-in-law," said Mr. Pan. "Having your assistance he will fittingly be an employee in the yamen and nobody will dare try to deceive him. What business are you engaged in, may I ask?"

"My father was a butcher," said Shih Hsiu.

"And do you follow the same occupation?" asked Mr. Pan.

"As a boy I of course got to know all about the trade," said Shih Hsiu laughingly.

"I followed the same trade," said Mr. Pan, "until my son-in-law here got a position in the yamen when of course I had to give up that trade."

When they had drunk some more wine together Yang Hsiung paid the bill, and they took their departure, Shih Hsiu shouldering his load of firewood. Upon reaching the door of Yang Hsiung's house he called out, "Wife, come and be introduced to my newly sworn brother."

A voice inside the curtain asked, "Who is this new sworn brother?"

"You need not ask questions," said Yang Hsiung; "you can come and see for yourself."

The curtain was raised and a woman stepped forth. She had been born on the 7th day of the seventh moon, and therefore had the name of "Clever Clouds" (the seventh moon is called Ch'iao Yueh, the clever month). She had first married an official clerk called Wang, who had died after two years of married life. Her second husband was Yang Hsiung and they had been married almost a year.

Shih Hsiu saluted her, but she objected, "I am much younger than you, and cannot accept such marks of respect."

"We have become sworn brothers to-day," said Yang Hsiung, "so that you are the elder brother's wife, and therefore can receive at least half of these salutations." Accordingly Shih Hsiu kotowed four times. The woman responded with two kotows, and then invited them inside. She also prepared a spare room for Shih Hsiu's use.

We need not go into many details. The next day Yang Hsiung before he left for his office in the yamen told his wife to see that Shih Hsiu had whatever clothes he required.

When Tai Tsung and Yang Lin had left Shih Hsiu in the inn they went outside the town and found an inn there. The next day they continued their inquiries for Kung-Sun Sheng without any result. So they gave up their search, and returning to Yin Ma Chuan they joined Pei Hsuan and his company and started off with them for Liang Shan Po where they were all duly introduced and placed on the strength.

Mr. Pan discussed with Shih Hsiu the question of reëstablishing a slaughter house. He said that behind his house there was an alley with a dead end and also an empty house. There was also a well, and he thought it a very suitable place for a slaughter house. Shih Hsiu could live on the premises.

Shih Hsiu was much pleased at the proposal, and agreed at once. Mr. Pan made inquiries and soon found suitable assistants. He suggested that Shih Hsiu should keep the accounts. They soon purchased the stock in trade, knives, benches, etc. and after selecting a lucky day they started business. All the neighbors and relatives came to take part in the feasting on the opening day.

Matters proceeded smoothly for a long time. One day during the winter Shih Hsiu went into the country to buy pigs, and upon his return three days later he found that the butchery was closed. Upon going inside he discovered that all the tools and fittings had been removed. He thought, "There is a saying, 'Men cannot be good for a thousand days, and flowers cannot bloom for a hundred days.' Yang

Hsiung has to go to his office every day, and cannot look after the home affairs. His wife must have been talking behind my back, and finding fault because I have been away for three days. He has suspected me, and has closed the business. I will not trouble to even ask for an explanation, but will just return to my old home." So he made up his accounts, changed his clothes, packed up his own things, and entered by the back door. He found that Mr. Pan had prepared a vegetarian feast in readiness for Shih Hsiu's return. Mr. Pan said, "You have been a long way, and must be very tired."

"Sir, that's my duty," replied Shih Hsiu. "Now I have squared up the account book, and everything is in order. If there is any error may Heaven and Earth destroy me."

"Why do you talk like this?" asked Mr. Pan. "There is no necessity for it."

"I have not been home for nearly seven years," said Shih Hsiu, "and as I must now go I have squared up all the accounts."

Mr. Pan laughed loudly and said, "You are mistaken. Please listen to me."

<blockquote>
Revenge is sought, so toll the knell,
And send an unfaithful priest to hell.
</blockquote>

CHAPTER 44

YANG HSIUNG WHILE DRUNK CURSES HIS WIFE; SHIH HSIU PLANS THE KILLING OF THE PRIEST HAI

OLD Mr. Pan spoke to Shih Hsiu, "Uncle, do not go. I understand your ideas. After an absence of two days you return, and find the butchery closed, and things cleared out, so you thought the business was finished. Even if the business was a failure you could still stay at our home. It is just two years since my daughter's first husband, Wang, died, and she wished to have a memorial service by priests. Therefore we closed the butchery and sent to the Gratitude Temple for priests. We would like you to take charge of the arrangements made. I am too old, and would be continually falling asleep in the night."

"In that case," said Shih Hsiu, "I will stay here for sometime."

"After this I must ask you, uncle not to have any suspicions of what we do here," said Old Mr. Pan.

Early the next day the priest assistant arrived to arrange the room for prayers. He erected an altar, arranged the drums, cymbals, gongs, and musical stone, and set out the lamps and incense. He then went into the kitchen to prepare the feast.

When Yang Hsiung came he told Shih Hsiu that he was on duty and would not be back that night. He must therefore not wait for him. He left all the matters in his hands.

"You need not worry about anything," said Shih Hsiu. "I will look after everything."

Yang Hsiung then departed and Shih Hsiu took charge. Shortly afterwards the door curtain was raised and a young priest entered who gave Shih Hsiu a priestly salutation. Shih Hsiu also saluted, and asked the priest to be seated. He then called out to Old Mr. Pan in the next room, "Father-in-law, the priest has arrived."

Mr. Pan came in, and the priest spoke to him, "My adopted father, why have you not been to our temple for such a long time?"

"We have opened a new butchery here so that I have had very little spare time," said Old Mr. Pan.

"This is the anniversary of the death of Wang and I have not sent you any presents, but I hope that you will accept this vermicelli and some dates I have had prepared for you," said the priest.

"Why do you spend so much money? How unreasonable!" said Old Mr. Pan. He asked Shih Hsiu to take them, and the latter carried the tray with the presents into the next room. Shih Hsiu soon returned with tea which he offered to the priest.

Just then Mrs. Pan, the Clever Cloud, came down the staircase into the room. She was plainly dressed, and had no rouge on her face. She spoke to Shih Hsiu, "Who has sent the presents?"

"They are from a priest who called your father his adopted father," said Shih Hsiu.

Mrs. Pan, Clever Cloud, laughed and said, "I know. They are from Pei Ju-hai, the priest whose religious name is Hai She-li, a very honest man. He is the son of Mr. Pei of the woolen goods shop, and is now at the Gratitude Temple. He is two years my senior, and therefore I can address him as elder brother; uncle, you can listen to his recital of the prayers this evening, as he has a very good tone."

"Is that so?" said Shih Hsiu. In listening to her, however, he suspected she had some hidden desire.

Shih Hsiu did not follow her, but looked on through the bamboo curtain. He saw that the priest gave her a very elaborate salute. The woman asked the priest, "Why did you spend so much money for the presents?"

"Sister, the presents are so small that they are not worth mentioning," replied the priest.

"As you have become a priest, how can we accept your presents?" said the woman.

"At our temple we have just begun a prayer for the dead which we should like you to participate. I hope that your husband will raise no objections to that."

"I do not think he will mind that," said the woman. "When my mother was dying I made a vow that I would offer prayers, and sooner or later I will trouble you to fulfill my vow for me in your temple."

"That's my business; whatever you order me I will do as you desire," said the priest.

"Sometime I will ask you to recite the prayers for my late mother's benefit," she said.

Just then a maid-servant entered with tea. The woman took the cup, wiped it clean with her sleeve, and then offered it to the priest. The priest took the cup, but at the same time he gazed amorously into her eyes. The woman returned his gaze with a smile.

Neither of them suspected that their exchange of flirtation was being closely watched by Shih Hsiu behind the bamboo curtain. He now began to understand the woman a little better. He thought, "How deceptive are appearances. She always spoke to me in a very free and open manner, but I thought it was because I was a sworn brother of her husband. Now I think she cannot have been a very virtuous woman. She is now however in my hands, and I must deal with the matter for Yang Hsiung." He raised the curtain, and entered the room.

The priest immediately put down his cup of tea and said, "Brother, please be seated."

The woman interposed, "This is the sworn brother of my husband."

The priest had suspicions at once and hurriedly inquired, "Brother, may I ask where you are from, and also your name?"

"Me! My name is Shih Hsiu. I am from Nanking! I help other people to revenge their wrongs and therefore they call me the Desperado. I am however only a stupid fellow, and if I intrude in your affairs I hope that you will not resent it."

"Never mind! Never mind!" said the priest hurriedly, "I am just now going to summon the priests to come and commence the service." He left the room at once.

That fickle woman called after him, "You must soon come back." She then went into the inner room.

Shih Hsiu stood near the door with bowed head in deep thought. It was not long before the priests arrived, lit the candles, and began to burn incense. They began their intoning of the prayers accompanied by drum beating, cymbals, etc., when Shih Hsiu and Old Mr. Pan had supplied them with tea and hot soup.

Soon that fickle woman entered, burnt her incense, and offered prayers and her priest increased the sound of his intoning. The other priests nudged each other as they witnessed this display of the two lovers, and the service was soon in disorder. When the service was over the priests were asked to dine in the next room. The priest Hai maneuvered his way to the rear of the priests, and turning his head to the woman he laughed. The woman smiled, but placed her hand over her mouth as though to avoid an explosion of laughter. They again exchanged lovers' glances and clearly made known their passions. Shih Hsiu had noticed all this and was more upset.

The priests in the other room had all sat down, and partook of the vegetarian food. Old Mr. Pan wished them all a good time, and asking to be excused he withdrew to go to sleep. After the meal the priests strolled about the rooms. Shih Hsiu said he had stomach ache, and begged to be excused—he thereupon lay down on a bench and pretended to go to sleep.

The woman now felt her passions rising so to divert her own thoughts she busied herself in making tea and serving it to the priests. The service went on until about 1 a.m. when most of the priests were drowsy, but priest Hai still continued reading the prayers with great vigor. Mrs. Pan, the Clever Cloud, was behind a screen, and noticing this she allowed her passions to arise. She called a maid-servant and sent her to summon the priest Hai to come to her. The young priest continued his intoning as before but slowly made his way towards the screen. When near Clever Cloud she seized his sleeve and said, "You must come here and collect the fees, and do not forget to speak to my father about the vows I made when mother died."

"I will not forget," said the priest. "I will tell him that you wish to redeem your vows as soon as possible. What about your uncle—is he not an awkward man?" Clever Cloud shook her head and said, "You take no notice of him. He is not a blood relation of ours."

"In that case I shall feel more at ease." So saying he clasped the woman's hand under cover of his sleeve and she moved the curtain to cover the act also. He laughed, returned to his place, and continued intoning the prayers as before. They did not realize that all this had been clearly seen by Shih Hsiu who was pretending to be asleep on the bench.

About 4 a.m. the service was finished, and the priests departed. Clever Cloud went upstairs to sleep.

Shih Hsiu thought, "My adopted brother, Yang Hsiung, is a great hero, and it is a great pity that he married a loose woman of this kind." He could not avoid being angry at the position of affairs.

The next day Yang Hsiung returned, but Shih Hsiu did not speak about the matter. As soon as he had had his meal he (Yang Hsiung) however left again. Shih Hsiu saw the young priest arrive, but this time he was dressed in his best clothes. Clever Cloud hurried downstairs, received him, and ordered tea to be brought. She said, "I am afraid that we put you to a lot of trouble last night, but we have not repaid you yet."

"That was only a very small affair. Last night we talked about your vows, and now we are reading prayers at our temple. You could just come to our temple, and get a written statement. That would be all right."

She agreed, and sent a girl servant to ask Old Mr. Pan to come, and discuss the matter. When he arrived he saluted the young priest, and apologized for retiring so early the previous night, but he had been very tired. "Uncle Shih Hsiu fell sick, and also retired early so that there was no one to look after you. I am sorry."

"Do not be so courteous," said the priest.

Clever Cloud now spoke, "I want to redeem the **vow I** made when my mother died. Our friend tells me that tomorrow there will be a service at the temple, and we might avail ourselves of the opportunity, and attend to pray for atonement."

"Very well," said Old Mr. Pan. "But I am afraid that we might be busy at the butchery to-morrow, and there will be nobody there to attend the matters."

"You can ask Shih Hsiu to look after the business," she said.

"Just so," said Old Mr. Pan. "We can go to the temple to-morrow."

Clever Cloud then got the money for the services rendered by the priests, and handed it to the young priest. After returning suitable thanks he left for the temple.

Yang Hsiung again returned home, and after supper Old Mr. Pan told Yang Hsiung of the proposed visit to the temple the following day. Yang Hsiung asked his wife why she did not speak to him herself, to which the woman replied that she was afraid that he might refuse her.

The next day a sedan chair was obtained for Clever Cloud and she set off about 11 a.m. accompanied by Old Mr. Pan and the girl servant Ying Erh, carrying the candles and incense. The young priest Hai was waiting for them at the temple gate, and he was much pleased to see them. Clever Cloud emerged from the chair, and thanked the priest for meeting them. The priest said, "The priests have been praying in the temple since early this morning, and we have awaited your arrival. He led the way into the hall where there were still about ten priests reading the scriptures.

Clever Cloud saluted, and gave three kotows to the Buddha. After burning incense and paper, the priests were asked to go, and get their meal, and priest Hai requested Clever Cloud and Old Mr. Pan to go to his private apartments for tea. Tea was duly served in silver cups with red saucers. When tea was finished the priest Hai asked them to go into the adjoining room. It was a very small room with a black lacquer couch, and many pictures on the walls. On a small table was a vase with burning incense. Old Mr. Pan and Clever Cloud took their seats on the couch with the priest facing them.

"What a nice place you have," said Clever Cloud, "and how quiet and secluded!"

"Do not joke about my humble bare quarters," said the priest "it is a mere barracks compared to your honorable mansion." Old Mr. Pan said, "We have given you much trouble, we will now depart."

"All the food has been provided because of your visit, why you depart without taking any? He then ordered the servant to bring in the food, and this was soon done. The meal was of the best food.

"Why you prepare food for us; we give you a lot of trouble," remarked Clever Cloud to the priest.

"I am afraid the meal does not by any means equal my respects and feelings for you," he replied. He then pressed Old Mr. Pan to try the wine provided.

"What a fine taste!" said Old Mr. Pan.

"Yes, the brewing method I learned from a donor of our temple and used quite five piculs of rice in making it. I will send a bottle of it to your house to-morrow as you like the flavor."

"That is quite unnecessary," said Old Mr. Pan.

The servants kept filling Old Mr. Pan's cup with wine, and the girl servant who was sitting with them also drank several cups of wine. Old Mr. Pan wanted to summon the sedan-chair carriers also to drink of the wine, but Hai, the priest, said that it was unnecessary as they had already had some with their food outside. In fact the priest had prepared this strong wine especially for Old Mr. Pan in order to further his own plans. Very soon Old Mr. Pan was drunk, and the priest suggested that he should now have a sleep. He summoned the servants to take Old Mr. Pan into another room to sleep on the bed there. Clever Cloud had also drunk some wine, and was feeling rather confused. She asked, "What was the use in getting me merely to drink the wine?"

The priest whispered, "Because I love you. Will you now come into another room to have a look at Buddha's tooth?"

"Very well, I should like to see it," she replied.

They went upstairs to a room which was the priest's private apartment and was nicely furnished. She was much pleased and said, "What a nice chamber, and how clean!"

"Yes, but it is short of the adornment of a woman."

She laughed, "Then why don't you get one?"

"Where is the donor who would present me with one?"

"But you asked me to come here to see Buddha's tooth."

"Well, first send away your girl servant, and then I will show it to you."

She told the girl to go downstairs, and see whether Old Mr. Pan had awakened. The girl went, and the priest closed the door after her.

Clever Cloud was now alone with him and she laughed. "Why do you close the door?"

"I am in love with you, and have waited for two years for this opportunity. I hope that we shall now complete our desires." He embraced her.

"You must not forget that my husband would be annoyed. You must not try to cheat me. If he finds out he will never forgive you."

He knelt down and said, "I hope that you will take pity on me."

"You are so skillful in dealing with me but I like to give you big blows upon your face with my hand." He laughed, "You would enjoy beating me."

Thus they enjoyed themselves for a long time, after which the priest embracing her said, "If I die now I shall have no regrets. But to-day our pleasure has been brief and I should like to arrange a whole night's assignation."

"You must not worry about that. I have a plan. Twenty days out of one month my husband is on duty at the prison. I will bribe my girl servant and she will wait outside the back door. A table will be placed there with incense, and you can easily get in that way. You must arrange for a wandering priest to come at daybreak, and beat a wooden fish at our back door, and then you can depart in due time. You can, of course, bribe him to keep a lookout to see that no one is coming."

He was much pleased at this proposal and said, "Admirable! That will do. There is a Taoist wandering priest here, named Hu, and I will arrange with him to do so."

"I cannot stay here much longer. I am afraid that somebody will suspect me. I must go at once." She quickly combed her hair, rouged her face again, opened the door, and went downstairs. She told the girl servant to see if Old Mr. Pan was now ready, and she went into the original room. The chair-bearers were waiting at the gate. The young priest had followed Clever Cloud, and now conducted her to the gate. She entered her chair and with Old Mr. Pan and the servant girl returned home.

Hai, the priest, soon arranged matters with the wandering priest named Hu who lived at a small temple close by. His duty at the temple was to arise before sunrise, and beat the wooden fish to summon all the priests to prayers.

The next day the wandering priest went to Old Mr. Pan's house, and met the girl servant who asked him, "Why do you come to the back door?"

The priest commenced to recite the prayers. Clever Cloud inside heard this, and coming out said, "Are you not the priest who announces the dawn?"

"Yes, I do that every day. You will also burn some incense to Buddha in the evening."

She was much pleased at this, and sent the girl servant upstairs to get a string of cash for the priest. As soon as the girl had gone the priest spoke, "I am the confident of the priest Hai who asked me to come here, and keep a lookout."

"I understand," she said, "you must come again this evening, and have another look. If there is an incense table here you can report to him and he can visit me."

The priest nodded his head as the girl just then returned, and handed him the money. He went his way.

Clever Cloud went upstairs, and there told the girl servant her plan, and gave her some money.

That evening Yang Hsiung left for his duty in the prison. The girl servant duly placed the incense table near the back door, and shortly afterwards a man wearing a hat (contrary to priestly custom) entered the gate, and the girl asked who he was, but the man did not reply, but continued on his way. Clever Cloud who was near, however, took the cap from the man's head, and seeing then the shining skull of the priest she exclaimed, "What an excellent disguise!" They embraced, and went upstairs. The servant took the incense table inside and closed the door. The lovers passed a happy night together. The next morning they were both aroused by the sound of the wooden fish being beaten. Hai, the priest, quickly dressed and said, "I must go now, but I will come again this evening."

From that day the priest visited Clever Cloud in this way every time that the husband was away from home. Old Mr. Pan was always asleep, and they had to hoodwink only Shih Hsiu. This affair went on for more than a month.

Now Shih Hsiu was attending to the affairs of the butchery and although he had some suspicion about the conduct of

Clever Cloud he had not seen anything further to convince himself. He was a very early riser and every day he heard the wandering priest strike the wooden fish at daybreak. But Shih Hsiu hearing the sound knew that it meant something.

On the 15th day of the eleventh moon Shih Hsiu was awake very early, and he listened to the beating of the wooden fish, and then also heard the traveling priest say, "Buddha saves everyone from trouble and difficulties." Shih Hsiu got up, and peeping through a crack in the door he saw a man wearing a cap go out by the back door, and depart with the wandering priest. A short time afterwards he saw the girl servant close the back door. He ejaculated, "Why does my adopted brother tolerate such a woman! She is evidently deceiving him, and does some underhand affair." He went about his business in the abattoir as usual, and then in the afternoon went into the town to collect some accounts, but instead went to the yamen to see Yang Hsiung. On the way he saw him who asked him, "Where are you going?"

"I came to collect accounts," said Shih Hsiu, "and then thought of finding you."

"I have always been very busy, but now we can have a little wine together if you will come with me," said Yang Hsiung. He then took Shih Hsiu to a wine shop near at hand where they sat down in a quiet corner, and Yang Hsiung ordered wine and food.

They drank three cups of wine, and then Yang Hsiung noticed that Shih Hsiu was hanging his head down as though lost in thought.

Yang Hsiung was a quick-tempered man. "I see that you have been upset by something. Is there someone at our home who has said anything against you?"

"There was nothing of that kind at our home," said Shih Hsiu. "Elder brother, you have always treated me well as your own brother, but there is something I do not dare to speak to you about."

"Why do you talk, my younger brother, in this unusual way to-day? Whatever is in your mind you may tell me!"

"Elder brother, you go to your office every day so that you cannot know what is happening at home. Your wife is not a good woman, but although I have known this for some time I did not dare to tell you before this. But to-day all has been made quite clear so that I can tell you the truth. I hope you will excuse my straightforwardness."

"I have no eye at my back," said Yang Hsiung, "so please tell me who the man is."

"Some days ago when you had Buddhist prayers at your house, I noticed that the priest Hai was exchanging love glances with your wife. Three days afterwards she and Old Mr. Pan went to the temple to fulfill a vow, and upon their return I noticed that they were both drunk. Nowadays I have heard a priest striking a wooden fish in the alley behind your house. As I thought it strange, so to-day I got up very early, and saw the priest Hai leave your house wearing an ordinary cap. What do you want this woman for?"

Yang Hsiung was very angry at this, and said, "How dare that rascal do this?"

"Please do not lose your temper," said Shih Hsiu. "You must not mention this matter to-day, and to-morrow you must tell your people that you are going to the office. Then you can return about midnight, and knock at the door of your house. The priest will try to leave by the back door. I will wait there, and seize him and hand him over to you."

"A good idea," said Yang Hsiung, "I will do as you say."

After finishing their wine they separated. Yang Hsiung spent the afternoon with some colleagues practicing with fencing sticks, and he drank so much wine that he was drunk by evening. When he returned home his wife undressed him, and assisted him to bed. When Yang Hsiung saw his wife doing this he remembered what he had heard about her. There is an old saying, "When drunk, people talk of affairs." Pointing at his wife he now said, "You deceiver! I shall kill you some day or other."

She was startled, but did not reply. She waited upon him, and heard his rambling remarks, "You loose woman! You deserve—deserve—deserve to be killed. I—I cannot— I cannot spare your life."

She dare not take any notice of this, and waited until he fell asleep. About 5 a.m. Yang Hsiung awoke out of his drunken sleep, and asked for water which his wife got for him. He asked her, "Wife, why did you not undress?"

"I saw that you were drunk, and being afraid that you might vomit I did not undress to sleep."

"What did I say in my drunkenness?" asked Yang Hsiung.

"Previously you have always been quiet when drunk, but last night you seemed to be cross about something."

"For quite a few days I have not drunk with Shih Hsiu so I want you to treat him to some wine."

She did not reply to this, but sat down on a couch and cried bitterly.

"Wife, I came home drunk last evening, and yet I did not provoke you. What are you troubled about?"

She did not reply to this, but only put her hands over her eyes. He again asked the question without getting a reply, and she now pretended to cry. He thereupon took hold of her, and carried her to his bed, and repeated his question. Still crying she now answered, "When my parents married me to the clerk Wang they thought that I was settled for life, but who would have expected that in mid-life he would die, and leave me a widow. When I met you, and saw that you were a great hero I married you, but I never expected that you could not protect me."

"You talk in a strange manner. Who has deceived you, and where did I not protect you?"

"I would not say just now, but I am afraid that you have been cheated by him, and if I told you you would only be angry."

"You can say just what you have to say."

"Then if I tell you, you must keep your temper. When you first brought Shih Hsiu here he had good manners, but since then he has shown his true habits. Now when you stay away from home he would approach me saying, 'Your husband will not return to-night so that you will find it very dull and cold by yourself.' But I gave him no notice although he said that every day. But what is more important is this. Yesterday morning I was washing my face in the kitchen, and he entered by the back door. Seeing no one else about he came up and stroke my bosom with his hand. I pushed him away, but was afraid to call out as I did not want our neighbors to hear as that would have made them talk about your disgrace. I intended to tell you when you returned, but alas! you were too drunk to understand. I detest that man and yet you ask about his condition."

Yang Hsiung was very angry at this, and said, "'In drawing a tiger, you show its skin, but not its bones; in knowing man, you may know his face, but not his heart.' He told me that it was the young priest Hai who was doing this, but it was evidently he himself, who has been guilty. He is no longer my sworn brother, and to-morrow he shall get out." In the morning Yang Hsiung went downstairs, and spoke to Old Mr. Pan, "That butchery business is finished. I want you to close the business, and take down all the fittings and furniture at once." This was done.

That morning when Shih Hsiu came to open the abattoir he found that all the tools, etc. had been removed. But he was very understanding, and soon guessed what had happened. He laughed, "So, this is the way! Yang Hsiung has let the cat out of the bag while drunk. He has told his wife what I said, and in order to protect herself, she has manufactured some slander about me, and got her husband to close the business. If I tried to defend myself it would lead to other people knowing of the trouble, and so my friend Yang Hsiung would lose face. I will give way (literally retreat one step) and think of some other plan of clearing myself." So he went inside the abattoir, and packed up his things.

Yang Hsiung was afraid that Shih Hsiu was too ashamed to come to see him, so he went off to his office.

Shih Hsiu took his sword and baggage to Old Mr. Pan's house and said, "I have given you much inconvenience, and as my sworn brother has now closed the business I will go. I have settled the accounts, and you will find everything in order. Should there be some slight mistakes in the accounts then may Heaven punish me for it."

As Yang Hsiung had told Old Mr. Pan to close the business the latter could not do anything, and so Shih Hsiu departed. He soon found an inn in the town where he engaged a room. There he meditated, "I am an intimate friend of Yang Hsiung, and if I do not make the whole affair clear it would ruin his life. Just now he is hoodwinked by his wife, and I am not going to raise any objection. Eventually, however, I must make the matter clear to him. In the meantime I will find out when he is on duty, and then watch what goes on at his home during the night."

After staying in the inn for two days, he made inquiries at Yang Hsiung's neighborhood. In the evening he saw a messenger from the jail came to take Yang's beddings so he concluded that Yang Hsiung would sleep at the jail that night. He went to the inn and slept until about 3 a.m. when he got up, took his sword, quietly slipped out of the inn and going to the alley at the back of Yang Hsiung's house he hid there in a dark spot. About 4 a.m. he saw the wandering priest arrive, and begin looking around. Shih Hsiu crept up behind the priest, and seizing hold of him placed the blade of his sword across the back of the priest's neck. He said, "Keep quiet or I will kill you. Speak the truth! Why does priest Hai tell you to come here and do this?"

"Kind sir, spare my life and I will tell you the truth."

"Be quick then! I will not kill you."

The priest said, "The priest Hai comes here every night to stay with Yang Hsiung's wife. I come in the evening to report whether there is an incense table outside, and if so he enters the house. At 5 a.m. I come and beat the wooden fish to awaken him to leave the house."

"Where is he now?" asked Shih Hsiu.

"He is asleep in the house. If I strike the wooden fish he will come out."

"Well, let us change clothes," said Shih Hsiu. The priest took off his clothes, and then Shih Hsiu killed him on the spot. Shih Hsiu put on the priest's robes, and then struck the wooden fish. Priest Hai in bed heard the sound, dressed and quickly left the house. As Shih Hsiu was still beating the wooden fish the priest Hai spoke in a low voice, "That is enough! I am here!"

Shih Hsiu took no notice of this, but coming up to the priest Hai tripped him. Shih Hsiu held the priest down and exclaimed, "Hold your tongue! If you make a noise I will kill you. I am going to take away your gown." The priest now recognized Shih Hsiu, and was afraid. He let Shih Hsiu take all his clothes so that he was soon stark naked.

Then Shih Hsiu took his sword and killed him. He then placed the sword in the hand of the first priest he had killed, wrapped up the dead men's clothes, and made off to his inn.

He very quietly opened the door, and shut it after him and went to sleep without being seen by anyone.

That morning a hawker of cakes and congee happened to pass the dead bodies, and fell over them in the dark. The small boy who accompanied him called out, "Here is a drunken priest." The hawker got up, and found his hands covered with blood, and was much upset. He made such a noise that the neighbors came out with lights, and disclosed the two dead bodies lying in blood. They seized the hawker, and took him to the yamen.

> Misfortune dropped from Heaven,
> And fell on this poor man.

CHAPTER 45

YANG HSIUNG MURDERS HIS WIFE; SHIH HSIU SETS FIRE TO AN INN

UPON reaching the yamen the neighbors went into the court, and the magistrate soon came and took his seat. The neighbors all knelt down, and made a statement: "This hawker fell down with his load of cakes and congee. When we came we saw two corpses on the ground—one was a priest, and the other a traveling priest—and they were both naked. There was a sword by the side of the traveling priest."

The hawker then stated: "I always go out early every morning selling my cakes and congee. This morning as I was going along I stumbled over something at that spot, and all my food was spilt, and my cups and plates broken. Sir, please have pity on me! I was surprised to see the two dead bodies. When the neighbors came they arrested me, and brought me to your yamen. I request your honor to have the matter carefully investigated."

The magistrate had this statement duly recorded, and issued an order for the Tipao and the coroner to examine the case and report. These men held a post-mortem and duly made their report in detail. They gave their opinions that the traveling priest for some unknown reason had murdered the priest Hai, and then being conscious of his guilt had committed suicide. The magistrate summoned all the priests of that temple to come to court, but when he explained to them the conclusions of the coroner there was not a single one who could throw any light on the mystery.

The magistrate released the neighbors on bail and ordered the temple to arrange for the burial.

On this strange amorous affairs some neighbors composed a song:

> We laugh at the priest of the Gratitude Temple,
> Who loved a woman willing,
> And risked their lives for pleasures gay,
> The idle moments filling.
>
> For pleasure which was uncontrolled,
> The blind, dumb Gods consented,
> For well they knew the sin unfold,
> They'd both be unlamented.
>
> They should have waited and avoid
> The trial—who was stronger;
> The ground from blood would have been free,
> And they had lived much longer.

Other neighbors listening to this song also composed one as follows:

> Lust invites murder,
> Without failure;
> And lays down the cleaver,
> By a naked figure.
>
> Big baldhead died to-day,
> With little baldhead lusty;
> Pursued by bosom comrade,
> In all faith mighty.

These two songs were sung in every street in that neighborhood. The wife of Yang Hsiung heard them with a distracted stare, but she dared not say a word and felt much worried.

Yang Hsiung heard of the two murders, and understood who had done the deed. He thought, "I had unjustly condemned him on insufficient evidence. I have leisure to-day, so I will go and find Shih Hsiu, and ask him what he knows about the case."

Yang Hsiung left the yamen, and had just crossed the bridge when he heard someone behind him calling out, "Elder brother, where are you going?" Upon turning round he saw that it was Shih Hsiu and said, "Younger brother, I was looking for you."

"Elder brother, please come to my place where we can talk matters over." They both went to Shih Hsiu's inn where they sat down in a small room. There Shih Hsiu asked, "Elder brother, did I not tell you the truth?"

"Younger brother, please excuse me for the mistake 1 made. I got drunk that day, and accused my wife, and she turned round and said many bad things about you. I was now coming to find you, and was going to confess my fault."

"Elder brother, I may not be without a fault, but I am a perfectly honest man so how could you think of me as capable of doing such things? I was afraid that you had been deceived by some ruse, and therefore, I came to find you, and show you a proof of my innocence." He thereupon spread out the priests' robes.

When Yang Hsiung saw the robes he became excited, and said, "Younger brother, excuse me. To-night I will hack that woman into small pieces, and so appease my wrath."

Shih Hsiu laughed, "You are getting angry again. As you work in the yamen you are supposed to know all about the law. How could you kill her when you have not caught her in the act? Also if I have been telling you nonsense, you would make a mistake in killing her."

"Then what should I do?"

"It would be better if you follow my advice. Outside the East Gate there is Tsui Ping Shan, a very lonely spot. To-morrow you can tell your wife that you want her to accompany you to sacrifice at a temple. She can also take her maidservant with her. I will go there beforehand and when you arrive you can confront her with me, and we will go over the whole matter. Then you can sign a bill of divorcement and release her. Would not that be better?"

"You need not go into details. I know your innocence. That woman is the liar."

"Of course I want you to know all that has passed between those two."

"Your plan is admirable," said Yang Hsiung. "I will go to-morrow with my wife, and I hope that you must not ail to come."

"If I do not turn up to-morrow then you can assume that I am the liar," said Shih Hsiu.

The two friends then took leave of each other, and Yang Hsiung returned to his work at the yamen. Upon reaching home that evening he did not say a word, but let everything be as usual. The following morning when he got up he, however, said to his wife, "Last night I dreamt that a spirit accused me of having overlooked some vow. I now remember that I once took a vow at a temple outside the East Gate, and have not yet fulfilled my oath. As I have leisure to-day, I will go there and would like you to come with me."

"Why not go alone," replied his wife. "What is the use for me to go with you?"

"My oath concerned our marriage so that it is necessary for both of us to go."

"In that case we will get away immediately after breakfast," said his wife.

"I will go and hire a sedan chair, and buy some incense," said Yang Hsiung. He also told the maidservant to get ready, and go with them. He then went to the inn and spoke to Shih Hsiu of the arrangements made. Shih Hsiu asked him to leave the sedan chairs when halfway up the hill, and walk the remainder of the distance, as it was not advisable to have outsiders about the temple. Yang Hsiung agreed to this, and then went to buy the incense and paper. When he got back he found that his wife and servant were dressed up in their best. The wife got in the sedan chair, and Yang Hsiung and the maidservant walked behind. When outside the East Gate Yang Hsiung quietly told the carriers that they were to go to Tsui Ping Shan, and that he would pay them well. They duly reached the mountain in about two hours as the place was only about seven miles from the town. The mountain was covered with green grass, and tall poplars, but there was no temple there. When halfway up the mountain Yang Hsiung stopped, and told the chair carriers to rest at that place while the three of them would walk the rest of the way.

His wife asked, "Why have we come to such a place as this?"

But Yang Hsiung told her not to ask useless questions. The three then started off, and soon reached the top of the mountain where they met Shih Hsiu.

The wife then asked, "How is it you did not bring the paper and incense up here?"

"I told one of the men to bring that up here," replied Yang Hsiung. He took his wife towards an ancient grave that was there. Shih Hsiu put his bundle and sword and stick against the trunk of a tree after which he saluted Mrs. Yang Hsiung (Clever Cloud).

She hurriedly asked, "How is it that you have come here?" As she spoke she stared with fear.

"I have been waiting here for you for a long time," he replied.

Yang Hsiung turned to his wife, "A few days ago you made some serious charges against my sworn brother that he laid his hand on your breast. There is nobody about here so you two can now discuss that matter, and make things clear.'

The wife exclaimed, "Ai Ya! Why talk about bygone matters?"

Shih Hsiu stared at her, "Madame, why not?"

"There is nothing to talk about unless you yourself have said something," she replied.

"Madame! Is that so?" He then opened his bundle and spread out on the ground the dead priests' clothes. "Do you recognize this clothing?" asked Shih Hsiu.

Mrs. Yang Hsiung blushed scarlet, and did not reply.

Shih Hsiu seized the sword, and handed it to Yang Hsiung, saying, "You had better ask the maidservant."

Yang Hsiung seized the girl, and made her kneel down before him. He spoke in a loud voice, "Now you speak the truth and I will forgive you for what you have done. But if you speak only one lie I shall most certainly kill you on the spot."

"Sir," replied the maidservant, "this is not an affair of mine. Do not kill me, and I will speak the truth." She then told him all that had occurred between his wife and the priest, and how she had been bribed to do her part of the plot.

Yang Hsiung now seized his wife and called out, "Now woman, tell me the truth, and if you say no falsehood I will not kill you."

"It was my mistake," said his wife. "As we are man and wife, I beg for your forgiveness."

"We cannot pass this over so easily, elder brother," said Shih Hsiu. "Why should she not give a full explanation?"

"I agree! Woman, give me the whole truth!" shouted Yang Hsiung.

The woman then confessed completely, and told all that had been arranged and carried on with the priest.

Yang Hsiung then told Shih Hsiu to strip his wife naked which was done. Yang Hsiung then took his sash and tied her to the tree. Shih Hsiu took the ornaments out of the servant's hair, and said to Yang Hsiung while he handed him the sword, "Why should we spare this little plotter. If she remains there will always be a source from which trouble might grow."

"That is so," said Yang Hsiung; "I will kill her myself."

The maidservant saw that she was in a dangerous position, and attempted to shriek, but Yang Hsiung, with one blow, killed her on the spot.

The woman tied to the tree called out, "Brother-in-law, please intervene!"

"This is not my affair," replied Shih Hsiu.

Yang Hsiung stepped up to the tree, took hold of the woman's tongue, and cut it off with his sword. He then pointed at her and said, "You worthless woman! I have almost been deceived by you. You nearly estranged me from my sworn brother, and might put an end to my life some day. I think you must have some strange viscera inside your bosom so I am going to have a look at them." He plunged his sword into her breast, ripped open her belly. He took out her heart, spleen, liver, kidneys, and lungs, and hung them up on the tree. He then asked Shih Hsiu to come near and discuss matters. He said, "Now we have killed the adulterer and the adulteress too. But where shall we now go for safety?"

"We have both committed murder," said Shih Hsiu, "and the only thing left for us is both to join the brigands at Liang Shan Po."

"Stop a bit! Neither of us know a single person at that place so it is unlikely that they will accept us."

"You overlook the fact, elder brother, that Sung Chiang is in charge there, and he is famous everywhere as a man who is always on the lookout for heroes. We both have military skill so how could he turn us away?"

"When things are difficult at first and quite easy afterwards, there will be no regret. But as I am an ex-official I am afraid that I should arouse their suspicions, and that they would not be willing to welcome us."

Shih Hsiu laughed and asked, "Was he not a clerk in a yamen himself at one time? But you must not forget that on the day we first drank in an inn I had been with two men, and they were leaders from Liang Shan Po. They even gave me a present of silver, and they will remember me."

"Very well, younger brother, you go on the road to Liang Shan Po, and I will return home and get some money to cover our traveling expenses."

"That will not do, because if you enter the town you would have a difficulty in getting out if they hear of what has happened to-day. People would undoubtedly inquire about your wife's absence. I have however enough money in this bundle to cover all our traveling expenses. So we had better both go together straightway by the road on the other side of the mountains."

They both then packed up their things, and set forth. They had only gone a short distance when they heard a voice behind them, and turning round saw a man emerging from the trees. He called, "I have been listening to all that you have said, and after committing murder in broad daylight you are now escaping to Liang Shan Po." Yang Hsiung recognized the man as Shih Ch'ien, a native of Kao Tang Chou, who however had lived in that neighborhood for many years. He was well known as a housebreaker, and was particularly good in scaling walls. He was known as the Flea on the Drum.

"What are you doing here?" asked Yang Hsiung.

"Nowadays I had nothing to do," replied Shih Ch'ien, "so I came here to open some ancient grave and take the things. I happened to see you arrive, and was a witness of what happened but I dare not intervene. I heard you two talking about going to Liang Shan Po and joining the bandits. For a long time I have been stealing all kinds of things (even chickens, cats, and dogs) so I thought I had better join you. Would you mind if I go along with you?"

"I think they would be pleased to have you at Liang

A CHICKEN STOLEN

Shan Po," said Shih Hsiu. "You can accompany us if you like."

Shih Ch'ien knew a small footpath, and led the other two. The two sedan chair carriers waited until evening without seeing the three persons return. Although Yang Hsiung had told them not to go up the mountain yet at last they went to see what was the cause of the delay. They saw a flock of crows on a grave making a great noise, and upon approaching they saw that the crows were eating the viscera hanging from the tree. They were startled, and immediately hurried down the mountain, and informed Mr. Pan who went with them to the yamen to report the case. The magistrate heard the reports, and ordered the coroner to investigate the case on the spot.

Upon his return he reported all that he had seen, and gave the names of the victims. The magistrate at once recollected the murder of the two priests, and cross-examined Mr. Pan who told him all that he knew of the seducing affairs. The magistrate correctly summed up the case that Shih Hsiu had killed the priests, and Yang Hsiung had killed his wife and the girl servant. He issued summons for the arrest of those two men.

Yang Hsiung, Shih Hsiu, and Shih Ch'ien continued on their way, and one evening, at dusk when near Hsiang Lin Wa they stopped at an inn near a stream. They told the waiter that they had walked about thirty miles that day and were hungry. The waiter said there were no other guests at the inn, and if they liked they could cook the food themselves as the pans were quite clean.

"Have you any meat here?" asked Shih Ch'ien.

"We had some meat early this morning, but people in the surrounding villages have bought it all during the day," replied the waiter. "We have a little wine left, and also some vegetables."

"All right, that will do," replied Shih Ch'ien. "Give us also some rice and we will do our own cooking."

This was done, and while Shih Ch'ien did the cooking, Shih Hsiu arranged their baggage and spread out their beddings. Yang Hsiung took a woman's silver hairpin, and gave it to the waiter as payment for the food, etc. Shih Ch'ien got a bucket of water for them to wash their feet and hands. When the wine was ready they asked the waiter to drink with them. Shih Hsiu noticed that there were many swords hanging on the wall under the eaves of the inn so he asked the waiter why they had so many arms.

"Those belong to the landlord of this inn," replied the waiter.

"What kind of man is your master?"

"As you are travelers, why do you not know the name of this place?" replied the waiter. "The mountain here is called the Solitary Dragon Mountain. The high ridge is the Solitary Dragon Ridge. Our master lives on the top of that ridge. Within a radius of about five miles round this place is the Chu's Village. Our headman is Chu Chao-feng, and he has three sons who are known as the three heroes. In this area there are about five hundred laborers who all work for our headman, and he supplies them with these swords. This inn is called the Chu Family Inn, and we generally have about ten men staying here who act as a guard, and those are their swords."

"But what do they use the swords for in such a quiet place as this?" asked Shih Hsiu.

"This place is not very far from Liang Shan Po, so that we are always afraid of those bandits coming here to borrow grain from us."

"If I give you some money will you sell me one of those swords?" asked Shih Hsiu.

"I cannot do that," said the waiter. "All the swords are numbered, and I have to account for the lot. If one was missing I should be beaten with sticks. Our master has very severe rules about such matters."

"I was only joking," said Shih Hsiu laughingly. "You must not be afraid of us."

"I have now had enough, and will now retire, and go to sleep. You gentlemen can go on drinking," said the waiter.

When the waiter had gone the three men went on drinking, but Shih Ch'ien suddenly asked, "Wouldn't you like some meat with this?"

"The waiter said they had sold all the meat so that there is none left," replied Yang Hsiung.

Shih Ch'ien laughed loudly at this, and going to the kitchen came back with a large chicken.

"When I went outside to relieve bowels I noticed this bird in the roost," said Shih Ch'ien. "As I could find no meat, I went and killed this chicken, plucked it and cooked it. So that is how we can have it now."

"You are still a thief when you take things like this," answered Yang Hsiung.

"He evidently has not reformed his old habits," said Shih Hsiu laughingly.

The three still laughing set to, and soon tore up the whole bird for their meal.

But the waiter could not go to sleep, and very soon he took a stroll round. He saw on the table the bones and feathers, and going to the roost found that the bird was missing. So he hurried back into the room, and asked, "Gentlemen, you seem to have no manners. Why did you steal our chanticleer?"

"No! No!" exclaimed Shih Ch'ien. "We bought a bird on the way here, and have not seen yours."

"Then where has our bird gone to?"

"Perhaps a stray cat, a weasel or a kite has taken it. But we know nothing about it," said Shih Ch'ien.

"The bird was in the roost when I left you," said the waiter, "so if you have not stolen it who has?"

"We will not wrangle any further," said Shih Hsiu; "we will pay for what you have lost."

"But the cock was our dawn announcer so all our affairs will be upset now that it has gone. Even ten ounces of silver would not be enough, and I must ask you to return us our cock."

"Who are you trying to fool?" asked Shih Hsiu in a temper. "If we do not make up for your loss what would you do?"

The waiter laughed and replied, "You should not make trouble here, as this inn is unlike others, and you might be arrested on a charge of being bandits from Liang Shan Po."

Shih Hsiu cursed the man saying, "Even if we were from Liang Shan Po how could you arrest us, and get a reward from your headman?"

The waiter without replying called out, "Robbers," and immediately about five men rushed into the room. But Shih Hsiu met them, and one by one he knocked the men down with his fist. As the waiter was still complaining, Shih Ch'ien slapped his face, and stopped his noise. The five men picked themselves up, and retreated through the back door.

"Those men will soon bring others, so we better have a big meal and get away," said Yang Hsiung.

The three friends after a hearty eating, picked up their things, and helped themselves to a sword each from the inn's stock.

Shih Hsiu said, "If we are going to be hung we might as well be hung for a house as for a cock," so saying he rushed into the kitchen, lit a torch, and began to set fire to the inn. Very soon the whole place was in flames. The three friends set off, but they had not gone far when they found themselves surrounded in the distance on all sides by many hundreds of men with torchlights.

Shih Hsiu said, "Let us keep cool, and try to find a footpath somewhere."

Yang Hsiung said, "It would be better to stop in one place, and kill these men one by one as they come up to us. We may not go until daybreak." While he was speaking, some of the men were quite close, and they were armed with sticks. Yang Hsiung attacked them, and soon killed about seven men, when the rest retreated. Shih Hsiu had done the same thing in another direction with the same result. The three friends continued on their way, but did not notice the men hidden in the grass one of whom grabbed hold of Shih Ch'ien with a hooked pole, and pulled him down into the tall grass. Shih Hsiu went to his assistance, but another pole grabbed hold of him. Yang Hsiung saw this, and struck the pole with his sword, and freed his friend. He then stabbed in the grass at the hidden men, and shouting in pain they soon all ran away. But Shih Ch'ien was missing, and the two friends saw no means of rescuing him. They therefore continued on their way, and following any small path they saw they went towards the east. They soon found themselves outside the circle of flaming torches. They walked during that night, and early the following morning they stopped at an inn. There they had just finished their breakfast when they noticed a man outside who had big eyes and ears. He had a rough appearance, wearing brown silk clothes, with a white belt.

A CHICKEN STOLEN

He called out to the waiter, "Our master tells you to go to his village with a load."

Yang Hsiung recognized the man, and asked him what he was doing there. The man then recognized Yang Hsiung and saluted.

> Union, 'twixt three hamlets broken,
> Roaring tigers make much sorrow.

CHAPTER 46

THE STRIKING HAWK TWICE WRITES A LETTER;
SUNG CHIANG FIRST ATTACKS
THE CHU VILLAGE

YANG HSIUNG raised the man and then introduced him to Shih Hsiu as Tu Hsing of Chung Shan Fu. He had a fierce face, and therefore people called him the Devil Faced Man. Previously he had come to Chi Chow Fu, and had entered into business with some other men. During a quarrel with his partner he had lost his temper and killed him. He had been arrested and tried, but Yang Hsiung, knowing that he was very skillful with the cudgel and lance, had saved his life by getting a light sentence passed.

The man asked, "On what official business do you come here, my benefactor?"

Yang Hsiung whispered in his ear, "I committed murder at Chi Chow Fu, and am now escaping to Liang Shan Po, where I shall join the brigands." He then told him about all the trouble at the inn and how Shih Ch'ien had been captured.

"You need not worry about that matter," said Tu Hsing, "because I can arrange for Shih Ch'ien to be released."

They asked him to join them at the wine. Tu Hsing then explained that at that village he was entrusted by the headman with important matters, and he had great influence there. There were three villages in close alliance, and altogether they supported an armed force of about 20,000 men. The most influential headman was Chu Chao-feng who had three valiant sons named Dragon, Tiger, and Tiger's Cub. They had a drill instructor named Luan Ting-yu, nicknamed Iron Staff, who was invincible. In the western village was a headman who had a son called Hu Cheng, nicknamed Flying Tiger, who was very courageous. His sister, Hu San-niang, nicknamed Pure One, was a skilled rider, and could fight with a sword in each hand. At the village on the east side was a man Li Ying, nicknamed Striking Hawk, who was his master who always carried five swords on his back, and could throw these a hundred paces, and kill men at that distance. These villages supported each other whatever the risk or danger, and were prepared to fight against the brigands of Liang Shan Po when they came to command the grain. He (Tu Hsing) offered to take them to Li Ying and get him to release Shih Ch'ien.

They accepted this offer, and settled their accounts with the innkeeper. They then followed Tu Hsing to the village. Yang Hsiung noticed that it was a big village, with a moat all round. The banks of the moat were very high, and on the top were many hundreds of large willows. They crossed a drawbridge and passed through a gate in a wall. They came to the principal hall in front of which were over twenty racks filled with spears, swords, etc., all of which were polished bright and in good order.

Tu Hsing asked the other two to wait outside while he went inside to announce their arrival. It was not long before Li Ying came out, and after being introduced invited Yang Hsiung and Shih Hsiu to come inside. When they had had some wine Yang Hsiung explained the object of their visit, and as a result Li Ying told his scribe to write a letter asking for the release of Shih Ch'ien, and sent a mounted messenger with it to the neighboring village. It was not long before the messenger returned and reported that the headman had at first been willing to release Shih Ch'ien. But when his three sons heard of it they objected, and insisted upon Shih Ch'ien being sent to the magistrate for trial.

Li Ying was surprised at this, and wondered what was the use of the alliance when even his urgent letter had been ignored. He asked Tu Hsing to go there himself, and try to secure the release.

Tu Hsing agreed to go, but asked Li Ying to write a letter by his own hand which he would take with him. This was done, and mounting a horse Tu Hsing galloped off.

It was almost night time before Tu Hsing returned. As he dismounted they saw that he was in a towering rage. His face was red with passion, and as he raised his lips he showed the tightly set teeth. For some time he could not speak.

"Take your time and tell us all about it," said Li Ying at last.

Tu Hsing slowly repressed his anger, and then spoke, "I took your letter to the village and dismounted at the third gate where the three sons of Chu Chao-feng were seated. I saluted them separately and then Tiger's Cub called out, 'Well, what do you come here for?'

"I replied in a respectful manner, 'I have here a letter from my master.' I presented it. Tiger's Cub showed annoyance as he replied, 'Why does your master not understand human affairs? Early this afternoon he sent some fellow here with a letter asking for that brigand Shih Ch'ien to be released. Just now we are going to send him to the magistrate so why have you come here?'

"I replied that Shih Ch'ien was not a bandit, but was a guest on his way to visit my master. He made a mistake in setting fire to his inn. That you would go tomorrow and make full compensation for the damage done, and hoped that they would overlook the offense and accept a full apology.

"Then all replied, 'That cannot be done.' So I requested them to kindly read your letter, but Tiger's Cub simply took it from me, and tore it into bits without reading it. He then ordered me to get out of their village at once. They also warned me not to incite them to anger any further or they would . . . I would not dare to speak the whole truth —but they said they would arrest you, sir, also as a bandit of the Liang Shan Po, and send you to the yamen. They told their servants to seize me but I jumped on the horse and galloped off. It is evident that the sworn alliance between our villages is no longer of any value, as those fellows are quite unreasonable."

While Li Ying listened to this he became more and more annoyed, and at last called out, "You men! Quickly get my horse ready."

Yang Hsiung and Shih Hsiu asked him to keep cool as they did not wish to see the peaceful relations between the villages disturbed by what they had done. But Li Ying took no notice of this, went indoors, put on his metal mail, with a large silk gown over it, put his five swords on his back, and took a spear in his hand; put on his iron helmet; and summoned three hundred men to accompany him. Tu Hsing also put on his mail armor, and got twenty horsemen to follow him. Yang Hsiung and Shih Hsiu took their swords, and also followed.

It was late in the afternoon when they reached the other village, and there the men stood in ranks. The village was situated on raised ground and had three protecting walls, one inside the other. The walls were built of stone, and were about twenty feet high. The village was surrounded by a moat, over which were two drawbridges in front of the north and south gates. In the towers at the gates were drums, gongs, etc. for summoning the men to fight.

Li Ying reined in his horse before the bridge, and shouted, "Why have you three sons of Mr. Chu defamed me?" At once the gate of the village was opened, and a body of about fifty horsemen galloped out. In front rode the third son, Tiger's Cub, on a roan-colored horse.

Li Ying pointing at him shouted, "You fellow still have your milk teeth and childhood's tufts of hair. Your father entered into a sworn alliance with me to defend these villages. If your family had trouble we would render unlimited assistance, or if short of something we would supply it. To-day I sent a letter which you tore up. Why did you insult my messenger in that way? Have you no decency?"

Tiger's Cub replied, "Our family entered into an alliance with you so that we could together resist the encroachments of the bandits at Liang Shan Po. But now you have become intimate with them and intended open rebellion."

"Why do you say that I am intimate with bandits? Why have you arrested an ordinary man, and falsely accused him?"

"The prisoner has already confessed that he is a thief so why do you talk in this wild disorderly manner? You cannot hide his crime. You clear off at once, or I will arrest you also."

Li Ying was now very angry, and whipping his horse he galloped forward. Tiger's Cub crossed the bridge, and did the same. They met in combat, and charged each other about eighteen times. As the Tiger's Cub could not overcome Li Ying he at last turned his horse round and retreated. Placing his spear on the horse he took his bow and arrow, and turning his body shot at Li Ying who was following close behind. Li Ying tried to avoid the arrow, but it struck him in the shoulder, and he fell off his horse. Tiger's Cub pulled his horse round, and rushed forward to seize Li Ying.

Yang Hsiung and Shih Hsiu seeing the danger of Li Ying shouted, seized their swords, and rushed towards Tiger's Cub, who seeing that the odds were against him retreated. As the horse turned, however, Yang Hsiung struck it, and the animal reared with the pain. Tiger's Cub was almost thrown off, but kept his seat. The villagers now rushed forward, and as Yang Hsiung and Shih Hsiu were not wearing their mail they now retreated along with Tu Hsing, Li Ying, and their followers. They were pursued for about a mile when the villagers returned to the village as it was getting dark.

Upon reaching their village Li Ying had his wound dressed, and then the four men discussed the position. Yang Hsiung expressed regret that all this trouble had arisen through their affairs, and considered that there was no way of obtaining the release of Shih Ch'ien. They thought that the best thing was for them to proceed to Liang Shan Po, where they would petition Ch'ao Kai to send an expedition to avenge the insult to Li Ying.

Li Ying agreed to this, and pressed the two men to accept some silver to cover their expenses. At last they accepted the money and left at once for Liang Shan Po. Li Ying and Tu Hsing remained behind.

Yang Hsiung and Shih Hsiu soon reached the neighborhood of Liang Shan Po, and stayed at the inn kept by Shih Yung as an outpost. When they inquired about the road to Liang Shan Po, Shih Yung asked where they came from, and what business they had at the stronghold. When Yang Hsiung said they came from Chi Chou, Shih Yung immediately asked if his name was Shih Hsiu, and when they had all been introduced Shih Yung explained that he had heard all about Shih Hsiu from Tai Tsung who had just returned, and was staying at the stronghold. Shih Yung then shot a whistling arrow across the lake, and soon a party of bandits appeared in boats. They crossed the lake, and were taken up to the stronghold where they were duly introduced to all the leaders. They explained fully all that had occurred at the Chu village, and how Li Ying had been grossly insulted.

When Ch'ao Kai had heard all the details he was angry,

and said, "We have gathered here many loyal and brave men, and have bestowed much benefit on the people in the surrounding country. When we go on any expedition we are never deficient in valor. All our brothers here are great heroes. But these two men have been implicated in a petty theft of a chicken, and if we associate with them we shall lose our great reputation. So we must kill these two men, and send their heads to the village to show the people that we have nothing to do with robbers. Then as the people in the village have reviled us we must go there and destroy their village. Thus we shall preserve our reputation for valor."

Sung Chiang however spoke, "That will not do. These two men did not take part in the theft as that was the affair of Shih Ch'ien who was traveling with them. What they have done was not disgraceful. We have heard several times that that village has been unfriendly to us. Elder brother, restrain your anger. We have not got a big stock of grain or money, but let us not make too much of that. As they however have insulted us we can go and punish them for that. If we defeat them we shall have food supplies for at least five years. You cannot go yourself because you are our leader, but I will go and command the punitive expedition. If I fail then I will not return. I finally propose that Li Ying be admitted to our numbers."

"What you say is extremely proper," said Wu Yung. "It would not do to kill our brothers who are willing to join us."

"It would be better if you kill me instead of these men," said Tai Tsung.

All the other leaders expressed their support of these views, and Ch'ao Kai agreed. Yang Hsiung and Shih Hsiu expressed their apologies.

The following day Sung Chiang took three thousand bandits, three hundred mounted men, and nine other leaders. He also placed a similar number of men in charge of Lin Ch'ung and nine other leaders, and these were to be his reserves. They soon reached the neighborhood of the Chu village and encamped. A tent was erected for Sung Chiang, and there he discussed matters with Hwa Jung. "I have heard that round this village there are numerous small roads so that it would not be advisable to send our men there at present. We must first send two spies to find out all about the roads, and then we can advance with greater security."

Li K'wei offered to go as a spy, as he said he had not killed a man for a long time.

"You must not go now," said Sung Chiang, "because we shall want you when the fighting commences."

Li K'wei laughed at this. "There is no need to send spies. If you let me have two hundred men I could enter the village, and settle this matter quite easily."

"Don't talk nonsense!" shouted Sung Chiang. "You can wait outside until I call for you."

As he went out however Li K'wei called out, "Those villagers are only like flies. Why are you so nervous?"

Sung Chiang summoned Shih Hsiu, and instructed him to go into the village with Yang Lin.

"The people will already be on the qui vive as your men are here," said Shih Hsiu. "How can we enter the village without being seen?"

"I can get into the village disguised as a priest," said Yang Lin. "I will carry the prayer rings, and shake them as I go along. You (Shih Hsiu) can follow me some distance behind."

"At Chi Chou I sold firewood," said Shih Hsiu, "and I think that I may get in the village with a load of firewood."

Yang Lin thought this a good idea, and they both agreed to start off that evening. They started off about 5 p.m. and had about three miles to go. They noticed the numerous paths and roads on all sides, and that the country was well covered with dense trees. Shih Hsiu put down his load, and spoke to Yang Lin as there was no one about. "There are so many footpaths about that I have not yet recognized the road I was on with Li Ying. As it is now getting dark we cannot make out our way very clearly."

"We need not worry about that," replied Yang Lin. "Let us follow what appears to be the main road."

They continued their way, and soon came to a place where there were shops and inns, and Shih Hsiu stopped in front of an inn. There were many men there with uniforms bearing the character Chu. He spoke to an old man, "Sir, what is the reason for these swords being staked at every door?"

"Where do you come from?" asked the old man. "As you do not know you had better go on your way."

"I am from Shantung, and having no money I brought this firewood into the village to sell it. I do not know the customs of this place."

"You had better get away at once and seek refuge," said the old man. "It will not be long before there is big fighting here."

"What will the fighting be about?"

"You evidently do not know, but I will tell you. This village hates the bandits of Liang Shan Po, but they are now encamped just outside the village. Our chief has summoned all the men to assemble here."

"And how many men are there in this village?"

"In this village there are about ten thousand men, but the other village would also join us in any fighting."

"Why are you afraid of Liang Shan Po brigands when you have so many men?"

"Even I myself was nearly seized when I first came here. There is an old saying that the roads round this place are so well arranged that men might enter the village, but they could not get out."

Shih Hsiu burst into tears, and bowing said, "What hard lines for me! I cannot go back even if I sell my firewood. So I will give you this firewood if you will tell me how I can get away."

"I cannot accept your offer, but I do not mind buying the firewood from you. Please come inside my house, and take a meal before returning."

Shih Hsiu thanked him for this, and followed the old man into the house. After partaking of the congee offered, Shih Hsiu again asked to be shown the way out.

"You just go your way in the village until you come to a poplar tree where you can turn. You must not turn if there is no poplar tree, or there would be death. No other trees will do—take no notice of them. If you make one mistake your position will be hopeless, as on the other roads there are hidden pointed stakes and hooks."

Shih Hsiu thanked him for the information, and asked for his name. The man's name was Chungli. Shih Hsiu then departed promising to reward him for the food, and wine some other day. Just then there was a great uproar outside, and voices were calling out, "A spy is seized!" Looking out Shih Hsiu saw about eighty armed men with a prisoner whom he recognized as Yang Lin. Shih Hsiu was much surprised, and turning to the old man asked, "Who is the man? Why have they bound him?"

"Have you not heard them say that he is a spy? He has evidently got in the village in the disguise of a priest, and not knowing the roads he has taken the wrong road and has been captured. Somebody has recognized him as the bandit, Yang Lin." Just then a patrol of about fifty men came up in charge of a young man on a white horse. Shih Hsiu recognized him, but asked the old man who he was.

"That is the third son of Mr. Chu, our headman, and is named Tiger's Cub. The Pure One is betrothed to him."

Shih Hsiu again thanked him, and asked to be shown the road. The man urged him not to go that day, as there was great danger and it was getting dark. After further pressing, Shih Hsiu again went indoors. Shortly afterwards there was knocking at the street door, and a voice called out, "The red lamp will be the signal to-night, and when you people see it, you must join the attack on the brigands." When the man had gone Shih Hsiu asked who he was, and was informed that he was the official thief-catcher and that that night he hoped to arrest Sung Chiang. Shih Hsiu thought matters over, and then taking a fire, he bade the old man good night and went to the room at the back, and sleep there.

Sung Chiang was waiting in his tent for a long time, and at last as Shih Hsiu and Yang Lin had not returned he sent out O Peng to see whether he could get any news. When he returned he reported that he had heard cries in the village about a spy. The paths were so numerous and complicated that he dared not go any farther.

Upon hearing this Sung Chiang was very angry. "Evidently they have captured our two brothers so why should we wait here any longer as we cannot get any inside information. We must attack at once, and try to save the lives of our brothers. What do you think of that?" he asked the other leaders.

"I will fall on slaughtering," offered Li K'wei.

Sung Chiang issued orders that all the men should prepare for an immediate advance. Li K'wei and Yang Hsiung were to be in charge of the vanguard; Li Chun in charge of the rear guard; Mu Heng on the left wing; Huang Hsin on the right wing, while Sung Chiang, Hwa Jung, and O Peng took charge of the main body. There was at once a great hubbub, waving of flags, beating of drums and gongs, and a great display of swords and axes. It was evening. Upon reaching the village Li K'wei found that the bridge had been drawn up, and as there were no lights showing in the village he thought of going through the water. But Yang Hsiung held him back, and said, "As the village gates are closed it may be only a plot or trap for us. We will wait until the other leaders arrive, and then we will discuss matters."

Li K'wei could not endure any delay so lifting aloft his two axes he yelled, "That fellow Mr. Chu! You come out! The Small Whirlwind is waiting here for you."

No reply came from the village to this challenge. Just then Sung Chiang and the other leaders came up, and were told of the position. Sung Chiang was surprised not to see even a single man on the other side, and also became suspicious. Suddenly he remarked, "I have made a mistake. In the three Divine Books I received it was stated quite clearly, 'In warfare make no undue haste.' I forgot about this in my haste to save the lives of our comrade and have brought troops here without proper plans for entering the village. Now that I am here the enemy hides. There is evidently a plot, and I must at once give orders for a retreat."

Li K'wei said, "But as we have come so far we cannot retreat without doing something. I will go forward, and you can follow me."

While he was speaking a skyrocket went up from the village, and instantly on all the hills surrounding the village there were numerous lights from torches. From the tower above the village gate came a shower of arrows. Sung Chiang gave the orders for retreat, but Li Chun, leader of the rear guard, came and said, "The road we arrived by is now all obstructed, and there is probably an ambush." Sung Chiang gave an order for a number of horsemen to try and find some other road. Just then another skyrocket went up on one of the surrounding hills, followed by loud shouts from all sides. Sung Chiang was quite perplexed.

Even the strategist with the most elaborate plans could not avoid getting into a tight corner?

> Plans to catch a tiger,
> Or a dragon in its den,
> Are ready to capture,
> The extraordinary men.

CHAPTER 47

MISS HU ARRESTS WANG YING; SUNG CHIANG ATTACKS THE CHU VILLAGE

WHEN Sung Chiang gave the orders for retreat there soon arose from his men many cries, and when he inquired the reason he was told that the roads were like a maze, and although they had retreated they had all got back to where they started from. He then gave orders that they were to advance to those places where there were torches displayed. Very soon further cries were heard, and he was then informed that his men had tried to get to the lighted torches, but had found the roads studded with bamboo spikes and iron pricks so that they could not advance.

Sung Chiang was very much distressed and had no plans. Just then, however, a cry arose in the left wing of his armed men, "Shih Hsiu has returned!" Very soon Shih Hsiu appeared, and spoke to Sung Chiang, "Keep cool, sir! I know the road. Tell our men to follow the road, and when they come to white poplars they must turn there, and not at any other place."

Orders were given accordingly, and when the men had gone about two miles they found themselves face to face with a large body of armed villagers.

Sung Chiang asked Shih Hsiu about the position.

They have a lamp as a signal," replied Shih Hsiu.

"Do you see that lamp among the trees? I have noticed that as we go eastward that lamp also moves eastward, and if we go westward the lamp moves in the same direction. That is evidently done to indicate our directions and movements," said Hwa Jung.

"How can we stop this movement of the lamp?" asked Sung Chiang.

"That is quite easy," said Hwa Jung. Running forward

in front of the vanguard he shot an arrow at the lamp and brought it down. The village guard not seeing the lamp any longer did not know where to go, and were soon in confusion. Sung Chiang gave orders for a speedy advance. Shortly there was a great uproar in front, and the torchlights were moving in all directions. Sung Chiang called a halt, and sent Shih Hsiu to find out the position. He soon returned, and reported that the relief party from Liang Shan Po had now arrived, and was attacking the village guard in front. Sung Chiang ordered an attack so that the village guard was soon between two fires. The villagers soon gave way, and scattered. The united bandits now halted, and encamped on some high ground to await the dawn. The roll was called, and they discovered that Huang Hsin was missing. His men said that during the night attack they had got on the wrong road, and Huang Hsin had been dragged off his horse by hooks from tall grass.

Sung Chiang was very angry with the men because they had not duly reported this, and threatened to kill those responsible for this dereliction of duty.

Yang Hsiung tried to pacify Sung Chiang, "There are three villages in alliance here, but Li Ying's village is now free from that alliance. Why not go there and talk matters over with Li Ying?"

Sung Chiang admitted that he had forgotten about Li Ying, and at once decided to go to see him. He left Lin Ch'ung and Chin Ming in charge of the temporary camp. Sung Chiang took three other leaders and about three hundred cavalry with him. Upon reaching the village they found the drawbridge raised and the gates closed. A drum was sounded on the tower over the gate. Sung Chiang called out, "I am Sung Chiang from Liang Shan Po, and have come here only to pay a visit to your headman Li Ying."

Tu Hsing was on the tower, and he recognized some of the leaders. He at once had the gate opened, and taking a boat came across the moat. Upon landing he saluted Sung Chiang, and was introduced by Hwa Jung and Shih Hsiu. Their object in visiting the village was explained, and Tu Hsing agreed to go back, and report the matter to the headman, Li Ying. When he reached the village hall he found Li Ying seated on a bed with a blanket over his shoulders nursing his wound. When Tu Hsing had delivered his message Li Ying replied, "Sung Chiang is a bandit of Liang Shan Po so I cannot agree to receive him here. I am above disloyalty, but if I saw him, people would suspect a double game. You can go back, and tell him that I am sick, and as I cannot leave my bed I cannot meet him now, but may see him at some future date. I request him to take back his presents, as I cannot receive them."

Tu Hsing returned, and duly conveyed this message to Sung Chiang who understood Li Ying's meaning. Tu Hsing then told Sung Chiang of the girl Hu San Liang who was betrothed to Tiger's Cub, and was famous as a great warrior. She lived in the Hu Village, and that was the place that Sung Chiang must be on guard against as Li Ying would remain neutral on account of having been wounded and discourteously treated by the Chu Family Village. The last-named village had two gates, and to succeed he must attack both gates at the same time. To attack one gate only would lead to disaster. The roads near the front or main gate had been specially made to confuse strangers, but the clue was in following the poplar trees.

Here Shih Hsiu interrupted, "But those poplar trees have all been cut down now, so that clue will be missing."

"Even if they have cut them down there will still be the stumps left," replied Tu Hsing, "so that there would be no difficulty in broad daylight."

Sung Chiang thanked Tu Hsing for the information, and then rode back with his cavalry to the temporary camp. There the leaders had a conference, and heard the news. They all agreed to join in an attack on the Chu Village. Li K'wei was very keen on again going in front of the attack, but Sung Chiang ordered him to stay behind which rather upset Li K'wei, and he sat with head bowed down. Sung Chiang selected Ma Lin and three other leaders to accompany him in the vanguard. Tai Tsung and eight other leaders were to take men by the moat. While Lin Ch'ung, Hwa Jung, and two other leaders were to bring the reserves by two separate roads.

After all the men had had their food Sung Chiang started off displaying a large red flag with the character "Shwai," i.e., commander in chief. Upon reaching the Chu Village, Sung Chiang halted his men, and noticed that over the gate were two white flags bearing the announcement, "We will fill up the lake and capture Ch'ao Kai. We will tear down the hill at Liang Shan Po and seize Sung Chiang." Sung Chiang was very angry upon reading this, and swore, "If I do not raze this village to the ground I will never go back to Liang Shan Po." The other leaders were also angry. Sung Chiang waited until he saw that all his men had arrived, and that the two reserve bodies were there, and then gave the order for a general assault on the front gate. He then led part of his men to the other gate. The rear gate was strongly guarded. Approaching from the west (outside the village wall) was a large body of armed men who were shouting and making a great noise. Sung Chiang ordered Ma Lin and Teng Fei to take half the men and guard the gate while he took the other half under O Peng and Wang Ying to oppose the advancing force. As the force came round a smal mound it was seen that it consisted of about thirty horsemen under the command of a young girl—the Pure One—who rode in front, and carried a sword in each hand. This body was followed by about five hundred armed men on foot.

"I suppose this must be the powerful Amazon we have heard so much about," said Sung Chiang. "Who is willing to meet her in single combat?"

Wang Ying came forward and shouted, "I will go," and spurring his horse he dashed forward. Now this man had a weakness for woman, and when he saw this girl his only desire was to make her his prisoner.

The Pure One whipped her horse, and rushed forward for a fight. She was very skillful with the sword, whereas Wang Ying was a superior spearman. They met and after about ten bouts Sung Chiang perceived that Wang Ying could not overcome the girl. Wang Ying had thought that he would seize her at once, and at first had only played with his spear. But when he realized that he could not take her easily, he began to use his extreme strength and skill, but found that he was nonplused.

The girl was quite well educated and intelligent. She thought, "This fellow is very impolite, and treats me too lightly," so she attacked him very strongly. Wang Ying could not stand this, and he pulled his horse round to retreat.

The girl was however too quick for him. Placing her sword in a rest she raced her horse after Wang Ying, and seizing hold of him pulled him out of his saddle. The villagers rushed forward, and seizing him led him away as a prisoner. O Peng seeing this galloped forward to try to save Wang Ying, but found himself in mortal combat with the girl. O Peng was the son of a military officer who had instructed him in the use of the lance with which he was very skillful. Sung Chiang watched the fight with secret satisfaction. But in spite of his skill O Peng could not overcome the girl, he had met his equal. Teng Fei considering the position critical now rushed forward armed with an iron chain. Chu, the Dragon, in command of the villagers now rushed forward to assist Miss Hu by capturing Sung Chiang, but was met by Ma Lin with whom he fought. Seeing this Teng Fei returned to protect Sung Chiang. Sung Chiang seeing these two deadly combats was nonplused, but just then a detachment of horsemen came in view led by Chin Ming who hearing the noise of combat had brought up the reserves. Sung Chiang called out, "Chin Ming, you take the place of Ma Lin in this fight!" Now Chin Ming was very hasty, and was already irritated because these people had arrested Huang Hsin who had been one of his pupils. Seizing his mace he whipped his horse, and rushed forward to attack Chu, the Dragon. Ma Lin seeing Chin Ming retired, and went off to try to rescue Wang Ying. The girl Miss Hu (the Pure One) seeing this movement left O Peng, and rushed to attack Ma Lin. These two were armed with two swords each, and now there was a brilliant flash of steel as the four swords were lashed, and thrust backwards and forwards. Sung Chiang could not distinguish any particular sword as they were so quickly crossed and withdrawn. Chin Ming and Dragon Chu fought about ten bouts without either gaining an advantage. There now came on the scene another combatant—Drill Inspector Luan Ting-yu, who emerged from the village gate on horseback, armed with a lance and a heavy iron mace.. O Peng was free, and advanced to fight this new man. Luan Ting-yu retreated, and O Peng galloped after him. Luan Ting-yu seeing his opponent near at hand flung the iron mace and knocked O Peng off his horse. Seeing this Teng Fei called out, "To the rescue!" and galloped up to engage Luan Ting-yu. Sung Chiang ordered his men to go and rescue O Peng. Dragon Chu had retreated as he could not overcome Chin Ming, and that individual now charged forward also to attack Luan Ting-yu. After about twenty bouts with Chin Ming, Luan Ting-yu watched his opportunity and also retreated. As Chin Ming was pursuing, Luan Ting-yu went into a place where the grass and reeds were very tall and dense. Chin Ming followed him, never suspecting that he was merely going into a trap. Suddenly his horse was pulled down by a lasso, and as he fell he was seized by men who had been waiting in ambush. Teng Fei had seen Chin Ming disappear from his horse, and galloping into the tall grass to rescue him met the same fate, and was also made a prisoner. Sung Chiang seeing this, called off O Peng and Ma Lin as he saw that they could not overcome their opponents. The three leaders then galloped off in retreat followed by their men. They were pursued by Dragon Chu, Luan Ting-yu, and the young Amazon Miss Hu (the Pure One).

Sung Chiang saw in the distance a horseman approaching followed by about five hundred men. He soon recognized him as Mu Heng. There was also another large body of men to the east of these who he saw were led by Yang Hsiung and Shih Hsiu. He also was pleased to see another body of men approaching in charge of Hwa Jung. Sung Chiang gave orders for his men to fight a rearward action, but not to delay their retreat too much as it was getting dusk. Sung Chiang was in advance finding the proper road, and while by himself he found that the Amazon Miss Hu was chasing him to cut him off from his men. Not being a match 'or her Sung Chiang retreated, and now there was a very speedy race between the two. Just as they reached a small hillock a man appeared who called out, 'Why is that woman pursuing my elder brother?" He was none other than Li K'wei. The girl seeing this rescue party turned her horse towards a wood near at hand. Just then Lin Ch'ung also appeared accompanied by about ten horsemen. Lin Ch'ung shouted, and the girl Amazon without hesitation galloped towards him waving her two swords. They fought for about ten bouts, and then Lin Ch'ung saw her weakness. He allowed her to strike at him with both swords, and warding off the blows with his spear he at the same moment dropped his spear and seized hold of the girl with both hands. He held her firmly, and soon had her bound by his men with ropes. Sung Chiang issued an order for all the men to fall back to the place they had started from, and sent Li K'wei to carry this order to all the leaders.

It was now evening. Sung Chiang and Lin Ch'ung with their men and prisoner soon reached the rendezvous. The villagers had all withdrawn into the village for the night.

Sung Chiang summoned four sergeants, and about twenty men, all mounted, and gave them instructions to take the girl Amazon Hu to Liang Shan Po, and hand her over in the custody of his father. Most of the leaders concluded from this that Sung Chiang wanted the girl for himself, but they said nothing.

The following morning a scout came to the camp, and reported that another body of about five hundred men under the commander of Wu Yung was approaching. Sung Chiang went out of the camp to receive Wu Yung. Wu Yung had brought a large quantity of rations for the troops.

Wu Yung said, "Ch'ao Kai heard that you had not been successful yesterday, so he dispatched me with these men, and rations to help you. How did the fight get along these days?"

"That is a long story," replied Sung Chiang. He then explained what had taken place the previous day. He added that he had no plans but that if he could not succeed in defeating those villagers and rescuing the four comrades he would prefer to die at that place instead of returning to Liang Shan Po. He dared not face Ch'ao Kai after being in such disgrace.

Wu Yung laughed at this, and said, "The Chu Family Village ought of course to be defeated. Just now we have a fortunate opportunity and we can succeed very soon."

"But how can we defeat those people?" asked Sung Chiang surprisingly.

Wu Yung still laughed, and took his time to explain matters. Holding up two fingers he explained the position.

> A hand stretching forth to seize a cloud,
> Just helped a man enmeshed in net.

CHAPTER 48

HSIEH CHEN AND HSIEH PAO ESCAPE FROM PRISON; SUN LI AND SUN HSIN RESCUE MEN FROM PRISON

"THE favorable opportunity lies in this," said Wu Yung, "that our Shih Yung has introduced to our band a man who is a personal friend of Luan Ting-yu of the Chu village. This new recruit knows that you did not succeed in attacking this village, and has suggested a plan of attack. He is now on his way here and in five days his plan will be carried out. What do you think of that?"

Sung Chiang was much pleased upon hearing this.

Now at Teng Chou in Shantung there were two hunters Hsieh Chen and Hsieh Pao who were very skillful in the use of the trident. Of all the hunters in that district they were the best. Hsieh Chen was known as Double Headed Snake, while Hsieh Pao had a nickname Double Tailed Scorpion. Both of them had neither father, mother, or wife. They were both over seven feet in height, had broad shoulders, small ordinary waists, and brown complexions. Hsieh Pao had a rough temper, and at times would "shake heaven and earth."

The officials had issued a proclamation that the hunters would be held responsible for killing the tigers in Teng Chou, and if they did not kill the tigers in due time they would be punished. These two hunters had received the order and had prepared poisoned arrows, and then proceeding to the mountains where the tigers were known to be they hid themselves in a tree to wait for the tiger. After waiting there a whole day they returned home without having seen or even heard the tiger. They did this again the following day with the same result. At about 3 a.m. on the third day they again waited in a tree and were so tired that they leaned against each other and fell asleep. They had not yet closed their eyes when they were awakened by a sound of their trap, and springing up they looked around, and saw a big tiger writhing on the ground with the poisoned arrow sticking in its body. Seizing their tridents they ran forward, but the tiger seeing the hunters ran off carrying the poisoned arrow in its body. They followed it. The poison however was taking effect, and very soon the tiger roared loudly and sinking to the ground rolled down the hillside.

Hsieh Pao recognized the place down below as the garden of a Sire Mao. They went down the hillside, and knocked at the door of the farmstead. It was now daylight and upon being admitted they explained to Sire Mao that they had come to take the tiger in his garden they had shot that morning. Sire Mao agreed to this, but as he was afraid they were hungry after their nights work he invited them to take food and wine with him, and then go and look for the wounded tiger. They agreed to this and after the meal Sire Mao took two of his men, and went with the hunters into the garden, but although they looked everywhere they found no tiger. Sire Mao suggested that the hunters had made a mistake as there was no tiger. Hsieh Pao, however, pointed to a spot where the grass had all been leveled, and there were marks of blood of the tiger on the ground. "It looks as though someone had moved away the tiger," he said.

"Do not make such statements," said Sire Mao. "My farm servants did not know anything about a tiger being here, so how could they have had anything to do in the matter? You noticed that when we entered the garden the lock on the gate was rusty and we had to break open the gate. I also came with you to look for the tiger."

"Sir, you must hand the tiger over to us so that we can take it to the yamen and get the reward."

"What you say is quite unreasonable," said Sire Mao. "Your statements are not correct in suggesting that I have taken the tiger away."

"Why should we make false charges?" asked Hsieh Pao. "Evidently you have taken the tiger, and sent it to the yamen so as to get the reward yourself. We shall be beaten by the magistrate."

"That is not my business," said Sire Mao.

"Well, will you let us search your buildings?"

"I cannot agree to that. You a couple of beggars, now have no decency," said Sire Mao.

The brothers became angry, and began to damage his things by force.

Sire Mao called out: "The Hsiehs are plundering in broad daylight!" Seeing that an ambush was lying in the farmstead, the brothers left the yard saying that they would bring a charge against him in the yamen. They had not gone far when they saw the son of Sire Mao on horseback with a group of men, and upon their explaining what had happened he said that some mistake had been made, and asked them to go back to the farmstead with him. They agreed to do this, but upon getting inside the gate of the farmyard the brothers were seized by the farm laborers by order of the son.

The son then said that the previous day they had shot a tiger themselves. He would hand the hunters over to the yamen for making false claims and trying to make trouble.

Sire Mao had the brothers bound with ropes, and sent them to the yamen for trial. At the yamen the case was dealt with by a recorder named Wang Cheng who was a son-in-law of Sire Mao, and he reported the case to the prefect who ordered the two brothers to be beaten for making false claims. In order to avoid the punishment the brothers made a forced confession. They were then put under heavy cangues and sent to prison. Sire Mao and his son talked matters over, and agreed that they could not feel safe until the hunters died in prison so they went to see Wang Cheng, and said they wished the case dealt with more thoroughly, and were willing to bribe the prefect themselves.

The jailer Pao Chi was also bribed with the request to kill the two prisoners. But the under-jailer was a cousin of Hsieh Pao and disclosed the plot against the brothers, although they had never met before. The name of the jailer was Yueh Ho, and his nickname was Iron Flute. He was well skilled in all military drill, and also in the use of the spear. He knew that the prisoners were good men suffering from gross injustice, so he decided to assist them in escaping. He told them that the head jailer had received a bribe to put them to death. Hsieh Chen then asked the under-jailer to take a letter to his aunt's daughter, Mrs. Sun, who was called Ku Ta Sau, and who kept an inn outside the East Gate. She was very kind to both the prisoners, and upon the matter being explained to her she would make arrangements to rescue them.

Yueh Ho agreed to do this and asking another under-jailer to take his duty he slipped out of the prison, and duly told Ku Ta Sau, the Tigress, the story, and asked her to rescue the two prisoners.

She considered the situation bad, and sent a servant for her husband Sun Hsin whose nickname was Small Wei Chih. This was a powerful man, and was very skillful with the iron bludgeon and the spear. He soon arrived, and upon being informed of the trouble he asked Yueh Ho to return to the jail, and they would think of some plan of helping the prisoners to escape. He gave Yueh Ho some money to distribute among the other jailers, and the latter then went back to the jail.

Sun Hsin said that to rescue the prisoners he must go to bring two of his friends. He went straight away, and that evening returned with them. One was Tsou Yuan, noted for his honesty and generosity. Because of his fearless disposition he was called the Forest Dragon. The other one was Tsou Jen, the Horned Dragon, and he got this nickname through once having knocked down a fir tree with his head. Tsou Jen upon hearing the details said he had only twenty loyal followers and after attacking the jail and releasing the two prisoners, the district would not be safe for them to stay in and they must all of them make straight for their refuge at Liang Shan Po. He said he knew the leaders at that place.

Mrs. Sun thought it an excellent plan, and said she would kill any man who would not go with them.

"But there is still one doubtful point," said Tsou Jen. "If we are pursued by cavalry what shall we do?"

Sun Hsin said he had a plan and the next day he went to see his elder brother Major Sun Li who had charge of the cavalry in the town, and by threatening to use force Mrs. Sun, the Tigress, made him agree to join with them in their plots, and afterwards go with them to Liang Shan Po.

The following day Yueh Ho was near the entrance to the jail when he heard the doorbell ringing. He asked who was there, and Ku Ta Sau gave her name, and said she had brought some food for a prisoner. He knew her object, and admitted her. The jailer Pao Chi had been liberally bribed by Sire

Mao, and when he was told by Yueh Ho that the woman was a relative of Hsieh Chen and Hsieh Pao, and had brought food for them, he said the food must be left at the gate to be sent in to the prisoners. So Yueh Ho took the food into the inner prison, and handed it to the two prisoners. He told them who had brought it, and said they would soon meet her. He then unlocked the bolt which fastene them to their beds. Just then he heard at the gate an attendant jailer report that Major Sun was at the gate waiting to enter. The jailer Pao Chi replied, "He is in command of troops. What does he want in my prison? Don't open the door."

Now Mrs. Sun had got near Pao Chi. Again a voice outside the room called out, "Major Sun is outside, and insists upon being admitted."

Jailer Pao Chi was very annoyed at this, and came out of the room. Mrs. Sun asked him in a loud voice, "Where are my brothers?" She took two swords out of her belt, and threatened jailer Pao Chi. He understood the situation, and walked away. He had not gone far before he met the two prisoners Hsieh Chen and Hsieh Pao who had both got rid of their cangues. Jailer Pao Chi was unarmed, and picking up a piece of cangue Hsieh Pao hit him on the head, and brained him. Mrs. Sun had already killed about three jailers now joined the two prisoners and Yueh Ho. Going to the prison gate they opened it, and they all set off. The people closed their doors, and those policemen or soldiers who were about seeing Major Sun in charge of the party did not dare even ask a question. The party duly left the town, and reached Major Sun's home.

There Major Sun's wife got in a cart, and Ku Ta Sau mounted a horse. Sun Hsin and Yueh Ho went with the women as guard while Major Sun, Hsieh Chen, Hsieh Pao, Tsou Yuan, Tsou Jen, and the men went off in another direction to have revenge on Sire Mao who was the cause of all this trouble. Upon reaching the farm they killed him and his son, and then took all the valuables available. They found eight horses in the stables, and loaded four of them with the valuables, and saddled the others for riding. They then set fire to the farm buildings.

They soon caught up to the cart, and all proceeded on their way to Liang Shan Po.

Upon reaching the inn kept by Shih Yung they were told of the defeat at the Chu Village and that the enemy had three great warriors on their side.

When Major Sun heard this he laughed, and said, "We are going to join these heroes, but we have not done any meritorious service yet. But if we now go and help in the attack on that village we shall be in a much better position to be admitted to Liang Shan Po. Now I know all the same military drill as Luan Ting-yu, as he and I were taught by the same teacher in those matters. I will go and say that I was just passing his village on official business, and he will admit me. While inside we can easily act in concert with the heroes outside." He had hardly finished saying this when a man reported that Wu Yung was leaving Liang Shan Po to go to join Sung Chiang. Shih Yung at once told the man to ask Wu Yung to come immediately to that inn as there was a very important matter for discussion. This was done, and very soon Wu Yung arrived with about five hundred men.

After the strangers had been introduced by Shih Yung and their object explained, Wu Yung was pleased, and urged that they should at once join with them in an attack on the Chu Village. As they agreed to this he said that he would ride in advance, and announce the arrangement to Sung Chiang and the other leaders. Upon arriving at the camp he found Sung Chiang with a melancholy expression. He told him of the new recruits, and mentioned that one of them Major Sun was taught by the same teacher as Luan Ting-yu of the opponent village, and that he was prepared to enter that village as a friend, but would act in concert with the attackers outside.

Sung Chiang was much pleased to hear of this, and ordered a feast for the new recruits.

Wu Yung arranged the plans, and explained them to the leaders under strict secrecy. Having received the instructions, Major Sun departed with the new recruits for the Chu village while Tai Tsung was instructed to go to Liang Shan Po to bring four other leaders.

> The eagle old on Liang Shan Po
>   Receives new wings to help its flight;
> At the mountain stronghold
>   A renovation will be in sight.

CHAPTER 49

WU YUNG COMPLETES HIS PLANS; SUNG CHIANG AGAIN ATTACKS THE CHU FAMILY VILLAGE

WU YUNG sent Tai Tsung to Liang Shan Po to bring four other leaders to the camp.

That day Hu Cheng, brother of the girl Amazon, arrived in the camp, and addressed Sung Chiang, "My sister was very stupid in provoking your anger, and she deserved to be captured by you. I hope, however, that you will forgive her for her youthful rashness."

Sung Chiang asked him to be seated, and then said, "The people of the Chu Village have no sense of decency, and have repeatedly tried to deceive us. Therefore we have had to fight them yet we are on good terms with your village. Your sister had one of our leaders arrested so we had to treat her in the same way. We might exchange the prisoners, and so settle accounts."

"But our prisoner has already been taken away to the Chu Village," said Hu Cheng. "I have no means of getting them to hand over the prisoner to you."

"In that case," said Sung Chiang, "how can we release your sister?"

"There is another way," said Wu Yung, addressing Hu Cheng. "Your village must decline further assistance to the Chu Village, and when they send a messenger to call for help you can arrest that man. If you do this then you can exchange that prisoner with us for your sister. You can now return and need not worry about her."

"We will never help them again," said Hu Cheng. He then departed.

Major Sun displayed a flag bearing his late official position, and duly arrived at the gate of the Chu Village with his retinue. His arrival was duly reported, and Luan Ting-yu at once recognized his old schoolmate. He went to the gate, had it opened, and welcomed Major Sun. They all entered the village.

Luan Ting-yu asked how Major Sun came there at such a time, and the latter explained, "I have just been appointed to take command of the troops at Yun Chou, and guard the district against the brigands at Liang Shan Po. As I was passing quite close to your village I thought that I would call and visit you."

Luan Ting-yu then explained that the brigands had been attacking his village for several days, and that he was trying to capture the leader Sung Chiang. The arrival of Major Sun was very opportune, like rain for dry grass.

Major Sun laughed, and said that he had no special ability, but he would help them in capturing the brigands. He made arrangements for quarters for his men and the horses and carts, and then changed his dress, and went to see Sire Chu.

After the introduction and the usual salutations Major Sun said that as the village was in his district he would specially look to the advice and assistance of Sire Chu. He then inquired how their fighting against the brigands had resulted.

"We have not been very successful," said Dragon Chu.

Major Sun then arranged for Ku Ta Sau and Yueh Ta Liang Tze to be introduced to the women's apartments. He then introduced Sun Hsin, Hsieh Chen, and Hsieh Pao as his younger brothers who were traveling with him. He introduced Yueh Ho as a clerk of his yamen, and Tsou Yuan and Tsou Jen as minor army officers.

Upon the third day after this an outpost reported that Sung Chiang's troops were moving for another attack upon the village.

Tiger's Cub Chu said he would go, and arrest the brigand's chief. He took about a hundred mounted men, and lowering the drawbridge left the village. He soon met a body of about five hundred brigands. He halted his men, and went forward alone. Hwa Jung also advanced by himself to engage in combat. They met, but after about fifty bouts neither had any advantage. Hwa Jung tried a ruse, and retired as though defeated. Tiger's Cub turned to pursue him when one of his men called out, "Do not pursue him as he may have some secret trap for you. Your opponent is a skilled bowman." Tiger's Cub listened to this advice, and stopped to pursue, but instead ordered a retreat into the village. Hwa Jung also withdrew his men.

Upon reaching headquarters Tiger's Cub told Major Sun about the fight, and how both had retired. They then all feasted together until well into the night.

The next day about noon Sung Chiang's men were again advancing for an attack, and the three brothers Chu all went with their men to repel the attack. There was a great noise of gongs and drums and a big display of flags. Chu Chao-feng, the village headman, went on the gate tower, and sat down there with Luan Ting-yu and Major Sun. Very soon they saw Lin Ch'ung ride out from the brigands, and coming near the village gate he cursed loudly.

Dragon Chu was annoyed at this, and mounted his horse. The drawbridge being lowered, he went across supported by a loud crashing of gongs and drums. He engaged in combat with Lin Ch'ung, but after about thirty bouts neither had any advantage, and they both retired.

Tiger Chu now mounted and dashed over the drawbridge. He was met by Mu Heng, and they had about thirty bouts without any definite result.

Tiger's Cub Chu now took to the saddle, and was met by Yang Hsiung, but again there was a draw.

Major Sun now called for his spear, and mailed armor, and mounted his horse. He rode out to the bandits troop, and challenged the best man to come out and fight against him. Very soon Shih Hsiu came out on horseback, and they had about fifty bouts. Then Major Sun by a trick let Shih Hsiu thrust in with his spear, and by evading it, Major Sun suddenly seized hold of his opponent, dragged him off his horse, and carried him to the village gate. He was greeted by all the men as a great conqueror. Major Sun asked how many men had been captured so far, and was informed that this made the seventh. He said they must treat the prisoners well, because when they got Sung Chiang they would send the whole lot in carts to the district city.

Major Sun sent Tsou Yuan and Tsou Jen to visit the prisoners, and secretly told them of the plans for the coming struggle.

On the fifth day Sung Chiang again had his men advancing for an attack. Major Sun now suggested that the defenders be not excited but be prepared to take prisoners instead of trying to kill the enemy. This was agreed to and arranged. Chu Chao-feng again took his seat at the observation post on the tower above the gate. He saw large bodies of men on all sides, and it looked as though this was to be the final mass attack. The three brothers and also Luan Ting-yu were ready to take their men out of the four gates to meet the bandits.

The war drums were beaten, and a rocket fired in the village, the four gates were opened, the drawbridge lowered, and the armed men rushed out of the gates. Major Sun had charge of his own men, and took up his position on the bridge in front of the main gate. His brother Sun Hsin took the official flag, and stuck it on the tower over the gate. Upon a signal from Yueh Ho the other leaders of the bandits inside the village blew whistles and attacked the villagers who were guarding the prison van. They soon broke open the van, released the seven brigands, and armed them. Ku Ta Sau seized two swords, and went into the rooms of Sire Chu, killing any woman she met. Chu Chao-feng saw all this on the tower over the gate, but before he could raise an alarm he was killed by Shih Hsiu. The brigands under Major Sun now attacked the villagers at the gate. Hsieh Chen and Hsieh Pao went to the stables, and set fire to the fodder storage. The brigands under Sung Chiang seeing the great fire pressed onward their attack.

Tiger Chu seeing the fire, galloped back towards the village, but was stopped at the gate by Major Sun. He realized the treachery, and beat a hasty retreat. But he was confronted by Lu Fang and Kuo Sheng who soon overcame him and killed him. The villagers, seeing their leaders killed, scattered in all directions. The bandits under Sung Chiang now had a clear road, and advancing on the main entrance were admitted by Major Sun and his men.

At the other gate, Dragon Chu had also failed to defeat Lin Ch'ung in personal combat, and seeing the fire at the rear gate had also galloped back to the village. At the gate he saw Hsieh Chen and Hsieh Pao throwing the dead bodies of villagers from the wall, and he retreated. He then met Li K'wei with his two axes, and in a short encounter was soon overcome, and killed.

Tiger's Cub Chu got reports of the treachery in his rear, and realizing that it was useless to retreat he led his men in the direction of the Hu Village. Upon arriving there he was arrested by Hu Cheng who intended to send him bound as a prisoner to Sung Chiang. Shortly afterwards, however, Li K'wei appeared and he at once took the Tiger's Cub and killed him on the spot. The villagers seeing this all scattered. Li Kwei now advanced to attack Hu Cheng who mounted his horse and galloped off. Li K'wei continued his way through the Hu village killing the whole family of Sire Hu. Li K'wei and his men looted the farmstead, and then set fire to it.

The leaders of the bandits assembled in the main hall. Sung Chiang was highly elated at the victory, but expressed his regret at the death of Luan Ting-yu. When he heard that the Hu Village had been looted and burnt, he asked why that had been done seeing that the headman Hu Cheng had been friendly towards them only a few days ago. Li K'wei stepped forward. He was covered with blood, and had his two axes stuck in his belt. He said, "I killed the Dragon, and Tiger's Cub, but Hu Cheng got away on horseback. I made a clean sweep of the whole family of Sire Hu. I now report my meritorious conduct."

"It has been reported already that you have killed Dragon Chu, but nobody has confirmed your other statements," said Sung Chiang.

Li K'wei then gave details of what he had done.

"But why did you do such a thing in defiance of my order that Hu Cheng and his village should be spared."

"You forget, but I remember," said Li K'wei. "The Amazon Miss Hu was sister of Hu Cheng, and she wanted to kill you a few days ago. You must not expect to make her your wife."

"Iron Cow, you should not talk such nonsense," said Sung Chiang. "Why should I want her as a wife when I have other plans for her? How many prisoners did you take alive?"

"None. If I saw one alive I killed him at once."

"You do not observe my orders. I ought to have you executed for that, but this time I will excuse you because you killed Dragon Chu, and Tiger's Cub Chu, and many others. In future, however, if you do not carry out my orders I shall certainly have you executed."

Li K'wei laughed and said, "I may have no merit, but I certainly have had the pleasure of killing people."

Sung Chiang then discussed with Wu Yung as to whether they should kill everybody in the village, and make a clean sweep of their enemies. But Shih Hsiu pointed out that there were some good and innocent people in the village, and mentioned, as an instance, Mr. Chungli who had shown him the roads in the village. Sung Chiang asked Shih Hsiu to go, and find the man, and bring him there. In a short time Shih Hsiu returned with old Mr. Chungli who saluted Sung Chiang and Wu Yung. Sung Chiang presented him with some silver and said, "Because of your benevolent assistance to one of our leaders I show mercy to all the people in this village. We have thought of exterminating everybody, but on account of your great virtue we will spare their lives. We have been victorious, and have killed all those who were really opposed to us. We will even give each family in this village a picul of rice, in order to show our good intentions. We will entrust the distribution of the rice to you, as you are a good upright man."

All the valuables in the village and also the cows, sheep, and horses were sent to Liang Shan Po. After the rice had been distributed as promised there was still about 50,000 piculs left which were also sent to Liang Shan Po. The new recruits with Major Sun were duly admitted to the band, and all then went to Liang Shan Po.

Now Li Ying had been wounded by an arrow, and he did not take part in all this. He remained in his village, and had messengers who reported to him all that had taken place in the Chu village. When the bandits had all gone a messenger reported to him one day that an official had arrived in the village, and was making an investigation. Li Ying dressed up in his best silks, and went to meet the officials. The official was seated in the main hall of his farmstead. With him were a recorder, a clerk, several servants, and many jailers. Li Ying saluted, and stood to attention. The official asked him what he knew of the attack on the village.

"I was wounded by an arrow shot at me by Tiger's Cub Chu. I was confined indoors, and did not know the fighting."

"Nonsense!" remarked the official. "I received a petition from the Chu village stating that you had brought the brigands from Liang Shan Po to attack that village. They looted the village and you received their presents, but how is it that you did not go back with them?"

"I know the law in such matters," said Li Ying, "how dare I receive bribery from the bandits?"

"It is hard to believe what you say," said the official. "I must arrest you, send you to the court where you can answer the charges made against you by the villagers." Li Ying was arrested, and bound, Tu Hsing was also arrested, and then they all mounted their horses, and set off.

They had gone only about ten miles when they were stopped in a forest by Sung Chiang and four other leaders. With the brigands was Lin Ch'ung who shouted out, "We are from Liang Shan Po," and the official and his escort upon hearing this galloped away leaving the prisoners behind. Sung Chiang ordered a party to pursue the men, who soon returned and reported that they had all escaped. The two prisoners were released, and given horses to ride on.

Sung Chiang suggested to Li Ying and Tu Hsing, the prisoners, that it would be better if they both took refuge at Liang Shan Po.

"That will not do," said Li Ying, "because the officials were killed by you, and I had nothing to do with it."

Sung Chiang laughed, "The court will not discriminate as to who among us killed the prefecture. If we go and leave you the officials will arrest you as being implicated. If you do not care to join our band, then you can leave us after staying at Liang Shan Po until things settle down."

The two men saw no means of declining this offer as they were completely in the hands of the bandits so they fell in with the proposal, and accompanied them to the mountain. Upon arriving there they were duly introduced to all the leaders. Li Ying then asked that a man be sent to the village to find out how his people were faring as he was rather anxious about them.

Wu Yung laughed at this and said, "All your people are already here, and as the whole village has been burnt down what is the use for you to go back?"

Li Ying did not believe this until he saw many of his villagers about. Among the prisoners he even saw his wife who told him, "When you had left some officials and inspectors with about three hundred soldiers came to the village, and arrested us. They took all the cattle, and set fire to the houses and buildings." Li Ying was very much upset. Ch'ao Kai and Sung Chiang however bowed to Li Ying, and said, "We brought you all here because we heard that you are a good man. We hope that you will excuse us for taking such liberties."

Li Ying agreed to let matters remain as they were.

Sung Chiang then explained that the officials, inspectors, and soldiers who had taken him and Tu Hsing as prisoners, and had taken all the villagers to Liang Shan Po were his own followers who had acted the part of officials. When the men were pointed out to Li Ying he recognized them, and was astounded at the way in which he and his people had been duped.

Sung Chiang spoke to the Amazon Miss Hu, and suggested that she should marry Wang Ying. She agreed to this, and the marriage took place soon afterwards.

A few days afterwards a messenger arrived from Chu Kwei, and said that there was a guest staying at the inn who wished to meet Sung Chiang. Sung Chiang was pleased to hear this, and was willing to receive the man.

> Black and white all people know,
> Bandits know their enemies.

CHAPTER 50

THE WINGED TIGER HITS PAI HSIU-YING WITH A CANGUE; THE HANDSOME WHISKERS MISSES THE SON OF AN OFFICIAL

THE messenger stated that a few days ago they had stopped some travelers near a forest, and among them was Inspector Lei Heng of Yun Cheng Hsien, who was recognized by Chu Kwei, and the latter had got the former to stay at the inn. Sung Chiang and Ch'ao Kai were much pleased to hear this, and they went with Wu Yung to receive Inspector Lei Heng, and bring him to the headquarters.

Upon meeting, Sung Chiang said, "I have been thinking of you very often, and it is with great pleasure that I now meet you here. But what has brought you this way?"

Lei Heng after a deep bow said, "I was deputed by our magistrate to go to Tung Chang Fu, and I am now on my way back. I was however recognized by Chu Kwei when our party was held up by your people."

"Heaven fortunately arranged that," said Sung Chiang. He then took Lei Heng to headquarters where he was entertained for about five days. Ch'ao Kai happened to ask for news about Inspector Chu Tung, and was informed that he was a head jailer of the prison at Yun Cheng Hsien. He was held in high esteem by the newly appointed magistrate.

Sung Chiang gradually brought the conversation round, and suggested that Inspector Lei Heng join them, but the inspector rejected the idea. His mother was very old, and could not stay alone, but when she died he could join them. When at last he left the mountain they gave him many presents. Upon reaching Yun Cheng Hsien Inspector Lei Heng duly delivered the dispatches he was carrying, and reported to the magistrate the results of his journey.

One day as he was on his way to the yamen he heard someone behind call out, "Inspector, when did you get back?" Upon turning round he recognized a man named Li, the Second, and replied, "I came back some days ago."

"Then you cannot have seen that beautiful girl Pai Hsiu-ying who had just arrived here from the Eastern Capital (Kaifeng). She was inquiring for you, but you were away at the time. She sings splendidly, acts well, plays the lute feelingly, and is very popular with all the men. Would you care to see her? She is one of the best singsong girls."

Inspector Lei Heng was off duty at the time so he agreed to go with Li, the Second. At the door he noticed many announcements in golden characters. He entered, and took the first seat. There was an actress performing on the small stage. Li, the Second, disappeared as soon as Lei Heng was seated. When girl's song finished an old man came on the stage holding a fan in his hand and he spoke, "I am Pai Yu-chiao and I come from Kaifeng (the Eastern Capital). I am getting very old, and have to depend upon my daughter Pai Hsiu-ying for a living." A gong was then sounded, and his daughter came on the stage, and bowed to the audience. She went through a few tricks with a small gong, and then sang the following song:

> The young birds chirp; the old ones come;
> Old goats lean, but kids are fat;
> In life how hard to get a crumb,
> Let alone a little clothing;
> In love our men are frolicsome,
> So diff'rent to the mandarin duck.

Lei Heng applauded. The girl spoke, "To-day you will have noticed a bill at the door announcing that I would sing the gay and amorous song, 'At Yu Chang Cheng Mr. Su Ching was twice expelled.'" Her song was received with general applause." She sang some more verses of the above song, and then her father spoke, "Our repertoire is very select, but particularly suited for an intelligent audience like this. Now that the applause is over I will ask my daughter to go round, and collect your donations." The girl took up a tray, and said, "I begin with the wealthy,

KILLING A SINGSONG GIRL

and stop with the profitable pass he lucky spots, and go to the prosperous places. I hope you will all give something."

"They will all contribute," said her father.

She first came to Lei Heng when he felt in all his belts and pockets, but could not find a single cash. He said, "I have forgotten to bring my purse, but I will come again to-morrow and reward you."

"If you don't contribute the others will follow your example," said the girl. "You are sitting in the best seat."

Lei Heng blushed, and said, "When I left home I had no idea of coming here so I did not carry a purse."

The girl laughed, "You came here, and listened to my singing so why did you not bring some money?"

"Never mind! I will give you three ounces of silver to-morrow. Just now I have not a single cash."

"As you have no cash to-day you need not talk about giving silver to-morrow," said Pai Hsiu-ying. "It seems as though you were showing me a plum to quench my thirst and a painted cake to satisfy my hunger."

Her father also added, "My daughter! Have you no eyes? You ask people without looking whether they are likely to have money. You had better pass him by and ask more generous people for money."

"Do you wish her to infer that I am ungenerous?" asked Inspector Lei Heng.

"It would be easier for a dog to grow horns than for you to be generous," said the father, Pai Yu-chiao.

The audience all laughed at this joke. Inspector Lei Heng was angry, and said, "You foolish slave! How dare you insult me?"

"To insult a village cowboy is a small matter," replied Pai Yu-chiao.

A bystander interposed, "Don't talk like that. This is Inspector Lei Heng."

"I am only afraid of donkeys," replied Pai Yu-chiao.

Lei Heng could stand no more of this sarcasm. He jumped on to the stage, and gave Pai Yu-chiao a blow on the jaw which knocked some teeth out. Many bystanders intervened, and prevented further blows, and induced Lei Heng to leave.

Now the girl had known the magistrate when he was previously in the Eastern Capital (Kaifeng). When the daughter saw how badly her father had been mauled she took a sedan chair at once, and went to call on the magistrate. She told him how her father had been treated in the tea house. The magistrate was angry, and asked her to write out an accusation at once. This was done. The girl was so determined that she would not leave the magistrate's yamen, but stayed there crying. This prevented Lei Heng's many friends from seeing the magistrate and settling the matter in favor of Lei Heng. Lei Heng was arrested, and upon being brought into court was beaten with a bamboo. The magistrate also ordered that he wear a cangue, and be paraded on the street with it.

The girl wished to further display her influence with the magistrate so she again spoke to him, and asked him to order that Inspector Lei Heng be paraded in front of the tea house. The magistrate gave this order.

The men in the yamen were all friendly to Lei Heng, and would not do him any harm. The girl knew this so she went into a tea shop just near, and called out to his attendant to come inside. She said to him, "The magistrate wants to punish Lei Heng, but I know that you are the prisoner's friend and treat him well. I will go to tell the magistrate, and see what he will do."

"Please do not get angry," said the attendant; "I will punish him."

"In that case I will reward you for your service," replied the girl.

The attendant went to Lei Heng, and told him what the girl had said. Then he began to execute the punishment. There was a big crowd all round looking on, and soon Lei Heng's mother arrived with some food for him. When she saw her son was being abused she cursed the attendant: "You are a friend of my son like all the others in the yamen, but how much money did you get for doing this dirty work? Who will stand for you when it is your turn to be charged?"

"Madam, please listen to me," replied the attendant. "The plaintiff insisted upon your son being sent to be bound up here as the orders issued. So what else can I do? If we disobey orders, the plaintiff would complain to the magistrate, and we would be punished. I have no means of saving his 'face.'"

"What right has the plaintiff," said Lei Heng's mother, "to ask for details of the punishment to be executed in this way?"

The attendant whispered to Mrs. Lei, "The plaintiff is very friendly with the magistrate, and a word from her goes a long way."

Mrs. Lei went up to her son, and began to untie the fastenings while she was cursing, "That girl must be a mean thief to use her influence in this way. I will untie these ropes myself, and then see what she will do."

The girl Pai Hsiu-ying in the tea shop had heard all this, and she now came out on the street, and spoke to Mrs. Lei, "What did the old woman say just now?"

Mrs. Lei was annoyed at this, and pointing at the girl she replied, "You birch! Suitable for all and sundry! How dare you abuse me?"

The girl raising her eyebrows, and staring replied, "You old flea! Beggar-woman! You have insulted me."

"I have insulted you! Well, what then? You are not the magistrate of this district!"

The girl, Pai Hsiu-ying, rushed forward, and slapped Mrs. Lei's face. She followed this up with a vigorous assault of slaps and blows. Lei Heng saw all this, and could not stand it. He was boiling with rage, and seizing the cangue, he broke it in two pieces, then seizing it he hit the girl's head with it, and broke her skull. She fell down dead.

The bystanders arrested Lei Heng, took him to the yamen, and made a full statement to the magistrate. The magistrate ordered the coroner and the Ti Pao to take Lei Heng to the spot, inspect the corpse, and make their report. Lei Heng confessed fully, and was sent to prison. His mother was released on bail. The jailer was Chu Tung, the Beautiful Whiskers. He gave his friend Lei Heng a good room, and supplied food and drink.

Chu Tung thought of finding a means of allowing Lei Heng to escape, but for a day he could not find a plan. He however arranged for a friend to interview the magistrate, and explain the case. The magistrate had some esteem for Chu Tung, but would not listen to any proposal made as he was still angry that his sweetheart had been killed. The girl's father was pressing the magistrate for prompt action, and wanted Lei Heng executed at once. After sixty days of detention in the prison Lei Heng was sent to the prefect at Chi Chou for trial. Chu Tung was placed in charge of the escort. When they had gone about four miles from Yun Cheng Hsien, Chu Tung ordered a halt at an inn by the roadside. While the escort was drinking wine Chu Tung took Lei Heng to a quiet spot at the back of the inn. He took off the prisoner's cangue, and said, "Younger brother, you are free. Go at once, and get your mother and then both of you can escape. I will face the case at the yamen."

Lei Heng replied, "I do not object escape. It would only get you into trouble."

"Younger brother, you do not understand. The magistrate was angry because you killed his sweetheart, and has worded the report so that you will be executed upon your arrival at Chi Chou. If I allow you to escape I shall not be executed for that crime. I have no parents now or even relatives, and can use whatever money I have for my own case. Go at once, and be more careful in the future."

Lei Heng argued no more, but escaped. He took his mother, and went to Liang Shan Po.

Chu Tung came inside the inn again and said, "Lei Heng has escaped. What can we do?"

"Let us go at once to his home, and arrest him, as he is sure to go there," replied the escort.

Chu Tung, however, remained undecided for a long time, and then took the escort back to the yamen.

He reported to the magistrate that owing to his own carelessness Lei Heng had escaped, and he held himself responsible for the misfortune.

The magistrate was inclined to save Chu Tung, but Pai Yu-chiao would not let the matter drop. So he sent Chu Tung to Chi Chou Fu, for trial. Chu Tung sent a man in advance with plenty of money to arrange matters with the officials. After his trial he received twenty blows with the bamboo, and was then sent to the prison at Tsangchou, Chihli province. He was put under the escort of two men. Upon arrival t Tsangchou the escort was dismissed, and sent back. The prefect liked the appearance of Chu Tung, and instead of sending him to prison gave him a post as a menial official in his yamen.

The minor officials treated Chu Tung with respect, as they soon saw that he had a very good easy disposition. One day while the prefect was sitting in court listening to a case he summoned Chu Tung, and asked him, "For what reason did you assist Lei Heng in escaping?"

"I had no intention of allowing him to escape," said Chu Tung, "and he only got away owing to my carelessness."

"Then your fault was not very serious," said the prefect.

"But the plaintiff claimed that I had done it purposely, and demanded severe punishment."

"Why did Lei Heng kill the singsong girl?"

Chu Tung then explained all the details of the murder.

The prefect considered that under the circumstances as Lei Heng had acted from strong sense of filial piety, Chu Tung had done the right thing in allowing the prisoner to escape.

Chu Tung told the prefect that he would not dare to deceive him so as to gain such a good reputation. Just then a son of the prefect about four years of age entered the court. The prefect regarded his child as a jewel of the greatest value. The boy approached Chu Tung, and wanted to be lifted up. Chu Tung took him in his arms. The child stroked Chu Tung's beard and said, "I like men with beards."

The prefect told his son not to annoy Chu Tung by pulling his beard.

"I want him to come and play with me," replied the child.

"I will just go, and play with him outside, but will soon come back," said Chu Tung.

The prefect agreed to this, and the pair left the court. Chu bought some sugared fruit in the street for the child, and then returned to the court with the boy still in his arms.

"Where did you go, my son?" asked the prefect.

"This old beard took me to the street, and bought for me some sugared fruit which I ate," replied the little boy.

"Where did you get the money from to buy such sweets?" asked the prefect to Chu Tung.

"Do not mention it," replied Chu Tung. "It is merely to express my reference to you."

The prefect ordered a servant to bring some wine for Chu Tung. A woman servant soon brought it in, and offered Chu Tung three large tumblers of wine. The prefect asked Chu Tung to look after the boy and play with him in future.

"Your orders shall be closely observed," said Chu Tung. After this Chu Tung was always with the child, playing with him, and always spent sums of money to buy things for him.

In another fortnight was the Festival of Departed Spirits (15th of the 7th moon), and many lamps were floated on the rivers for the spirits. A woman servant came to Chu Tung, and told him that the boy wanted to go in the evening, and see the lamps floating on the river. The prefect's wife had agreed to let him go with Chu Tung. The boy was dressed in green silk, and wore a cap with imitation beards at each side. Chu Tung carried him on his shoulder through the yamen gate to the Ti Tsang Temple where they could get a good view of the river. It was about 9 p.m., and Chu Tung carried the little boy round the temple to the Releasing Life Pool.[1] The boy leaned on the rail, and enjoyed watching the lamps floating on the water.

While there a man pulled at Chu Tung's sleeve and said, "Elder brother, please come here as I have something to say." Turning, Chu Tung was surprised to see Lei Heng. He told the boy to sit down at that spot while he went to buy some sugared fruit for him. He must not go away.

"Please come back quickly," replied the boy, "because I want to go to the bridge and see the floating lamps there."

Chu Tung agreed, and then went off to Lei Heng. He asked why Lei Heng had come there.

Lei Heng drew Chu Tung to one side where there was no one about. Then Lei Heng explained that he had taken his mother to Liang Shan Po and joined the bandits. But Ch'ao Kai and also Sung Chiang were so much indebted to the splendid assistance of Chu Tung that they had specially instructed Wu Yung to come with Lei Heng, and convey their deep gratitude to him.

[1] A pool where fish were to be released, as a symbol of saving life.

"Where is Wu Yung now?" asked Chu Tung.

A voice behind him said, "Here I am!" and turning he saw Wu Yung.

After the usual exchange of salutations Wu Yung invited Chu Tung to accompany them to Liang Shan Po. He urged him to go with them that night.

For some time Chu Tung could think of nothing to say, but at last he replied, "You are wrong. I am afraid that somebody will hear what you say. Lei Heng has committed a murder. I let him escape, and am now an exile here for his sake. After about half a year more I can return home, and see my people again. I cannot join your band. You had better return at once, and not get into trouble by staying about here."

"You have a job here," said Lei Heng, "but it is hardly suitable for a hero like you. It is not my idea to take you away, but I come because both Sung Chiang and Ch'ao Kai would like very much to see you, and thank you personally for what you have done."

"I do not understand you," replied Chu Tung. "I helped you to escape, and also to take your old mother away. But why do you come to-day, and endeavor to involve me in some trouble?"

"As you do not care to come with us," said Wu Yung, "we shall of course have to return without troubling you any further."

"Then please convey to our friends at Liang Shan Po my kind regards," said Chu Tung.

Upon returning to the spot where he had left the small boy, Chu Tung could not find him anywhere, and became alarmed. Lei Heng seeing the position said that his companion had taken the boy, and that Chu Tung should not worry so much.

"But this is a very serious matter for me," replied Chu Tung. "If the boy has any misfortune the life of the prefect will be in danger."

Lei Heng and Wu Yung got Chu Tung to go with them outside the town.

"Where are your companions who have taken the child away?" asked Chu Tung.

"Just come to our rooms and there we will give you the small boy," replied Lei Heng.

"Time is passing quickly," said Chu Tung, "and I am afraid that the prefect will blame me."

"Our companions are rather stupid, and will probably have taken the child to our rooms," said Wu Yung.

"What is the name of your companion?" asked Chu Tung, and was informed that he was Li K'wei. At this Chu Tung was very much upset, and hurried forward. They had gone about a mile when they met Li K'wei and Chu Tung asked him where the boy was.

After saluting Li K'wei replied that the boy was there, and Chu Tung wanted to see him at once. Li K'wei said the boy was sleeping in the wood. Chu Tung went to the place indicated, and there saw the boy lying on the ground. Upon going to pick the boy up Chu Tung saw that he was dead—his skull having been cleft in two. At this Chu Tung was boiling with rage, and rushed out of the wood. The three men had disappeared, but looking round Chu Tung saw Li K'wei some distance away, and ran after him. On the way he stripped his clothing ready for a fight. Li K'wei was a fast runner, and Chu Tung could not overtake him, and was soon out of breath. It was now dark except for the moonlight, and Li K'wei had no difficulty in keeping well in front. Soon they came to a farmhouse, and Li K'wei went inside. "Now," thought Chu Tung, "I will capture him, and kill him." Upon entering the farmyard Chu Tung noticed many military weapons arranged in front of the main building. He thought this place must belong to some official so he shouted out, "Is there anybody inside?" In response a man came out and asked, "Who are you?"

"I am Chu Tung, jailer from the prison, at Yun Cheng Hsien, and I am in pursuit of a criminal who entered this farmyard. He is named Li K'wei and he has murdered the son of the prefect of Chi Chou Fu. Please help me to capture him."

The man asked him to wait a little, but Chu Tung would not do so, and asked for his name.

"I am Ch'ai Chin, Small Whirlwind," replied the man. Chu Tung had heard of his reputation, and after salutations Squire Ch'ai Chin asked him to go into the house, and talk

A PREFECT'S SON KIDNAPED

matters over. They entered and Chu Tung then asked how such a man as Li K'wei could use that farm as a hiding place.

"I welcome all kinds of wanderers here," replied Squire Ch'ai Chin. "As I have a special iron tablet bestowed by the emperor to my ancestor as a distinction for great merit, no criminal may be arrested at my house. I received a special note from Sung Chiang, a friend of ours, asking me to allow Lei Heng, Wu Yung, and Li K'wei to stay at my house for a few days. They were on their way to request you to join them at Liang Shan Po. As you refused to join them, Li K'wei kidnaped the boy, and killed him, so that you could not return to the yamen and face his father."

Just then Lei Heng and Wu Yung entered the room, and after saluting Chu Tung they said, "Please forgive us for the crime committed. We did it only by order of our chief, Sung Chiang. If you come with us to Liang Shan Po all will be explained to you."

"Your asking me to go to Liang Shan Po was all right," replied Chu Tung, "but your method of inducing me to go was exceedingly cruel. I will go with you now, but I must first see Li K'wei."

Squire Ch'ai Chin agreed to this, and called in Li K'wei to make a full apology to Chu Tung. When Li K'wei entered he gave Chu Tung a kotow. Chu Tung was enraged at seeing the man, and rushing forward seized him to kill him on the spot. The other three men however intervened and held Chu Tung.

"Before I go with you," said Chu Tung, "I have something to say."

> Battle-axes break the law;
> Offspring of the emperor dies.

CHAPTER 51

LI K'WEI KILLS YIN TIEN-HSI; CH'AI CHIN CAPTURED AT KAO T'ANG CHOU

"I will go with you to Liang Shan Po on the condition that you kill Li K'wei," said Chu Tung. "Then my anger will be appeased."

Li K'wei was angry at this, and swore, "I was told by Ch'ao Kai and Sung Chiang to kill the boy."

Chu Tung again tried to get at Li K'wei, but was held back by the others. Squire Ch'ai Chin intervened, "This matter can be easily arranged. You three may go to Liang Shan Po according to Ch'ao Kai's wish, and leave Li K'wei behind here?"

"But the governor will order for the arrest of my family," said Chu Tung. "What about that?"

"I think that Sung Chiang has probably sent men to bring all your family to the mountain," said Wu Yung.

This appeased Chu Tung, and at last he agreed to go. That evening the three men mounted horses given them by Squire Ch'ai Chin, and left for Liang Shan Po. They duly reached their destination, and were received by the leaders of the bandits. During the reception Chu Tung asked if anything had been done about his family. At this Sung Chiang laughed, and said, "You need not worry about them because they have been here for several days."

Chu Tung was pleased at this, and was taken to see his wife. She told him that a letter had been brought to their home stating that he had joined the bandits, and that she was to join him there. After this Chu Tung lived with his family at Liang Shan Po.

At Tsangchou the governor became anxious at the non-return of his son and Chu Tung, and sent men to look for them. They all returned by midnight without having found a trace of them. The next day the body of the boy was found in the wood. The governor was filled with anguish, and went at once to see the corpse. The next day he issued an order for the arrest of Chu Tung. Inquiries made at Yun Cheng Hsien discovered that Chu Tung's family had left there some days before.

Li K'wei had stayed at Squire Ch'ai Chin's for a month when one day he saw a messenger arrive with an urgent message. Squire Ch'ai Chin read the letter and was startled. He said, "As things are like this, I must go and look into the matter myself."

"What is it about?" asked Li K'wei.

"I have an uncle at Kao T'ang Chou, and he is very ill because a man is trying to deprive him of his garden. As he is about to die he asks me to go, and hear his will. As he has neither son nor daughter I must go at once to him."

"I should like to go with you," said Li K'wei. "What do you say?"

"As you want to go I have no objection," said Squire Ch'ai Chin. He then selected about ten of his best horses and men to go with them. They started the following morning at daybreak, and reached Kao T'ang Chou the same day. Upon reaching the house they dismounted, and Squire Ch'ai Chin went inside to see his uncle, leaving the others with Li K'wei in a guest room. Squire Ch'ai Chin found his uncle on the bed in a very weak state. The wife said, "You have ridden a good distance to pay us this visit, but I hope that our trouble will not upset you." After answering several questions she continued, "The new prefect here, Kao Lien, is a younger brother of Kao, Minister for War. He does all kinds of bad things here, and relies upon his influence and position to hush any objection. He brought with him his brother-in-law, named Yin Tien-hsi, who has got the nickname Yin, the Prefect's Deputy; and he also acts just as badly as his brother-in-law. One of his hangers-on informed him that we had a very nice flower garden with a fine arbor in a pond. One day he came here with about thirty dissolute fellows, and after looking round our garden he said we must remove as he had decided to come and live here himself. My husband told Yin Tien-hsi that our family was of very high standing, and that we held an iron tablet inscribed by the emperor himself. Therefore we could not submit to such treatment. 'If you take our home, where can we go to?' But he would not listen to what my husband had said, and insisted upon our leaving at once. My husband got so excited that he tried to fight with Yin Tien-hsi, but the fellows around seized my husband and assaulted him. As a result of this he has been seriously ill ever since. Medicine has not improved his health, and he is expecting to die very soon. As you are his cousin you must devise some plan for this situation."

"Do not worry about it," replied Squire Ch'ai Chin. "Let us send for the best doctors, and see whether they cannot cure my uncle. I will send a man to my home to bring the imperial iron tablet here, and then I will discuss matters with the officials. We need not be afraid of these local mandarins when I have that tablet."

"Perhaps my husband has not managed the business properly," said Mrs. Huang Cheng, "and I hope that you will succeed."

After attending to his uncle's requirements Squire Ch'ai Chin went to the guest room, and explained the position to Li K'wei and the men.

Li K'wei was very angry at this and said, "These fellows are unreasonable. But I will go and ask them to bite my ax, and after that we can discuss matters with them."

"Don't be so stupid," replied Squire Ch'ai Chin. "This official has great influence, but when I show him my imperial tablet, if he will not listen to me, then I may go to the capital, and lay the case before the highest official."

"Laws! Laws!" said Li K'wei. "At the present time laws are of no use in our country. Better fight and discuss afterwards. Then if these fellows appeal to the mandarins against us we shall chop off the heads of the mandarins themselves."

Squire Ch'ai Chin laughed, "You should not forget that you cannot meet Chu Tung because he wants to fight with you. But still you must remember in this city you cannot act as you wish as you were on the mountain stronghold."

"What difference does this city make? When I was in Chiang Chou did I not kill many men there?"

"Wait until I have seen how the matter goes," said Squire Ch'ai Chin, "if I see a chance of using you I will let you know."

Just then a maid servant entered, and asked Squire Ch'ai Chin to go and see his uncle again. Upon entering the sick room Squire Ch'ai Chin saw that his uncle had tears in his eyes, and the latter said, "You are very courageous, and did nothing to defend our family. As we are blood-relations I want you to take the imperial iron tablet to the capital, and there bring a charge against Yin Tien-hsi of being the cause of my death. Revenge me, and then in the grave I shall rest contented. Take due care of yourself, and I have nothing more to say." After saying this he expired.

Squire Ch'ai Chin burst into tears, and his sister-in-law begged him not to be so much upset. "The imperial iron tablet has not yet arrived from my home," replied Squire Ch'ai Chin, "but as soon as I can get it I will proceed at once to the capital. But we can talk matters over after the corpse has been dressed and placed in the coffin." He then made all the usual arrangements, and observed the rites.

Three days after this Yin Tien-hsi went to the country with his followers armed with bows and arrows and all kinds of musical instruments. They all got more or less drunk, and upon reaching Squire Ch'ai Chin's house, they reined in their horses and called to speak to the master. Squire Ch'ai Chin upon hearing the message went to the gate dressed in his mourning clothes.

Yin Tien-hsi seated on his horse asked, "Who are you?"

"I am the nephew of Ch'ai Huang-cheng," replied the Squire.

"A few days ago I told him to remove from this house," said Yin Tien-hsi. "How is it that he has not done so?"

"My uncle was very sick after your visit, and could not remove," replied Squire Ch'ai Chin. "He died a few days ago, and after waiting the proper seven days we can remove the household goods."

"Absurd!" said Yin Tien-hsi, "I allow you only three more days. After that if you are still here I shall have you beaten one hundred times, and put a cangue on your neck."

"You must not insult me in that way," said Squire Ch'ai Chin, "because our family comes from very honorable ancestry. I am the possessor of the imperial iron tablet so who dare be disrespectful to me?"

"Well, let me look at your iron tablet," shouted Yin Tien-hsi.

"It is at my home at Tsangchou," replied Squire Ch'ai Chin, "but I have already sent a messenger to bring it here."

"You are talking very foolishly," said Yin Tien-hsi with anger. "Even if you have such a tablet it will not make any difference. You men! Beat this fellow!"

Li K'wei was standing inside looking through a crack in the door, and hearing all this. He now rushed out, and seizing Yin Tien-hsi pulled him off his horse. The followers of Yin Tien-hsi came to his assistance, but Li K'wei used his fists right and left, and drove them off. They all decamped. Li K'wei picked up Yin Tien-hsi, and gave him such a beating that the latter soon died.

Squire Ch'ai Chin was annoyed at this as it would lead to trouble, and told Li K'wei to go inside to discuss matters. There he spoke, "The officials will soon be here to investigate this case, and you must escape at once to Liang Shan Po. I will deal with the officials."

"If I escape you will be involved," replied Li K'wei.

"I have the imperial iron tablet," said Squire Ch'ai Chin, "and that will protect me. You must go at once."

Li K'wei agreed, and taking his axes, he left by the back door.

It was not long before about a hundred armed men arrived, and Squire Ch'ai Chin went out and spoke to them. "I will go with you to the yamen and give my evidence there." The men bound him with ropes, and then searched his house for Li K'wei without finding the latter. They then took Ch'ai Chin to the yamen as a prisoner, where he knelt down.

The prefect was very angry that his brother-in-law was killed, and he shouted at Squire Ch'ai Chin, "How dare you kill my brother-in-law, Yin Tien-hsi?"

"I am a descendant of Ch'ai Shih-tsung who received from the emperor an iron tablet. I live at Tsangchou. My uncle was very sick so I came here to see him. Unfortunately he died, but has not yet been buried. Yin Tien-hsi came to the house with about thirty armed men, and told us to clear out of the house at once. As I objected to this he set his men to beat me. A villager named Li Ta, came to my assistance, and during the fight he killed your brother-in-law."

"Where is this Li Ta?" asked the prefect.

"He was very much afraid of the consequences of this action, and ran away."

"He was a servant at the house, and must have done this with your approval. You purposely told him to escape, and now come here to try to deceive me. If I don't have you beaten now I suppose you will not speak the truth. Jailer, beat this prisoner very severely!"

"As it was Li Ta who killed the man that is not my crime," said Squire Ch'ai Chin. "I have an imperial iron tablet protecting me from injustice so how dare you torture me?"

"Where is the tablet?"

"I have already sent a man to bring it here from Tsang-chou."

The prefect was angry and shouted, "This fellow is doing his best to thwart the law. Beat him!"

The attendants seized Squire Ch'ai Chin, and beat him till the blood flowed. Then Squire Ch'ai Chin falsely confessed that he had told Li Ta to commit the foul deed. A heavy cangue was then fastened on his neck, and he was sent to prison.

The sister of Yin Tien-hsi was not satisfied with this, and got the prefect to arrest also the whole family, and put them in prison. She also got the house sealed up.

Li K'wei traveled day and night to get to Liang Shan Po, but on arriving there he was seen by Chu Tung who was angry at the sight of him. Chu Tung seized a sword, and Li K'wei took his axes. Ch'ao Kai and the other leaders interposed to stop the fighting.

Sung Chiang spoke in an apologetic tone, "Li K'wei killed the prefect's son in accordance with Wu Yung's order, and the latter only thought of that because you would not join us. Do not think of that affair any more, but let us work together here, and not let outsiders laughing at us." He then turned to Li K'wei and told him to apologize to Chu Tung.

Li K'wei stared at Sung Chiang and said, "I have been here a long time, and have done many meritorious deeds.

But Chu Tung has only been here a few days, and has done nothing so far. Why should I apologize to him?"

"Although Wu Yung gave the order yet you actually did the deed," said Sung Chiang. "But apart from that Chu Tung is your elder brother, and if you will salute him now and become friends, I myself will give you a salutation, and so end this trouble satisfactorily for all."

Li K'wei turned to Chu Tung and said, "I am not afraid of you. But as my elder brother Sung Chiang orders me to do it I will salute you as my friend, and here I apologize for what I did."

He gave Chu Tung two salutations, and the latter was appeased. Li K'wei then told the assembled leaders what had happened to Squire Ch'ai Chin. When Sung Chiang heard the news he was startled, and said, "You have escaped and let Squire Ch'ai be involved."

"Do not get excited," interposed Wu Yung. "I was afraid that Li K'wei would make some trouble at Squire Ch'ai Chin's place so I sent Tai Tsung there to investigate and report. If Li K'wei was not there Tai Tsung was to go on to Kao T'ang Chou and make inquiries there."

While he was speaking a scout entered, and reported that Tai Tsung was just arriving.

Tai Tsung soon entered the hall, and Sung Chiang asked for news about Squire Ch'ai Chin. He reported that not finding Li K'wei at Ch'ai Chin's home he had hurried on to Kao T'ang Chou. There he heard the news that a dark complexioned man had killed Yin Tien-hsi. That as Squire Ch'ai Chin was implicated he had been arrested, and was put in prison. All the furniture and also the house had been confiscated. Squire Ch'ai Chin was undoubtedly in danger of losing his life.

"That black fellow is always stirring up trouble," said Ch'ao Kai. "Everywhere he goes there is some strife."

"Squire Ch'ai Chin's uncle was killed by Yin Tien-hsi," said Li K'wei. "Then he came, and wanted to take possession of the house, and I heard what was said. Even if I were a living Buddha I could not have remained passive with such injustice."

"Squire Ch'ai Chin has always been on good terms with

us here," said Ch'ao Kai, "and now that he is in danger I will go myself to rescue him from the peril."

"How can you do that by yourself when you are our great chieftain?" said Sung Chiang. "As I am indebted to Squire Ch'ai Chin I will go in your place."

"Kao T'ang Chou is a small place, but the people and soldiers are many so that we must not consider this matter as only trifling," said Wu Yung. "We must send atleast five thousand men under the command of Lin Ch'ung, Hwa Jung, and ten other leaders, as an advance guard. The main body consisting of three thousand men must be in charge of Sung Chiang and nine other leaders."

They all left Liang Shan Po that very day, and upon nearing Kao T'ang Chou the prefect was informed by his own men of the advance of the brigands. Upon hearing this the prefect, Kao Lien, sneered and said, "These are bandits of Liang Shan Po, I will now capture them as they come here. Let all preparations be made for an immediate march outside the town. The people left behind can guard the city." He mounted his horse and went to the parade ground where the troops assembled, and soon began to march out of the town gates. His own bodyguard consisted of three hundred men called the "Flying Spirits." He commanded these specially selected men himself. They had mail armor, a double-edged sword on their back, and were mounted on horses. They formed the center of the army with the other soldiers on both wings.

The two armies duly met, and faced each other standing in readiness. Both sides sounded their ram's horns and beat their drums. Lin Ch'ung, armed with a big crooked spear, galloped forward, and coming near the opposing force shouted, "Kao, you thief! Come out!"

Kao Lien advanced with about thirty officers, and then halting shouted, "You fellow are not aware that you will soon die. How dare you come here!"

"You robber of the people!" replied Lin Ch'ung. "Very soon I shall go to the capital to kill that rascal Kao Chiu, Minister for War. When I cut him up into small pieces I shall be contented!"

Kao Lien was angry, and turning round asked his attendants who would volunteer to kill this thief. General Yu Chih came forward, and whipping his horse dashed towards Lin Ch'ung. They fought, and after about five bouts, Lin Ch'ung wounded General Yu Chih who fell dead off his horse.

Kao Lien was surprised, but called for another volunteer. General Wen Wen Pao next came forward mounted on a cream-colored horse which had many bells tinkling, and he was armed with a long spear. He galloped, and met Lin Ch'ung.

General Chin Ming seeing this called out to Lin Ch'ung, "Let me meet this man while you take a rest." Lin Ch'ung therefore retired, and left his opponent to General Chin Ming. They fought and after about ten bouts Chin Ming tried a trick, and hit his opponent on the head killing him on the spot.

Both sides raised loud shouts after this. Prefect Kao Lien, seeing that two of his champions had been killed, drew his precious sword from its sheath on his back, and holding it in front he muttered a charm, and immediately a large dark magical mist arose in his army. It rose upwards like a whirlwind throwing sand and stones in all directions, and moved towards the opposing brigands. The bandits could not see anything, and being thrown into confusion they began to retreat. Kao Lien waved his sword and ordered his special bodyguard to charge. The other troops on either wing also advanced to the attack. The brigands were now in hopeless confusion and in their retreat were cut down by the pursuing troops. During the general rout about a thousand bandits were killed. After pursuing about a mile Prefect Kao Lien recalled his men, and they returned to the town.

Sung Chiang at last got together Lin Ch'ung and Wu Yung, and they were surprised at the fatal defeat. Sung Chiang said, "What is this devilish charm that threw our men into confusion?"

"It was done by a magical spell," replied Wu Yung. "If we had had a trick of turning the wind we should have won."

Sung Chiang now remembered the divine books he had, and upon looking through these he found in volume three the description of a method of turning winds or fire. He was now much pleased, and carefully memorized the magic spell as given. He mustered all his men, and after they had partaken of a meal he ordered a general advance towards the town.

Prefect Kao Lien was informed by a scout of the return of the bandits and immediately gave orders. The town gate was opened, and the troops again marched out. When the two armies were close they halted, and Sung Chiang rode forward. He saw many black flags in Prefect Kao Lien's troops. Wu Yung said, "Those black flags must be part of the magic spell, and they will be used again. What are you going to do?"

"Do not be anxious!" replied Sung Chiang. "I have a means of gaining a victory this time. You tell our men this, and order that they must advance without any fear."

Kao Lien addressed his troops, "This time we will have no single combats, but instead you will all advance on hearing my signal. You must capture Sung Chiang this time, and I will reward you handsomely." His charmed breast plate was engraved with animals and seal characters. He carried his sword in his hand, and went in front of his bodyguard on horseback.

Sung Chiang pointed to him and cursed him, "Yesterday I was not here, and therefore my men were defeated by you. To-day I will see that you are killed."

Kao Lien replied in a loud voice, "Do not make me soil my hand, you rebellious thieves, but submit at once and become my prisoners." He then held his sword aloft and muttered a charm. Immediately a black mist arose, and began to whirl round.

Sung Chiang also took his sword, and uttered his spell. The black whirlwind immediately turned, and went back towards Prefect Kao Lien's army.

Kao Lien seeing the black whirlwind returning took his charmed breastplate and rattled his sword on it. Immediately a cloud of sand arose, and from this mass emerged strange monstrosities, snake and insects.

Sung Chiang was quite nonplused at this, turned his horse, and galloped off to escape these monstrosities, followed by the other leaders and all his men.

Kao Lien ordered a general advance, and his army pursued the fleeing bandits. They chased them for about five miles, and then a gong was sounded to stop the attack, and the troops returned to the town.

The brigands reached their camping ground, and Sung

Chiang held a consultation with Wu Yung as they had been defeated twice at Kao Tang Chou for the purpose of rescuing Squire Ch'ai Chin.

Wu Yung said, "As this man uses such supernatural agencies he will probably attack us to-night, so we must prepare for same." Sung Chiang then ordered Yang Lin and Pai Sheng to guard the camp with three hundred men while the other leaders retire to another place.

These two leaders posted their men at various points hidden in the grass. They waited until nearly 9 p.m. when a storm arose with wind and thunder. The two leaders then saw Kao Lien with his bodyguard, advancing upon their camp whistling. But finding nobody there Kao Lien and his troops returned. The two leaders hidden in the grass signaled to their men who immediately without showing themselves raised a loud shout. Kao Lien could not understand this, and fearing a trap in the dark ordered a retreat, and his troops scattered in all directions. The bandits now discharged arrows from their ambush and one of these hit Kao Lien in the shoulder. Many soldiers were killed. Kao Lien led some of his men back, and after pursuing them for some distance Yang Lin and Pai Sheng summoned their men to return. The rain had now stopped and it was a bright starlit night with a cloudless sky. They returned to the camp with about twenty prisoners, and reported the matter to Sung Chiang. He was surprised to hear the details because at his camp there had been neither wind nor rain nor thunder. It was the general opinion that Kao Lien had used his supernatural powers again. Yang Lin was sure that he had wounded Kao Lien with an arrow, and said that Kao Lien had his hair unbound and flying loose. Being afraid of another attack from Kao Lien, Sung Chiang ordered his men to take precautionary measures.

That night he sent to Liang Shan Po for reënforcements.

Kao Lien upon returning to the town issued an order that the gates and moat should be carefully guarded both day and night, but that no further fighting would take place against Sung Chiang until his (Kao Lien's) wound was healed.

Sung Chiang had a talk with Wu Yung. "Kao Lien has defeated us twice, and our losses have been great. What can we do if he gets reënforcements from other districts?"

SQUIRE CH'AI CHIN ARRESTED

"I know a man who can overcome these supernatural tricks of Kao Lien," said Wu Yung, "and if we do not get him to help us I do not see how we can attack the town or rescue Squire Ch'ai Chin."

To raise mist and cloud,
A supernatural man was brought.

We will now relate who this man was.

CHAPTER 52

TAI TSUNG FETCHES KUNG-SUN SHENG; LI K'WEI SPLITS OPEN TAOIST LO, THE TRUE MAN

WU YUNG said, "The only man who can overcome Kao Lien is Kung-Sun Sheng, and we must send for him at once."

"Previously Tai Tsung went to Chi Chou to find Kung-Sun Sheng without success;" said Sung Chiang, "so where can he go this time?"

"Chi Chou is a very big district," said Wu Yung, "with many villages, hsiens, and hamlets. I think he must be somewhere there. As he is a great Taoist he will probably be at some temple in some remote mountain, and we must tell Tai Tsung this time to make inquiries at all the mountains in isolated spots."

Sung Chiang sent for Tai Tsung, and then told him about their plans for finding Kung-Sun Sheng.

"I will go," said Tai Tsung, "but it would be better this time if somebody accompany me."

Li K'wei was there, and volunteered to go. "In that case," said Tai Tsung, "you will not eat meat while on the way with me, and also you must obey my order implicitly."

"Where is the difficulty in that?" said Li K'wei. "I will of course do what you say."

"On the way you must be careful," said Sung Chiang to Li K'wei, "as we do not want any trouble this time. When you find Kung-Sun Sheng you must return at once with him."

"There will be no row this time," said Li K'wei.

The two men started off at once, and when they had got about ten miles beyond Kao T'ang Chou, Li K'wei suggested that they should stop at an inn for some wine. But Tai

Tsung reminded him that he had promised to abstain from meat. They went on until evening, when they stopped at an inn. Li K'wei went and got the food, and soon brought in some vegetables for Tai Tsung.

"Why don't you also dine with me?" asked Tai Tsung.

"I do not feel hungry just now," said Li K'wei; "I will dine by and by."

"This fellow probably tries to deceive me," thought Tai Tsung, "and will get some meat behind my back." He however finished his meal, and then went stealthily to see what Li K'wei was doing. In a room at the back he found Li K'wei with a plate of beef and two horns of wine. He decided, however, not to disturb him at his meal, but would have a practical joke with him the following day. Tai Tsung then went to bed. The next morning he was up by about 4 a.m., and awakening Li K'wei they got their breakfast, and went on their way. They had only gone a short distance when Tai Tsung said, "Yesterday we did not travel by supernatural power so we have to hurry up to-day. Now pack up your things firm, I will apply the charm to you and you can travel three hendred miles, where you can stop. You can go in front, but when you come to an inn you wait for me there." He then put the enchanted greaves on Li K'wei, repeated the incantation, and blew at Li K'wei who sailed off. He took very long strides, and in fact was like a cloud floating along with a strong wind behind.

When Li K'wei had gone Tai Tsung laughed, "He will be hungry before the day is done." Tai Tsung then put on his enchanted greaves, and flew after Li K'wei.

Li K'wei did not suspect there was a joke being played on him. He felt the wind rushing past his ears, and saw the trees and houses whirl past him. The speed became so great that he became afraid, but when he tried to stop he found that he was quite helpless. He had the sensation of being swept along by some invisible force. When he saw an inn he was simply whirled past it although he would have liked to stop there and have a drink. He called out, "Sir, stop here! stop here!" His flight continued until the western sky began to redden for sunset, and he was now not only thirsty but very hungry as well. His body was covered with perspiration and he was panting for breath.

At last Tai Tsung caught up to him, and asked, "Elder brother Li, why did you not stop at some inn for a meal as I asked you?"

"Elder brother!" replied Li K'wei, "Save me! Save me, before I die from hunger!"

Tai Tsung took some cakes out of his breast pocket, and began to eat them. Li K'wei seeing this called out, "I cannot stop. Please give me a bite."

"Brother," said Tai Tsung, "if you will only stop I can give you some."

Li K'wei turned round, and reached out a hand, but found that Tai Tsung was nearly a furlong away. He himself was now traveling along at the same rate, but without seeing where he was going. He called out, "Elder brother! Elder brother! Let us stop here."

"Things are very strange to-day, as I cannot control my legs, and they will not stop," said Tai Tsung.

"Oh dear! My legs are the same. I am quite helpless. They won't obey me at all to-day. The only escape would be for me to cut off my legs with my ax."

"That appears to be the only way, because if we go on like this we shall never stop until the first day of the New Year."

"Elder brother, please do not play practical jokes with me. If I cut off my legs how can I go back?"

"Last evening you must have disobeyed my order, and I think that is why we are like this to-day. You must go on."

"Elder brother, please forgive me."

"I cannot do anything because you must have broken the important rule about abstaining from meat. If you have committed that sin you will probably have to continue your flight for very many years."

"What a prospect! I deceived you yesterday, and ate some meat. But it was not very much — only about six pounds. What can I do now?"

"No wonder that we cannot stop to-day. You have seriously injured me, and rendered me helpless."

Li K'wei hearing this threw his hands up towards heaven, and wept.

Tai Tsung could not help laughing, "If you would swear to always listen to what I say I might be able to find a way out."

"Sir, please say what you like in future, and I will obey every word."

"Well never dare again to deceive me about eating meat."

"If I do that again may my tongue be blistered. Yesterday I saw you eat the vegetables, but I did not like the taste, and so ate just a very little meat. I will never do that again."

"In that case I will forgive you just this time." So saying Tai Tsung hastened his speed, caught up to Li K'wei, and catching hold of his leg, pulled it hard, and shouted, "Stop!" They began to slow down, and soon stopped. Tai Tsung said, "I will now go in front, and you can come slowly behind." But when Li K'wei tried to go he found that he could not move. His feet were like cast iron, and he could not lift them. "Trouble again! I request you to assist me," he said.

Tai Tsung turned his head, laughed, and said, "Will you take an oath that you have spoken the truth?"

"You are my elder brother, and I will strictly do what you ask me to do," replied Li K'wei.

"Will you really do as I tell you this time?" asked Tai Tsung. So saying he took hold of Li K'wei, and saying, "Rise," and the latter began to walk.

"Please take pity on me as I am tired, and should like a rest," said Li K'wei. Soon they came to an inn and stopped there.

Upon entering the inn they bought some sacrificial paper, and burnt it to the gods.

"Well, what about to-day's journey?" asked Tai Tsung. Li K'wei rubbed his legs, and said, "These legs appear to be mine just now."

Tai Tsung got some warm water, and they both bathed their feet. They then partook of a vegetarian repast, and went to bed.

The next morning they were up early, and after breakfast they started off again on the road. When they had gone about a mile Tai Tsung took the enchanted greaves, and said he would put only a pair of them on Li K'wei's so that he could travel slower that day.

"I do not want them," said Li K'wei.

"You must do as I tell you," said Tai Tsung. "We are on important business, and I will not trifle with you. If you don't do as I wish I will leave you here rooted to the spot. I will then go to Chi Chou, and after finding Kung-Sun Sheng I will return here and release you."

"Do it! Put them on!" replied Li K'wei hurriedly.

They were put on, and that day the two men traveled together. Whatever Tai Tsung proposed Li K'wei agreed to at once.

They duly reached Chi Chou, and stopped at an inn there. The day following their arrival Tai Tsung dressed as a master with Li K'wei as his servant. All that day they made inquiries in all parts of the town without finding any trace of Kung-Sun Sheng. The next day was the same although they tried all the small alleys. At the end of that day Li K'wei lost his temper and said, "Where can this Taoist beggar have got to? When I find him I will take him by the hair and drag him off."

Tai Tsung frowned at him, "You are at it again! Don't forget what trouble you got into once before." Li K'wei laughed, and said, "I was only joking."

They returned to the inn that evening to rest, and the third day they spent all their time outside the town making inquiries in all the villages. But again nobody had ever heard of Kung-Sun Sheng. About noon as they were both hungry they entered an inn for a meal. The inn was very crowded, and they could not find a seat. The waiter however asked them to sit at a table where there was an old man. Tai Tsung saluted the old man, and they sat down. They ordered four bowls of vermicelli and Tai Tsung said to Li K'wei, "If I eat one bowl to your three bowls will that do?"

"Not enough!" said Li K'wei. "If they bring six bowls I could eat the whole lot."

The waiter laughed at this. After waiting a long time however no food was served. The other tables were however being served with vermicelli, and seeing this Li K'wei became angry. The waiter now brought a bowl of hot vermicelli, and set it in front of the old man at their table. The old man without any ceremony began to eat. He had his head bowed down to the bowl eating when Li K'wei called out, "Waiter, why have we to wait so long?"

So saying he struck the table so hard that the bowl of hot vermicelli was upset. The old man was annoyed at this, and taking hold of Li K'wei said, "Have you no reason? Why have you upset my bowl of vermicelli?"

Li K'wei held up his fist to strike the old man, but Tai Tsung interposed and told him not to do so. Tai Tsung addressed the old man, "Take no notice of this man as he is very stupid. I will supply you with another bowl of vermicelli."

"You do not understand," replied the old man, "I come from a distant place, and must hurry back as quickly as possible according to the order I received."

"Where did you come from, and who gave you orders?" asked Tai Tsung.

"I am from the Two Fairies Hill in Nine Palace Hsien in Chi Chou," said the old man. "I came here to buy incense, and must get back quickly because True Man Lo has promised to disclose to us the secrets of immortality."

Tai Tsung thought a bit, and then asked if he had heard of a man Kung-Sun Sheng.

"If you had asked anybody else they could not have answered you," said the old man. "He is a neighbor of mine, and lives with his mother. He is often away from home, and was once called Kung-Sun I-Ching, but now is known as Ching, the Taoist. People have forgotten his original name."

Tai Tsung repeated the old proverb, "You can wear out iron shoes in fruitless searching, and yet by a lucky chance you may find the lost thing without even looking for it." He asked the old man, "How far is this Two Fairies Hill? Is Ching, the Taoist, at home just now?"

"It is about fifteen miles from here. Ching, the Taoist, is a pupil of the True Man Lo who would not dispense with him."

Tai Tsung was much pleased and when they all had their food he paid the bill, and they left the inn. He then got full directions of the road and let the old man go in advance.

Tai Tsung and Li K'wei put on the enchanted greaves, and set off and soon reached the Two Fairies Hill. There they met a woodcutter, and asked him where Ching, the Taoist, lived. The man told them to cross a pass on the hill, and they would come to a house with a stone bridge opposite the door. That was where Ching, the Taoist, lived. They followed these directions, and found the house. There they asked a woman carrying a basket of fruit whether Ching, the Taoist, was at home. The woman replied that he was in a room at the back preparing a magic drug. Tai Tsung asked Li K'wei to wait outside while he went in by himself. Tai Tsung entered, and came to a room with a reed curtain in front of the door. Here he coughed, and a white-haired old woman came out. He saluted her, and said, "I come here to see Ching, the Taoist."

"What is your name?" she asked.

"I am Tai Tsung, and have come from Shantung."

"My son has not yet returned from his travel abroad."

"I am an old friend of his," said Tai Tsung, "and have a message for him."

"He is not here, but you can tell me the message, and I will tell him when he returns."

"As he is not here I will call again to see him," said Tai Tsung. He again saluted and went outside, and said to Li K'wei, "An old woman says that he is not at home so now I want you to go inside and see what you can do. If she tells you the same story you must make a row, but avoid striking the old woman. When I hear the noise I will come in, and intervene between you two."

Li K'wei put down his pack, and putting his two axes in his waist belt he entered the house and shouted, "Is anybody here?"

The old woman came, and asked, "Whom do you want?" When she saw Li K'wei, however, she was afraid.

"I am the Black Whirlwind from Liang Shan Po, and have orders to come here for a man Kung-Sun Sheng. Tell him to come here at once. If he comes I will be respectful, but if there is any obstacle I will burn down this house."

"Sir, do not get excited, this is not the home of Kung-Sun Sheng, but of Ching, the Taoist."

"Then tell him to come here. I know his face."

"He has gone abroad, and has not returned yet."

Li K'wei took his ax and striking the wall made a big hole in it. He then said, "If you won't call your son I will kill you at once." He then advanced with his ax in a threatening attitude, and the woman fell down. A door opened, and Kung-Sun Sheng came out saying, "You have no decency." Tai Tsung just then also entered, and said, "Iron Ox, why have you knocked this old lady down?" He went and lifted her up.

Li K'wei threw his ax on the ground, and said, "Please excuse me. I did this only because you would not come out to see us."

Kung-Sun Sheng took his mother inside, and then came and saluted both Tai Tsung and Li K'wei. He then took them into a small room, and Tai Tsung explained the position at Kao Tang Chou, and asked Kung-Sun Sheng to help them against the troops who had defeated them. Kung-Sun Sheng was unwilling to go and leave his old mother alone, but Tai Tsung pressed him, and said that if Kung-Sun Sheng did not help them they would be defeated again, and probably Sung Chiang himself would be captured.

Kung-Sun Sheng at last agreed to go to consult his master Lo, the True Man. He with Tai Tsung and Li K'wei then left the house, and went to the Two Fairies Hill. By the time they got there it was dusk. A small path through pine trees brought them to a small temple with three characters over the door, "Pole Star Temple." They entered an arbor in front of the door, and arranged and dusted their clothes. They then went inside. Two acolytes had seen them coming, and had announced their arrival to Lo, the True Man. He asked them to come into the Pine and Stork Room where he usually sat in silent meditation. Kung-Sun Sheng and Tai Tsung kotowed, and then stood in respectful attitude. But Li K'wei instead of following their example was staring about the room.

Kung-Sun Sheng then explained the object of the visit, and asked Lo, the True Man, to advise him whether he should go to rescue Sung Chiang.

"You sought refuge here from the wicked world," said Lo, "and wished to attain immortality. So why do you now think of returning?"

"We only want him to help us in defeating Prefect Kao Lien, and after that he can return here," said Tai Tsung.

"That is hardly a matter for a priest to interfere in," replied Lo "You can decide that question yourself."

Kung-Sun Sheng and the other two then withdrew, and returned to Kung-Sun Sheng's house. Upon arriving there Li K'wei asked what the priest had said. "Did you not listen?" asked Tai Tsung.

"I listened but could not understand what he said," replied Li K'wei.

"He said that Kung-Sun Sheng should not go," said Tai Tsung.

Li K'wei was angry at this. "We have come so far, and undergone many tribulations, and now we have at last found Kung-Sun Sheng but the priest tells him not to go. I feel like killing that priest."

Tai Tsung frowned upon him, and said, "Must I again fasten your feet to the ground?"

"No! No! I was only joking," said Li K'wei.

That evening they talked over a plan, and at last Kung-Sun Sheng agreed to go with them the next day, and get the priest to agree to their proposal. But Li K'wei could not sleep as he was thinking the matter over. About 4 a.m. he got up, and heard that Tai Tsung was snoring while fast asleep.

He thought, "We are heroes so why should we ask a priest for his opinion about our own affairs. If I kill the priest there will be no obstacle in our way." He took his ax, and quietly opening the door he went towards Lo's temple, easily finding his way in the bright moonlight. Upon reaching the temple he found that the gates were closed. The wall was not very high, and he soon leapt over it. Then opening the gates from inside he went towards the temple. He soon found the room, and breaking a piece of the paper on a window he looked inside. Candles were burning on a table, and the priest Lo was slowly chanting the scriptures. Li K'wei thought, "That fellow deserves death." He pushed the door open, and going straight to Lo, the Priest, he struck him on the head with his ax, and killed him on the spot. Li K'wei saw that the blood was white, and laughed saying, "He evidently was a bachelor. He cannot stop Kung-Sun Sheng from going now." He left the room, but was stopped by an acolyte who called out, "You have killed our master. Where are you going?" Li K'wei without hesitation used his ax, and also killed the boy. He then quickly left the temple, and going down the hill soon came to Kung-Sun Sheng's house where he quietly opened the door and slipped into bed.

The next morning Kung-Sun Sheng was up early, and prepared the breakfast. While eating Tai Tsung reminded Kung-Sun Sheng that he had to take them to the temple again. Upon hearing this Li K'wei could hardly suppress a laugh. He said nothing, and accompanied the other two up the hill. Upon entering the temple they saw the two acolytes, and Tai Tsung inquired if Lo, the True Man, was in.

"He is sitting on the bed meditating," replied the acolyte.

Upon hearing this Li K'wei was dumbfounded, and stood with his mouth wide open, and his tongue hanging out. The curtain was raised, and looking into the room they saw Lo, the True Man, sitting on the bed. Li K'wei thought, "Last night I must have made a mistake."

"What do you three men want now?" asked Lo.

"We came to ask for your mercy," replied Tai Tsung, "and beg you to save us from calamity."

"Who is that dark man?" asked Lo pointing to Li K'wei.

"He came with me, and his name is Li K'wei," replied Tai Tsung.

Lo, the True Man, laughed, "I did intend to allow Kung-Sun Sheng to leave me, but I have changed my mind on account of that dark fellow." Tai Tsung saluted the priest, and then turning to Li K'wei told him what had been said. Li K'wei knew then that the priest was aware that he (Li K'wei) had tried to kill him.

"How would you like if I dispatch you three men to Kao T'ang Chou in a few minutes?"

Tai Tsung thought that a better way than using his enchanted greaves, and so they thanked the priest Lo. Lo then ordered the acolytes to bring three pieces of clothes, and asked the three men to follow him. He took them outside to a place and there spread a red cloth on a stone. He said, "Ching, the Taoist, you can stand on this." Kung-Sun Sheng did so, and Lo, the True Man, waved his sleeve, and said "Rise!" Immediately the cloth became a cloud which ascended carrying Kung-Sun Sheng upwards about fifty feet when Lo called out "Stop!" and there Kung remained stationary. He then spread a blue cloth on the stone, and invited Tai Tsung to stand on it. He did so, and the same process was gone through. Li K'wei was astonished, and gazed with open eyes at the two clouds in the sky on which stood his two companions.

Lo, the True Man, now spread a white cloth on the stone, and asked Li K'wei to stand on it. Li K'wei laughed, "This is no joke! If I fall I shall have a big lump on my head."

"Do you see those two men?" asked Lo.

Li K'wei took his position, and after the same process he rose up on a white cloud. "I do not feel safe," said Li K'wei "Let me come down!"

Lo, the True Man, hearing this, waved his sleeve again, and the red and black clouds descended. Li K'wei seeing this called out, "I also want to come down."

"I am a priest and have never offended you. Why did you attempt to kill me last night? If I had had no virtue you would have killed me. You also tried to kill my acolyte."

"It wasn't me! You must have made a mistake!" replied Li K'wei from aloft.

Lo, the True Man, laughed, and said, "You certainly broke two of my gourds last night. You are a bad man! I am going to punish you for that." So saying he again waved his sleeve. "Go!" he said, and a strong wind arose, and carried the white cloud right up into the sky with Li K'wei on it. On each side of the cloud were two men with yellow turbans, and looking downward Li K'wei saw houses, forests, and mountains skimming past under his feet. He was exceedingly afraid, and trembled in every limb. All at once he heard a great noise and the next moment he fell on the roof of the yamen in Chi Chou Fu, and rolled off into the courtyard. The Fuyin was sitting on the bench with a full court, and they were all startled by this strange and sudden appearance of a big man rolling off the roof of the court.

"Seize that man," ordered the governor.

The attendants seized Li K'wei, and brought him as a prisoner before the governor who asked, "What kind of magic is this? Where do you come from?"

Li K'wei could not speak as in his fall his head had been injured. "He must be a wizard," continued the governor,

"Use the means to exorcise evil spirits." The jailers took Li K'wei outside, and there an attendant took a bowl of dog's blood, and threw it over his head. Another attendant poured a bucket of urine and manure over him, and he was covered all over with the filth.

At last Li K'wei spoke, "I am not a wizard. I am only a servant of Lo, the True Man."

At that place they all knew Lo, the True Man, as a Living Buddha, so they ceased their activities against Li K'wei. They took Li K'wei into the court, and there a secretary spoke to the governor, "If this man is a servant of Lo, the Living Buddha, had we better not punish him?"

The governor laughed, and said, "I have read many thousand of books both ancient and modern, but have never read of a Living Buddha having this kind of servant. He must be a wizard. Jailers! Beat him!" The jailers forced Li K'wei on the ground, and beat him with the bamboo until he was almost unconscious.

"Now you fellow speak the truth, and I will stop the punishment," said the governor.

"I will confess," said Li K'wei, "I am a wizard, called Li Erh." A cangue was put on him, and he was sent to prison. Upon reaching the cell Li K'wei said, "I am a general of the Living Buddha, so how dare you put this cangue on me? I will duly report this indignity, and everybody in this town will die."

The jailers all respected the Living Buddha as they knew his great power, so they asked Li K'wei, "Now, who are you really?"

Li K'wei replied, "Truly, I am a confidential general of Lo, the Living Buddha. But as I had made a mistake, Lo sent me here so that I would be punished by you. He will send to rescue me in two or three days. If you don't treat me well and give me some meat and wine, I shall tell him, and he will kill all you people."

The jailers were afraid of him, and gave him a good meal. Li K'wei seeing their fear spoke wildly again, and the men being more afraid brought hot water for him to bathe, and also wash his clothes. He then swore that if they did not treat him well the next day he would fly away, and send trouble to them. They beseached him to take pity on them, and promised to treat him well.

Lo, the True Man, told Tai Tsung how Li K'wei had tried to kill him, and how he would punish him. Tai Tsung expressed his great regret, and begged Lo to spare Li K'wei. Lo asked Tai Tsung to come into the temple where they discussed the affairs of Liang Shan Po. Tai Tsung explained that both Ch'ao Kai and Sung Chiang distributed wealth in good cause and were acting like agents sent from Heaven. They had sworn not to injure good officials or patriots who were willing to die for their country; filial sons or worthy grandsons; men of high principles or chaste wives; and they had done fine work.

Lo, the True Man, considered this, without expressing an opinion. Tai Tsung stayed there for five days, and every day he kotowed to Lo, and begged him to have mercy for Li K'wei. The True Man however said that Li K'wei was a bad man, who was not deserving to be saved from his distress.

"Master, you do not understand," replied Tai Tsung. "He is a very simple fellow, but has good intentions. He is very straightforward, and the making of wealth has no attraction for him. Again he is not a flatterer and is loyal even in the face of death. Again he is not lustful and is very brave. Because of these qualities he is liked by Sung Chiang and if he does not return to Liang Shan Po I should not dare to face Sung Chiang again."

Lo, the True Man, laughed, "He was evidently born under a murderous star, and Heaven has sent him here to kill off those sinful people. I will not oppose the will of Heaven. I have punished him enough, and will now have him back to you."

Tai Tsung kotowed and expressed his gratitude. Lo, the True Man, then summoned his strong men who came, and stood awaiting orders. Lo said to them, "That man you took to Chi Chou has now finished his period of punishment. You must go and release him from the jail and bring him back here." The men vanished, and in about an hour they reappeared throwing down Li K'wei from aloft. Tai Tsung went forward to lift Li K'wei up, and said to him, "Younger brother, where have you been these last few days?"

Li K'wei noticed Lo, the True Man, and kotowed to him before replying, "Sir! I dare not offend you again."

"After this you must abstain from taking life," said Lo, the True Man, "you must exert all your strength to assist Sung Chiang, and must avoid bad thoughts."

Li K'wei again kotowed, "You are my newly adopted father, and I will certainly do as you say."

"But where have you been these last few days?" asked Tai Tsung.

Li K'wei then recited his experiences at the court and prison in Chi Chou, and how he had been brought back. When he was told that Lo, the True Man, controlled about one thousand of such stout men as had taken him to Chi Chou, Li K'wei said, "If I had only known all about this I would never have even tried to attack Lo, the True Man."

Tai Tsung again pressed Lo to let Kung-Sun Sheng accompany them to Kao Tang Chou. Lo said he would not place any obstacle in his way, though he did not like to let him go. He however had some advice to give him.

<blockquote>
To help the age and guard the country,
Magic power must now be used.
</blockquote>

We will now relate what that advice was.

CHAPTER 53

KUNG-SUN SHENG BY A MAGIC TRICK DEFEATS KAO LIEN; THE BLACK WHIRLWIND DESCENDS INTO A WELL TO RESCUE CH'AI CHIN

"DISCIPLE," said Lo, the True Man, the spell you have learned is the same as Kao Lien, but I will now disclose to you the means of controlling thunder so that you can help Sung Chiang to guard the country and pacify the people as an agent appointed by Heaven. You need not be anxious about your mother as I will see that she is well looked after. You are one of the stars of the constellation and therefore I let you go for some time. You must remember what I told you of the divine principles, and avoid being deceived by human desire, as this will upset your plans."

Kung-Sun Sheng kotowed, and received the method for controlling thunder. He, Li K'wei, and Tai Tsung saluted Lo and the other priests there. They then went to Kung-Sun Sheng's home where he put on his traveling dress, took his double-edged sword, and after bidding adieu to his mother they all departed.

When they had walked about ten miles Tai Tsung said he would go in advance to Kao T'ang Chou, and announce their approach. Kung-Sun Sheng agreed to this, and promised that they would follow behind.

"On the road I want you to wait upon Kung-Sun Sheng," said Tai Tsung to Li K'wei. "You must also be careful to avoid all further trouble."

"He has the same magic power as Lo, so how dare I deceive him?" asked Li K'wei.

Tai Tsung then put on his enchanted greaves and vanished from sight.

Kung-Sun Sheng and Li K'wei continued their way, and towards evening stopped at an inn. Li K'wei had felt the great powers of Lo, the True Man and therefore he dared not display his temper, but waited upon Kung-Sun Sheng with every attention. On the third day they came to Wu Kang Chen where the streets were very crowded. As they were both tired Kung-Sun Sheng said they would get some vegetarian food at that market town. They entered a small inn at the side of the street, sat down, and ordered food from the waiter.

"What kind of vegetarian cakes have you?" asked Kung-Sun Sheng.

"We have only wine and meat," replied the waiter. "But at the entrance of the street you can get cakes made with dates."

"I will go and buy the cakes," said Li K'wei. He went and after purchasing the food was on his way back to the inn when he heard the applause, "How strong!" Looking round Li K'wei saw a big crowd round a very big man who was holding a heavy iron hammer with a head as big as a watermelon. His face was pock-marked. The hammer, Li K'wei thought, must have weighed about forty pounds. The man swung it round, and brought it down on a stone in the street, and broke the latter into small bits. The crowd applauded this exhibition of strength, but Li K'wei did not think it amounted to much. So putting the cakes in his breast he stepped forward, and took hold of the mace.

"What are you doing? Who are you?" asked the owner.

"These people applaud you, but what for?" asked Li K'wei. "It does not seem very wonderful. You just watch me do it."

"You may try," said the man, "but if you fail the penalty will be a blow from my fist."

Li K'wei lifted the hammer, and after whirling it round his head brought it down on the ground lightly and with ease. His face was not red, his heart did not palpitate, and his breathing was regular. He looked quite cool and collected.

The tall man seeing this, saluted, and asked for his name.

"Where do you come from?" asked Li K'wei.

"I live just opposite," replied the man. He then conducted Li K'wei to his home, and upon reaching the house he unlocked the door, and asked Li K'wei to be seated.

Li K'wei noticed that the room contained all kinds of implements of a blacksmith, a hammer, a stove, tongs, steel punches, and so on. He thought that the man must be a blacksmith, and as they had no such person at their stronghold it would be a good thing to invite this man to join them. He asked the man his name.

"I am Tang Lung, and my father was a military official at Yen-an-fu, Shansi province. This year my father died, and through gambling I have lost all the money. I work here as a blacksmith, and like to practice the use of lance and stick. Because of my pock-marked face the people call me the Cash Marked Leopard. I beg to ask for your honorable name."

Li K'wei told him, and also that he came from Liang Shan Po. Upon hearing this the man saluted, and said he had heard of Li K'wei's fame, and was very fortunate to meet such a hero. Then Li K'wei suggested that he should go with him to Liang Shan Po, and join the bandits there. The man agreed to this at once. Li K'wei then asked him to go with him to the inn to be introduced to Kung-Sun Sheng. The man got a few things together, and left his house to follow Li K'wei.

Upon reaching the inn Li K'wei duly introduced the new partner, and explained fully how they had met. After a meal together they three all started on their journey. When near their destination they met Tai Tsung, and Kung-Sun Sheng inquired whether there had been any more fighting.

"Kao Lien's wound is nearly healed now," replied Tai Tsung, "and every day there is fighting. Sung Chiang has been acting merely on the defensive awaiting your arrival."

The four men then went on their way to Kao T'ang Chou, and soon reached the bandits' camp. There Tang Lung was introduced, and duly joined the brigands. They were all pleased to see Kung-Sun Sheng.

The next day there was a general council held of all the leaders to discuss their future plans. Kung-Sun Sheng said that orders could be issued for a general advance on Kao T'ang Chou. He would go and see what the opposing army was doing. The next day the bandits all moved forward fully equipped, with flying banners, rolling of drums, and clash of gongs. Sung Chiang, Wu Yung, and Kung-Sun Sheng rode in the front.

Kao Lien had been informed of the approach of the bandits, ordered his army to leave the town. The two bodies of fighting men soon met, and stood in ranks. There was a great display of banners, and a great noise of drums and gongs. Sung Chiang and the two leaders advanced. Kao Lien was seated on his horse surrounded by about thirty officers with a large flag. As Sung Chiang approached Kao Lien shouted, "You thieves! As you come here to fight I hope you won't run away this time when you are defeated. Running away does not look nice."

Sung Chiang turned, and asked who would volunteer for a single combat. Hwa Jung immediately set spurs to his horse, and dashed forward without saying a word.

Kao Lien also asked for a champion to meet Hwa Jung and Hsueh Yuan-hwei dashed forward.

These two fought for a long time, and then Hwa Jung retired. Immediately Hsueh Yuan-hwei pursued him, flourishing his sword. Hwa Jung, however, got his bow, and turning round in his saddle shot an arrow which wounded Hsueh who fell off his horse. The troops applauded.

Kao Lien was very angry at this, and taking his copper plate from his saddle he beat it with his sword. Immediately a yellow cloud of dust arose, and obliterating the sunlight made the field quite dark. Out of the cloud now emerged all kinds of strange animals, tigers, leopards, and insects. The troops shouted and moved forward. Kung-Sun Sheng however on his horse took his sword, and waving it towards the approaching troops called out, "Go!" A flash of light emerged from his sword, and meeting the weird animals they all fell down. The assembled troops now saw that these animals had only been made of paper as they were all consumed by the flame. The yellow cloud of dust also disappeared.

Sung Chiang now ordered his men to charge, and they meeting the opposing troops entered into conflict. It was soon over and Kao Lien and his troops retreated into the town. When Sung Chiang came up they found the bridge drawn up, and the town gate closed, and the troops on the wall shower stones and blocks of wood on them. Sung Chiang then gave the signal for his men to withdraw, and slowly they returned to their camping ground. The men were rewarded for the victory and Kung-Sun Sheng was loudly praised.

The next day the bandits surrounded the town on all sides. Kung-Sun Sheng said to Sung Chiang and Wu Yung, "Yesterday we defeated more than half of the opposing army, but we did not touch the bodyguard of Kao Lien. To-day we must attack with great force. To-night they will probably attack our camp so we will leave the camp deserted, and station our troops at other points all round. We must instruct our men to remain quiet until they hear a clap of thunder and see a large flame in the camp when they must rush towards the camp."

Orders were given accordingly, and in the afternoon the brigands were withdrawn from the town, and were given a good feed in the camp. When it was dark the men were divided under their various leaders and all left the camp. Sung Chiang, Kung-Sun Sheng, and several other leaders took up a position on a mound near the camp.

That night Kao Lien provided his bodyguard with iron gourds filled with saltpeter and gunpowder. Each man also had a hooked sickle, an iron broom, and a whistle. Near midnight the town gate was opened, and his men marched out. Kao Lien was on horseback, and used his magic spells. A strong wind sprung up which whirled stones and dust in all directions. The soldiers soon lit their gunpowder, blew their whistles, and advanced in the great confusion.

Kung-Sun Sheng now used his magic, and in the deserted camp there was a clap of thunder with many flashes of lightning. Kao Lien's troops saw that the camp was deserted, and being frightened by the spectacle they all tried to retreat. But they now found their way blocked by the bandits who attacked fiercely, and in the end not a single one of the three hundred troops was left alive. Kao Lien, however, had been able to get back to the town with about nine of his bodyguard of thirty men. Upon entering the gate he gave orders for the drawbridge to be raised and the gate closed. He then ordered all the people in the town to mount guard on the walls.

The next day Sung Chiang surrounded the town with his

bandits. Kao Lien considered that all his study of magic was of no avail as he had been thoroughly defeated. What could he do? He decided that the only thing left was to send to the surrounding districts, and ask for help. He wrote two letters accordingly and sent messengers with them. Both of the prefects concerned had been appointed by his elder brother in the capital so he thought they could not refuse assistance.

Wu Yung saw the two messengers leave the town, but said, "We must not stop them, but let them go. We can make use of their plot to defeat them."

"What is your plan?" asked Sung Chiang.

"Evidently there are very few soldiers in the town now," said Wu Yung, "and they are sending for reënforcements. We must get two companies of cavalry, and delude the people in the town that they are reënforcements for them. We must arrange for a sham battle, and let the supposed reinforcements win. Then Kao Lien will open the town gate and welcome them. When however he finds out his mistake he will probably try to leave the town by some means, and we must look out for him and capture him."

Sung Chiang applauded this plot, and sent Tai Tsung to Liang Shan Po to bring two companies of cavalry.

Kao Lien had gathered a great deal of straw and grass to a vacant spot on the wall with the idea of burning this at night so as to guide the reënforcements should they arrive after dusk.

A few days afterwards the outposts reported to Kao Lien that the bandits were fighting against some troops. Kao Lien went to the observation post, and saw a large body of cavalry fighting against the brigands. Many bandits were on the grounds, and others were running away. Kao Lien considered that these were the reënforcements so he mustered his soldiers, had the city gates opened, and marched out his soldiers to attack the bandits. He saw Sung Chiang, Hwa Jung, and Chin Ming leaving the battlefield by a small side road. He advanced to pursue them but just then many gongs were sounded on a hill some distance away, and suspecting some trap he ordered a retreat. As he retreated he found that he was surrounded by brigands on his left and right who were closing in. He hastened his retreat, but about half of his men were cut off and taken prisoners. Looking towards the town he saw the brigands' flags flying there. He looked round for the supposed reënforcements, but could not see a single man. He, therefore, led his men towards a small hill to escape, but when near he saw a large body of brigands already there. He turned to try to find another way, but saw bandits on all sides. He dismounted his horse with the idea of going up the hillside on foot. He soon realized that he was being hemmed in again, and reciting a spell he caused a black cloud on which he mounted himself and ascended into the sky. Kung-Sun Sheng had however seen this, and uttering a spell he caused the cloud to descend bringing Kao Lien to the ground. There Kao Lien was attacked by Inspector Lei Heng who soon killed him. Upon receiving news of the death of Prefect Kao Lien, Sung Chiang entered the town with his men, and issued an order that the people were not to be disturbed by his men nor anything looted. He then went to the city prison to release the prisoners, and found that all the jailers had left their posts and run away. He released about fifty prisoners without however finding any trace of Squire Ch'ai Chin. In one cell, however, he found the family of Ch'ai Chin's uncle, and then in another cell found all the family of Squire Ch'ai Chin. As Kao Lien had very little spare time he had postponed cross-examining them until a later time. But Wu Yung had come across a turnkey in the prison who told him that some days ago before Prefect Kao Lien had given him the special duty of attending to the prisoner Squire Ch'ai Chin, and had ordered him that in case of any disorder in the town he must kill Ch'ai Chin at once. Three days before, Prefect Kao Lien had sent to the prison for Ch'ai Chin to be executed. This turnkey thought Squire Ch'ai Chin a fine type of man, and declined to carry out the order. But he sent a reply that Ch'ai Chin had been killed. As he was afraid that further inquiry might be made he smuggled Squire Ch'ai Chin out of the prison, and lowered him into a dry well. Upon hearing this Sung Chiang went with the turnkey to the well. He looked down, but as it was quite dark he had no idea how deep it was. He called out, but got no reply. He then got a rope about 30 feet long and lowered it down the well. Again there was no result. Sung Chiang considered that Squire Ch'ai Chin was not there, and burst into tears. "Do not cry," said Wu Yung. "In order to make sure we must lower a man down the well."

Just then Li K'wei came on the scene and offered to go down the well.

"As you have involved him in trouble," said Sung Chiang, "you must make recompense for him."

"I will go down. I am not afraid," said Li K'wei laughingly, "but don't cut the rope."

"That is a villainous thought," said Wu Yung. "Of course we shall not cut the rope."

A basket was obtained, and fastened to the end of the rope, a three-legged derrick was erected over the well with the rope running over the top. Li K'wei got in the basket, and was slowly lowered down. Upon reaching the bottom Li K'wei got out of the basket, and began to feel around in the dark. He felt some bones, and was rather upset by this. He however felt around, but found nothing. It was all mud and water. He again searched round and found a small hole in the side of the well, and there he felt a man. "Mr. Ch'ai Chin," he called out, but got no reply. He took hold of the man who was still breathing. "Thanks to Heaven and Earth, I have saved your life," said Li K'wei. He took his seat in the basket; and rang a small bell that was fastened to the rope. The basket was pulled up, and upon reaching the top he explained that Squire Ch'ai Chin had been found.

"Then you must go down again, and send Squire Ch'ai Chin up first," said Sung Chiang.

"When I went to Chi Chou I was deceived twice, so that to-day I do not want to be fooled again," said Li K'wei.

"We certainly will not fool you," said Sung Chiang. "You quickly go down."

Li K'wei went down again, placed Squire Ch'ai Chin in the basket, and rang the bell on the rope. The basket was pulled up, and everybody was pleased to see Squire Ch'ai Chin again. He was almost unconscious, had big wounds on his thigh and head. A doctor was sent for at once.

Li K'wei thought they had forgotten him, and shouted loudly. Sung Chiang hearing this, had the basket lowered and they soon brought Li K'wei up in the basket. Upon getting to the top, Li K'wei was angry. He said, "You people are bad! Why didn't you lower the basket for me at once?"

"We saw that Squire Ch'ai Chin was very badly wounded, and for the moment forgot about you. Please excuse us," said Sung Chiang.

A cart was obtained and Squire Ch'ai Chin was laid down in it. Others were obtained for Ch'ai Chin's relatives and altogether about twenty carts, set off for Liang Shan Po. On the way the bandits did not trouble the people. Within a few days Squire Ch'ai Chin recovered and was given quarters near Sung Chiang's at Liang Shan Po.

The victory of the bandits under Sung Chiang was duly reported by the prefects of Tung Chan and K'eu Chou to the minister at the Eastern Capital. The Minister for War, Kao Chiu, was annoyed when he learned that his younger brother Prefect Kao Lien had been defeated and killed by the bandits. Early the next morning before dawn, he went to the palace to have an audience with the emperor. There were many ministers and high officials also waiting for the audience. About half past 4 a.m. the emperor appeared, and took his seat on the throne. An official called out, "Those who have business may now speak. If there is no business His Royal Majesty will retire."

Kao Chiu stepped out of the ranks of the standing officials, and addressed the throne: "At Liang Shan Po in Chi Chou there is a strong company of bandits under Sung Chiang and Ch'ao Kai. They have ravaged the surrounding country, and done great damage to the people and their property. This is a vile state of affairs. If they are not suppressed I am afraid the province will be in danger. I await Your Majesty's order."

The emperor was surprised at the news, and issued a decree that Kao Chiu use all the necessary military forces to suppress the bandits at once.

Kao Chiu, Minister for War, decided to send to Juningfu in Honan province for a famous general named Huyen Sho to take charge of the expedition, and the imperial decree was issued accordingly. Upon that man's arrival the

A DESCENT INTO A WELL

emperor presented him with a black horse. Kao Chiu and Huyen Sho then discussed details and the latter recommended two other generals to assist him.

Merit should be comprehended,
Virtue entered honors list.

CHAPTER 54

KAO CHIU ASSEMBLES THREE TROOPS; HUYEN SHO USES HIS CAVALRY

"WHOM do you recommend as the commander for the vanguard?" asked Kao Chiu.

Huyen Sho replied, "I have confidence in Colonel Han Tao at Chen Chou. He is a Shantung man and is skilled in all military strategy. His nickname is Hundred Victories General. Another fine man is Colonel Peng Chi at Ying Chou. He comes from Kaifeng and all his ancestors have been military men. He is also skilled in strategy and has the nickname of Heavenly Eyes General."

Kao Chiu was much pleased at this, and immediately had dispatches prepared for those two colonels to come to the capital at once. Within a few days they duly arrived and had interviews with Kao Chiu and Huyen Sho, and were promoted to their new posts. They discussed plans for the coming campaign against Liang Shan Po. They had altogether five thousand cavalry, and five thousand infantry. Kao Chiu ordered that three thousand cavalry and five thousand infantry be sent to the front at once.

Huyen Sho, however requested several days' postponement of the start of the expedition as the troops were not well equipped.

Kao Chiu gave them permission to draw freely from the imperial stores at the capital for whatever armor, etc. were required. They must make all arrangements, and when they were ready to leave for the front he would dispatch a staff officer to inspect the troops, and report direct to himself.

Huyen Sho visited the ammunition depots, and dispatched large quantities of war materials including five hundred rockets. Before their departure Kao Chiu gave them three thousand more battle steeds, and also many presents in silver and gold.

The general and his two colonels then distributed their supplies of equipment, and had everything ready and within half a month their troops were assembled at Guningchou. Two staff officers arrived from the Capital to inspect and encourage the troops. After a general parade the armies were mobilized towards Liang Shan Po.

The bandit scouts duly reported the arrival of the troops, and a council of war was held by the leader of Liang Shan Po.

"I have heard of the great fame of this General Huyen Sho," said Wu Yung, "this is a man not to be slighted. We must employ our bravest men in the first battle and afterwards we can try strategy."

Li K'wei here interposed, "I will go to capture that fellow."

"How can you go?" said Sung Chiang. "I have a plan. We must fight the battle with five detachments in turn; first, General Chin Ming; second, Lin Ch'ung; third, Hwa Jung; fourth, the Amazon Miss Hu San; fifth, Sun Li. They must follow each other in that rotation so that each will have a rest between bouts." He then announced how he himself and other ten leaders would be divided into three parts. He then gave orders where the bandits should proceed to and await the attack.

On the following day the enemy came in view, but they had not all taken up their position before it was evening. Early the next morning the drums were beaten, and both armies were on parade. General Chin Ming rode forward with his heavy mace. General Huyen Sho spoke, "This is the Imperial army, and you had better surrender at once. If you refuse to do so then your body will be hacked up into thousand pieces. I am going to wipe out the nest of bandits here. Many will be killed, and all the rest will be captured and sent as prisoners to the Capital."

General Chin Ming took no notice of this, but advanced waving his mace. Colonel Han Tao accepted the challenge, and rode out to meet Chin Ming. They fought for some time without any result, and then Han Tao retired.

The next combatants were General Huyen Sho and Lin Ch'ung. After about fifty bouts these two retired.

Then came Hwa Jung who fought about twenty bouts with Colonel Peng Chi.

These were followed by the Amazon Miss Hu who fought against Colonel Peng Chi for about twenty bouts and then she retired. Peng Chi thought that he had won so he pursued her. She, however, only put aside her sword, and now took a long red rope with numerous hooks. She waited until Peng Chi was quite close, and then suddenly turning in her saddle she cast the rope, caught Peng Chi, and pulled him off his horse. Sun Li was quite close, and he galloped forward with a few men and took Peng Chi captive.

General Huyen Sho was very angry at this trick, and rushed forward to engage Miss Hu himself. But after ten bouts he found that he could not overcome her. He decided to beat her by a trick. He waited until she rushed at him, and met her with an iron whip in each hand, and used both at the same moment. She parried both blows with her swords—the swords met the whips with a loud crash, throwing off sparks—and she rode away unhurt. He pursued her on horseback, but was intercepted by Sun Li who fought with him. These two fought for about thirty bouts. Han Tao now gave orders for a general advance, and upon seeing this movement Sung Chiang issued similar orders to his men. The troops of General Huyen Sho were all well protected by mail armor, and the only exposed spots were their eyes. The bandits now shot arrows, but did no damage on the enemy because of the armor. But when the two thousand archers of General Huyen Sho discharged their arrows they took effect on the bandits who had not the armor. Sung Chiang seeing the position ordered a general retreat. Upon reaching their camp they stopped, and Sung Chiang sent for the prisoner Peng Chi. Upon reaching his tent Sung Chiang himself unbound the ropes on the prisoner, and invited him to sit down.

"I am your prisoner," replied Colonel Peng Chi, "and am quite ready for death. But why are you treating me like this?"

"As we have no safe place to live in," replied Sung Chiang, "we have to take our position at Liang Shan Po for the time being. When the émperor sent you here to capture us, we would have surrendered if we were not afraid that we should all be killed. Therefore we are forced to fight against you. It is quite unintentional that we oppose your power, and we must plead for your mercy."

"For a long time I have heard of your love for justice and benevolence," replied Peng Chi, "and that you are always assisting those in distress. Now I know as a fact that your chivalry is real. If you now spare my life I shall be extremely grateful to you."

That day Sung Chiang sent Peng Chi to Ch'ao Kai at Liang Shan Po where he was to be quartered, but treated well.

Upon General Huyen Sho reaching the camp he discussed with Han Tao what steps should be taken to defeat the bandits.

"To-day," said Colonel Han Tao, "the brigands felt the effect of our advancing army so they retreated. To-morrow we must pursue them, with all our cavalry and defeat them completely."

General Huyen Sho agreed that that must be done. He accordingly issued orders that the following day three thousand cavalry must be linked up in small rings of thirty each. They were to wait until the bandits were close, and then rush forward with spears. These 100 squads of cavalry should be supported by five thousand infantry. There would be no single combats, and the General and Colonel Han Tao would take up their position in the rear instead of in front of the army.

The following day Sung Chiang arranged his men in five companies in front in charge of ten leaders. On either side was a company in ambush. Chin Ming again rode in advance to challenge the opponent, but no one came out to meet him. Sung Chiang was suspicious, and ordered his rearguard to withdraw a little. He then rode to the front to see what happened. All at once a series of rockets was fired in the opposing army, and the infantry in front opened out into two divisions, and the cavalry dashed forth. The infantry on both sides discharged a shower of arrows. Sung Chiang signaled for his men also to use their bows and arrows. But this could not resist the opposing troops which still advanced nearer. Now the bandits could not sustain the severe attack, and were soon thrown into confusion. They gave way all along the line, and were soon scattered about. Li K'wei and Yang Lin, now led forth the men in ambush and attacked the opposing troops. Sung Chiang and a number of men embarked on boats which were waiting in the creeks. When the troops reached the banks they found that their arrows had no effect on these boats which had boards at the sides to protect the men behind. The boats withdrew to a spot where the men disembarked on the opposite bank, but there were not many men there. Of the leaders six had been wounded, and among the men there were a great many casualties. Just then Ch'ao Kai and Wu Yung arrived on the scene, having heard of the disastrous defeat. Sung Chiang was very depressed and Wu Yung spoke to him, "Elder brother, do not be sad. In fighting victory or defeat is inevitable. Do not worry too much. We must think of some plan to defeat our enemy." Ch'ao Kai issued orders for the boats to be ready to meet another attack by the opposing troops. He asked Sung Chiang to retire to the mountain stronghold, and take rest there. Sung Chiang however refused to go, but insisted that the leaders who had been wounded should go there.

General Huyen Sho was highly pleased with the victory, and rewarded his men liberally. They had captured about five hundred men and three hundred horses. The matter was duly reported to the capital by special messenger. The Minister for War, Kao Chiu, was much pleased to hear of the defeat of the bandits. He duly reported the victory to the emperor who was pleased and ordered presents and money and wine to be sent to General Huyen Sho.

General Huyen Sho received the imperial edict, and distributed the reward among his men. He promised a further attack on the bandits whom he intended to completely exterminate. He, however, asked the imperial messenger to send a man from the capital, named Ling Chen, who was expert in making explosives, and could attack a place five miles distant. With that man's assistance he could easily crush the bandits. The messenger agreed to take this message, and duly delivered the same to Kao Chiu, who at once sent for Ling Chen who was a Yen Ling man, and was the leading expert in ammunition at that time. His nickname was Roaring Thunder. Kao Chiu gave him the new appointment, and dispatched him immediately to General Hu-yen Sho. Ling Chen loaded many carts with ammunition, and taking about forty men he set out for Liang Shan Po. He duly reported his arrival to General Hu-yen Sho, and discussed the military situation. He had brought three kinds of firearms: (1) for incendiary bombs; (2) quick-firing explosives; and (3) for shrapnel bombs. Frameworks were erected on the banks of the lake, and the explosives placed in position.

Sung Chiang and Wu Yung were now discussing the situation, but could not decide on any plan for the defense of their stronghold. A scout, however, reported that Roaring Thunder Ling Chen had arrived from the capital, and was placing firearms in position all round the lake.

"That does not matter," said Wu Yung, "because we are surrounded by water, and the banks in places are a good distance away. However many firearms they have, the shots will not reach our stronghold. We can abandon the camp at the foot of our hill, and watch how they will attack us."

Sung Chiang accordingly issued an order that all men must withdraw to the main stronghold on the mountain.

Ch'ao Kai and Kung-Sun Sheng, however, asked how they were going to meet the expected attack. While they were talking, they heard the roar of the firearms. They saw two of the shots fall in the lake, but the third shot exploded in the camp at the foot of the mountain. Many of the leaders were upset by this new mode of attack.

Wu Yung said, "It would be a good plan if somebody would go and inveigle Ling Chen to the bank. Once we have captured him we can then easily defeat the enemy."

"We must appoint Li Chun, Chang Heng, Chang Shun, and the three brothers Yuan to go by boat, and do this decoy work," said Ch'ao Kai. "Two other leaders Chu Tung and Lei Heng can assist them on the bank."

These leaders agreed to go, and divided themselves into two parties. One party embarked on two boats with about forty men on each boat, and went into the tall reeds. Li Chun and Chang Heng on their boat got close to the framework of the firearms and overturned it. Ling Chen upon hearing of this led about a thousand soldiers to the spot. Li Chun and Chang Heng with about a hundred bandits seeing the troops coming retreated along the bank leaving their boats behind. When the soldiers were near, the bandits all dived into the water, and seeing this Ling Chen ordered his men to embark on the abandoned boats, and cross the lake to attack the bandits. On the other bank were Chu Tung and Lei Heng, who watching the position sounded their gongs and drums, and upon hearing this the bandits in the water turned, and taking off the rudders of the boats so that they could not be steered, and the water also began to leak into the boats. The men in the water now seizing the gunwale of the boats, capsized them. Ling Chen seeing the position ordered the boat to retire, but just then his boat was also held by the bandits and overturned. Ling Chen himself was thrown into the water. Yuan, the Second, was in the water, and he seized hold of Ling Chen and swam with him to the other bank. There Ling Chen was bound with ropes, and taken to the mountain stronghold as a prisoner. Altogether about two hundred men were taken as prisoners; five hundred were drowned; and three hundred managed to escape back to their base. When General Huyen Sho heard of the disaster he rushed many troops to the spot, but all the boats had reached the other bank. He was very much annoyed at this defeat, but led his men back to camp.

Upon receiving the report of the capture of Roaring Thunder, Ling Chen, Sung Chiang went down the mountain. Upon meeting the prisoner Sung Chiang himself took off the binding ropes, and said to the escort, "I told you to invite this general and conduct him to our stronghold. Why have you no decency and you treat him like this?"

Ling Chen saluted, and thanked Sung Chiang for his mercy. Sung Chiang sent for a beaker of wine, and offered it to the prisoner. When the latter had drunk the wine Sung Chiang conducted the prisoner up the mountain road. Upon reaching the stronghold Ling Chen saw Peng Chi acting as a leader of the brigands, and could not say a single word.

"The two leaders here, Sung Chiang and Ch'ao Kai," said Peng Chi, "are agents sent from Heaven. They have collected heroes from all parts, and are now waiting for the imperial edict to exempt them from punishment, when they will be quite ready to devote themselves to the service of the country. As I am here I now obey the orders of the leaders."

Sung Chiang courteously apologized to Ling Chen, and invited him to join them.

"It makes no difference to me," said Ling Chen, "that I stay here but my wife and family will be in danger when it is known that I have joined you."

"Do not worry about that," said Sung Chiang; "I will arrange to have them all brought here for safety."

Ling Chen expressed his thanks and said, "If you help me in that way I shall die with a peaceful heart."

Ch'ao Kai invited Ling Chen to a feast. At the feast there was a general discussion as to future military operations, and Tang Lung said that he had a proposal to make.

A plan to seize a monster,
Complete in all its detail.

We will now relate what the proposal was.

CHAPTER 55

SHIH CH'IEN STEALS ARMOR; TANG LUNG INVEIGLES HSU NING

"MY forefathers earned a living by making weapons," said Tang Lung addressing the assembled leaders. "Because my father was skilled in that work he was employed at Yenanfu by the Generalissimo old Chung, Guardian of the Frontier. At that time the battle horses were protected by mail armor, which was a great success. The only way of defeating such cavalry was by the use of hooked spear. I know how to make those hooked spears, but am not experienced in their use. I have a cousin, however, who understands how to use the hooked spears, and he is a drill inspector in the army. He however has kept this knowledge to himself, and his marvelous methods are equally effective either with cavalry or infantry."

Lin Ch'ung asked, "Is that man not Drill Inspector Hsu Ning?"

"Yes, that is the man," replied Tang Lung.

"If you had not mentioned it I should have forgotten all about him," said Lin Ch'ung. "His skill is undoubtedly the most marvelous. I knew him well in the capital where we often compared our various methods. Only how can we get him to come here?"

"He has a most valuable heirloom at home of which there is no equal anywhere," said Tang Lung. "I once went to the capital with my father, and saw it with my own eyes. It was mail armor made of gold rings coated with swan feather. This mail armor is both light and strong, neither sword nor arrow can penetrate it. It was called a habergeon. Many wealthy people wanted to have a look of it, but he would not let them see it. It is as dear to him as his life, and he kept it locked up in a leather box on the beam of his house. If we could get that mail armor he would follow us here."

"In that case we can easily arrange matters," said Wu Yung. "We have a capable man here, and for this work we have use of Shih Ch'ien, the Flea on the Drum."

Shih Ch'ien said, "If the mail armor is still there I could of course soon get it."

"If you steal the armor," said Tang Lung, "I will undertake to bring the man here."

"How could you induce him to come here?" asked Sung Chiang.

Tang Lung walked across to Sung Chiang, and whispered something in his ear. Sung Chiang laughed and said, "An excellent plan!"

"For this we must send three men to the Capital," said Wu Yung. "One of them is to purchase gunpowder, and the other two can bring the family of Ling Chen here."

Upon hearing this Peng Chi stood up and said, "Why should not one man go to Ying Chou and bring my family here?"

"Do not worry about that," said Sung Chiang. "We will send a man for your family." He then instructed Yang Lin to go to Ying Chou to do that work. He also deputed Hsueh Yung and Li Yun to accompany Yueh Ho and Tang Lung to the capital; the former to bring Ling Chen's family and the latter to buy gunpowder. Shih Ch'ien after making preparations departed by himself for the capital. The other four followed some time afterwards.

Shih Ch'ien duly reached the capital, and stayed at an inn. The next day he inquired for Hsu Ning's residence and one man told him, "Go through the Pan Gate, and you will find his house; it is the fifth house on the east side; it has a black door." Shih Ch'ien did so, and duly found the house. He first examined it both the front and the back door. There was a high wall all round the house with a two-storied tower inside, besides which was a large beam. He then went to the neighborhood, and asked whether Hsu Ning was at home and was informed that he attended his duties about 5 a.m. and would not return until evening.

Shih Ch'ien returned to the inn, and changed his dress.

He told the innkeeper that he might not return that night, and asked him to look after his room. He went, and had his evening meal at another inn. He then went to Hsu Ning's house, and prowled around outside. It was soon dark, and became quite cold. It was a bright moonlight night. He saw a big tree in the grounds of a temple for the local god, and climbed up hid himself in the branches. From this vantage point he saw Hsu Ning arrive and enter his house. The servant soon came out with a lamp, and fastened the gate. He waited until he heard the drum in the tower sounded for the first watch of the night (9 p.m.). It was very cold, and hoar frost was forming on the tree. Everything was now quiet so he got down the tree, and went to the back door of Hsu Ning's house where he climbed over the wall. He found himself in a very small courtyard. He went to the kitchen, where there was a light. Looking through the window he saw two maid servants cleaning and washing the dishes. He went to the tower, and climbed up the beam to a window on the second floor. Looking inside he saw Hsu Ning, his wife, and a boy of about seven years of age sitting round a fire. On the rafter of the bedroom where he saw a leather box. He also saw a sword, a bow with arrows, and some clothes hanging on a clotheshorse. At last he heard Hsu Ning call to the servant, "Fragrant Plum, fold up the clothes for me." One of the maid servants came upstairs, folded the clothes, and put them away in a wardrobe. About 11 p.m. Hsu Ning went to bed and his wife asked him, "Do you attend to duty to-morrow?"

"To-morrow the emperor goes to the Dragon Palace and I must go at 5 a.m."

His wife then told the servant, "My husband must be on duty by 5 a.m. to-morrow. You must have breakfast ready by 4 a.m."

Shih Ch'ien had seen and heard all this, and was quite confident that he would get the leather box without any difficulty that night. If he get it too soon he might disturb his people and could not get out of the city so he would wait till nearly 5 a.m. Very soon, everybody in the house was asleep, but there was a lamp still left burning on the table. Breaking a hole in the paper window he took a reed, and blew out the light. About 4 a.m. Hsu Ning got up, and called to the maid servant to get breakfast ready. When the servant came they were surprised to find that the lamp had gone out. Hsu Ning told them to go to the back chamber and get a light, The woman servant went downstairs, and Shih Ch'ien slid down the beam on which he had been perched so long. He went to the back door, and hid there in the shade. The maid opened the door, and went to the other chamber. Shih Ch'ien slipped into the kitchen, and hid under a table. The maid soon returned with the lamp, shut the door, and lit the fire. The other servant soon took the coal stove upstairs. Very soon the water was boiling, and some was taken upstairs for Hsu Ning to wash his face. Breakfast was soon served and finished. Hsu Ning came downstairs, and left for his duty. Shih Ch'ien now left his hiding place, went straight upstairs, and took his position on the rafter. The maid-servants returned after fastening the gate, and went to bed again. Shih Ch'ien waited until they were asleep, and then taking his reed he blew out the lighted lamp. Shih Ch'ien very quietly got down from the rafter taking the leather box with him when Hsu Ning's wife awoke, and hearing the noise called out, "What is that noise?" Shih Ch'ien made a noise like a rat chattering, and one of the servants replied, "It is the rats. They are only fighting." Shih Ch'ien now made a noise like rats fighting to cover his movements with the box. Slowly he got down the stairs, and at last reached the door, and then the outer gate which he opened, and was soon outside. He hurried off with the leather box, through the city gate as it was then nearly 5 o'clock and was open, and soon reached his inn. He immediately packed up his things, paid the innkeeper, and started off on the east road. After he had gone about ten miles he stopped at an inn for breakfast. While eating a man entered, and Shih Ch'ien recognized him as Tai Tsung. They held a whispered conversation, and Tai Tsung then said he would take the mail armor (habergeon) to Liang Shan Po while Shih Ch'ien could follow and take his time. Shih Ch'ien opened the box, wrapped the mail armor in a parcel, and handed it to Tai Tsung who donned his magic greaves started off for Liang Shan Po.

Shih Ch'ien continued on his way, and after going about seven miles met Tang Lung, and explained the position to him. Tang Lung told Shih Ch'ien to continue on his way, and that he must only stop at inns where there was a white circle chalked on the door. At those inns he must display the leather box so that everybody could see it. Shih Ch'ien agreed to do this, and started off while Tang Lung went on his way to the capital.

Early in the morning when the maid-servants in Hsu Ning's house got up they found the house door open, and also the outside gate unfastened. They did not notice anything missing, and going back upstairs said to Mrs. Hsu Ning, "It is strange that the gate is unfastened, but there does not seem to be anything missing."

"About 5 a.m. I heard a noise on the rafter, but you said it was some rats fighting. Go to see if the leather box is still there?"

The servants looked up, and were astonished. "We do not know where it has gone to!"

The wife upon hearing this got up quickly and said, "We must send a messenger to the palace to ask my husband to come back as soon as possible."

The maid-servant found a messenger and sent him off. When he returned he said that Hsu Ning was on duty inside the palace. Outside were guards who would not allow anyone to enter. The servants were very much upset, and hunted all round the house for the leather box like a lot of ants in a hot pan.

When the emperor had retired from the palace, Hsu Ning took off his uniform and returned home. When he was near the house a neighbor said, "There has been a thief in your house. They sent a messenger to tell you, but you did not come back immediately." Hsu Ning was surprised at this, and hurried to his home. At the gate he met the servants who said, "You left home at 5 a.m. and presently a thief secretly entered the house, and stole the leather box on the rafter. He did not take anything else."

Hsu Ning was dumbfounded at the loss. His wife said, "We do not know at what time the thief got into the house."

"Other thing does not matter," said Hsu Ning. "Only our precious family heirloom has been stolen. Minister Hwa Erh-wang offered me 30,000 strings of cash for that, but I refused to sell. I was so afraid of losing it that I hid it away on the rafter. Many men came to get a look at it, but I always said I had not got it. Now if people hear that it has been stolen, they will laugh at us. What shall we do?" Hsu Ning could not sleep, but was continuously thinking the matter over. "Who could have stolen it?"

"I think it was stolen by someone who coveted the armor," said his wife. "Perhaps he stole it because you would not sell it. You had better make inquiries in all directions, and see if we can get a clue as to who has stolen it. At present, 'we must not beat the grass to startle the snake,' i.e., drive the thief from his hiding place."

The next day Hsu Ning was very downcast, and stayed at home. After breakfast he heard someone knocking at the outer gate. A servant answered the door, and then announced that a man named Tang Lung of Yenanfu wished to see Hsu Ning. Hsu Ning told the servant to show him into the guest chamber. Upon meeting there they saluted each other. Hsu Ning said, "I heard of the death of your father, but owing to my official duties I could not come to see you. Your place was also such a long way off, and I could not go. Where have you been working, and what brings you here to-day?"

"I cannot tell you all that has happened since in one sentence," replied Tang Lung. "After my father's death I was very hard up, and in fact was at a loose end. I have just come from Shantung on a visit to you."

Hsu Ning ordered the servant to bring in food and wine. Tang Lung opened his bundle, and gave Hsu Ning two ingots of silver weighing about twenty ounces, saying, "Just before his death my father told me to hand you this silver. I had no intimate friend whom I could have asked to bring this present to you, so I had to keep it until I could give it you myself."

"I am extremely grateful to your late father for remembering me, and making such a valuable present," replied Hsu Ning. "I have been very undutiful to your father, and shall never be able to recompense him."

"Never mind that," said Tang Lung. "Before his death my father often spoke to me of your great skill. He could not come to see you as you lived so far away, so he decided to send you this thing as a memento."

Hsu Ning thanked Tang Lung, and asked him to dine with him. During the meal Hsu Ning several times looked troubled, and even frowned. At last Tang Lung said, "I see that you are worrying about something. What has upset you?"

Hsu Ning sighed, "Younger brother, you do not know, but last night a thief got into this house."

"Did you miss anything?" asked Tang Lung.

"He took the mail armor which is our great heirloom. Because of that I am rather annoyed."

"I remember seeing it some time before," said Tang Lung. "It was a very rare thing. My father often spoke of it as a splendid work of art. Have you any clue as to who took it?"

"The mail armor was in a box which I hid on the rafter of my own bedroom. I have no idea who can have stolen it."

"What kind of box was it?" asked Tang Lung.

"It was red goatskin box, and the armor was wrapped in fine muslin inside."

Tang Lung was startled. "A red goatskin box! Outside covered with white silk embroidered with a design of clouds in green, and lions playing with a ball!"

"Younger brother! Where did you see it?" asked Hsu Ning.

"Elder brother, last night I stopped at an inn about thirteen miles from here, and there I saw an old man with a sallow complexion who was carrying such a box on a pole. At the time I particularly noticed the box, and wondered what was inside. I even asked the man what was in the box. He replied that originally there was mail armor stored in it, but now there was only some clothes. That must be the thief with your box. I noticed that the man limped, and walked along very slowly. We must pursue him at once."

"If we succeed in arresting him it will be by Heaven's assistance," said Hsu Ning.

"We had better waste no time, but get away at once," said Tang Lung.

Hsu Ning quickly put on his boots and swords, and left immediately with Tang Lung. When they had gone some distance on the road they came to an inn with a white circle on the door, and Tang Lung suggested that they might make inquiries there. They entered and sat down. Tang Lung asked the innkeeper whether he had noticed a man with a red goatskin box. The innkeeper remembered the man well, and said he had been there the previous night.

The two men started off again, and that evening they stopped at an inn which also had a white circle on the door. Hsu Ning wished to push on, but Tang Lung said he was too tired. There again they made inquiries, and the waiter remembered the man, and even told them that the man had said he was going to Shantung.

"Then we shall overtake him," said Tang Lung.

After sleeping there the two men started off again early the next morning.

Again they made inquiries at the inns on the way, and always got news of the goatskin box. As it grew dark they came to an old temple, and there they saw a man resting with a load under a tree. Hsu Ning ran forward and seized hold of Shih Ch'ien (for he was the man). "How brave you are! Why did you steal that box from my home?"

"Wait a bit!" said Shih Ch'ien. "Do not get excited! I stole the box, but what do you want me to do now?"

"You have no decency," said Hsu Ning. "How can you ask such a question?"

"Well, look in the box, and see whether the mail armor is there," replied Shih Ch'ien.

Hsu Ning opened the box, but found it empty. "Where is the mail armor?" he asked.

"I will tell you," said Shih Ch'ien. "My name is Chang Ta, and I am a Tai An Chou man. In our town is a wealthy man who is a friend of Generalissimo old Chung, Guardian of the Frontier. He knew of the armor you had, and wished to present it to the general. But he knew that you would not sell it, and therefore engaged me and another man named Li San to go to your home and steal it. In getting the box I had a fall and hurt my leg so that I could not walk very quickly. So Li San took the armor away, and left me behind to bring the empty box. If you now beat me, or send me to the yamen I will not say a word as to where the mail armor has gone to. If you will forgive me I will go with you to get back the armor."

Hsu Ning was undecided how to act, and did not speak for some time. Tang Lung interposed and said, "Elder brother, you need not be afraid of him running away. We can go with him, and get the armor. If we cannot get the armor we can send him to the yamen."

Hsu Ning agreed to this. All three then went on the road, and stayed that night at an inn. Hsu Ning and Tang Lung were careful that Shih Ch'ien did not escape. Shih Ch'ien's leg was not injured, he only wrapped much silk round his leg. Because Shih Ch'ien limped Hsu Ning at last decided that it was not necessary to watch him closely. The following day they traveled far. They came at last to a place where the road divided, and there they met two men pushing a barrow, accompanied by a man who simply walked. They stopped and saluted Tang Lung who asked them what they were doing at that spot.

The man replied, "I have been trading at Chengchou, and am now on my way back to Tai An Chou."

"That is fine," said Tang Lung. "We are also going to Tai An Chou, and wish to hire a barrow."

"Our barrow could carry all three of you," replied the man.

Tang Lung then introduced Hsu Ning, and told him that last year he had been to Tai An Chou on a pilgrimage, and while there had met this merchant, Li Jung. He knew him as a chivalrous man.

"In that case," said Hsu Ning, "our man Chang Ta can ride on the barrow, and we can make haste." This was done. On the way Hsu Ning asked Li Jung whether he knew a wealthy man, named Kwo at Tai An Chou. Li Jung said he knew him, and this settled Hsu Ning's mind as he felt that now he was sure to get the armor.

That day they were not far from Liang Shan Po, and they stopped on the road while Li Jung sent his men to buy wine and food and bring it to them. When it arrived Li Jung took a gourd off the barrow, and filling it with wine offered it to Hsu Ning who drunk it off. Li Jung was filling the gourd a second time for the others when apparently the jug slipped, and fell to the ground, and all the wine was lost. Li Jung shouted to his man to go and buy some more wine. Before the man returned Hsu Ning was foaming at the mouth, and was lying down on the barrow. Who was this man Li Jung? He was Yueh Ho from Liang Shan Po. The men now wheeled the barrow off with Hsu Ning, and soon reached Chu Kwei's inn. There they put Hsu Ning on a boat, rowed him across the lake, and carried him up the mountain. There they were met by Sung Chiang and the other leaders. A drug was now administered to Hsu Ning who recovered his consciousness. Seeing such a crowd of men all around, Hsu Ning asked Tang Lung, "Brother, why did you deceive me and bring me to this place?"

"Elder brother, I will explain," replied Tang Lung. "I heard that Sung Chiang, the chief of these heroes, is always looking out for heroes to join his band. For this reason I came here and joined him. We have been attacked by troops under General Huyen Sho, and defeated. It was then I thought of the mail armor you had." He explained fully how the armor had been stolen, and brought to Liang Shan Po. He also invited him to join the bandits as a leader.

"Brother, you have seriously injured me."

Sung Chiang now stepped forward and spoke to Hsu Ning. "I, Sung Chiang, wait here with my men for the emperor to admit us to citizenship. We are quite loyal, and will devote our life to our country. We do not covet riches, and have no desire to kill anybody. Our motives are of the best, and will stand your closest scrutiny. We request you to join us to act as agents for Heaven."

Hsu Ning however again addressed Tang Lung, "You deceived me in bringing me here, and have exposed my wife and family to arrest."

"That is already arranged," said Sung Chiang. "You need not worry. I will be responsible, and see that no trouble happens to your family. I will see that they are all safely brought here."

Within a few days Hsu Ning's wife and family arrived. Hsu Ning was surprised, and asked his wife how she came there. She replied, "When you had left, there were many inquiries as to why you had not turned up for duty. I said that you were sick, and gave them money to silence the matter. Then some days afterwards Tang Lung came, and said that you had fallen sick in an inn on the road. He told us all to go with him quickly in order to see you before you died. He induced us to start at once, and brought us here."

Hsu Ning was pleased to see them, but said that now he could go back to the capital.

Ch'ao Kai and Sung Chiang both pressed him to stay with them, and gave him a separate house for his family.

The leaders held a conference regarding further military operations, and they asked Hsu Ning to instruct their men how to use the hooked spears, or halberds.

He agreed to do this, and selected the strongest men for his purpose.

> Three thousand troops defeated at one battle,
> A great hero surrendered on the spot.

We will now see how Hsu Ning instructed the use of the hooked spear.

CHAPTER 56

HSU NING DRILLS THE BRIGANDS; SUNG CHIANG GAINS A VICTORY

ONE day after choosing his men for the use of the halberd Hsu Ning entered the hall and took a halberd himself, and showed the assembled leaders some of his tricks. They applauded his skill. He then said to his men, "On horseback there are nine ways of handling the halberd, but on foot there are changes in every twelve paces." He then went through all these movements, and explained them. The leaders were much pleased at the exhibition and arrangements were made for a special company to be drilled in these methods from early morning till night. Within a fortnight there were fully five hundred men who could use the halberd.

During this time General Huyen Sho marched his men daily to the banks of the lake without meeting any opposition.

The bandits were in hiding watching these movements without showing themselves. Sung Chiang said, "Friends, I have a plan, but do not know whether you will approve of it. I propose that to-morrow we should attack on foot, not a single man should be mounted on horseback. The men will be divided into ten companies and when the enemy advances our men must retreat into the reeds and brambles. Then as the enemy is close our men must use their halberds and hooked spears, and drag them off their horses, and make them prisoners. We must select an open plain with many narrow paths leading off on all sides into grass. What do you think of my plan?"

"It is a good idea," said Wu Yung.

Hsu Ning also agreed with this. That day Sung Chiang divided his men into ten companies, and they all left the mountain and crossed the lake. By 3 a.m. the following morning they had all found their hiding places. The cannons had also been transported and stationed on high ground.

The next day about 10 a.m. Sung Chiang gave the signal, and all the men showed themselves with flags, and much beating of drums and gongs. General Huyen Sho was duly informed of this display, and sent Colonel Han Tao forward to attack. The horses were covered with mail armor. General Huyen Sho mounted his horse, and held an iron bludgeon in each hand. He ordered a general advance as he wished to annihilate the bandits. Colonel Han Tao came to have a final talk before the attack. He said, "On the south side there are many bandits on foot."

"Never mind how many there are," replied General Huyen; "attack them at once with the cavalry."

Colonel Han Tao led five hundred cavalry to the attack, but before he had gone far he saw two large bodies of men on foot towards the southeast and west. He therefore halted, and dividing his cavalry into three, gave each body its objective. He himself, however, returned to General Huyen Sho, and reported the position. The General said, "These bandits have not faced us for a long time, and they may employ some strategem." While he was saying this the bandits' artillery began to boom. "Those firearms must be the work of Ling Chen who has surrendered to the bandits." Looking round they now saw many bandits towards the north. He continued, "This must be a trick of the bandits, I will divide our troops with you. I will take half to the north while you take the rest towards the south." Again looking round he saw many brigands on the west side, and was surprised. There were booms on the north side, which sent shots quite near where they were then standing.

The shells exploded with great noise and about nine shots were thrown in all directions. Orders were given for a divided attack in all four directions, but as the troops advanced the bandits retreated on all sides. General Huyen Sho was annoyed at this, and galloped off towards the north side. He urged his cavalry to pursue the retreating bandits. When they reached a place full of reeds and bushes the cavalry became split up to follow the small paths. When they had gone some distance like this the troops heard a whistle blown in their rear, and immediately men sprang

THE HALBERD ADOPTED

from hiding places, armed with hooked spears. The troops on the two wings were surrounded, and dragged off their horses in less than no time.

General Huyen Sho seeing the position extracted himself, and galloped off towards the south side of the plain. Upon reaching there he found that Colonel Han Tao had met with the same fate. The two saw brigands on all the roads, but seeing a weak spot towards the northwest they galloped off in that direction followed by a few of their cavalry. However they had only gone about two miles when they found further progress blocked by a body of bandits in charge of two leaders who shouted out, "Defeated generals cannot pass!" General Huyen Sho was angry, and dashed forward to attack the two leaders. After about five bouts one leader retreated, but General Huyen Sho suspecting a trick did not pursue him. Instead he galloped off towards the north. Soon however he met another body of bandits with two leaders, and again he galloped to engage in combat. After about five bouts both leaders retreated. Huyen Sho pursued them, and he had only gone about a quarter of a mile when he was attacked on both sides by about twenty-four men with halberds. General Huyen had no mind to fight with them so he turned his horse and galloped off. He, however, found that Wang Ying and the Amazon Hu now blocked the road he had come. He saw that on either hand were many brambles so that there was no way of escape. He therefore urged the horse forward, and whirled aloft his two iron bludgeons.

He dashed past the two leaders who followed him. General Huyen Sho was now looking out for some of his men, but could not see a single one.

Just then Sung Chiang gave the signal for a general return to Liang Shan Po. About fifteen hundred horses had been wounded, and these were killed, and flesh used as food. An equal number of horses were captured, and were added to the bandits' stock. About five thousand soldiers were taken prisoners. The camps of General Huyen Sho were all destroyed, and the new buildings were erected as inns at the foot of the mountain. When Sung Chiang saw the prisoners he at once released Colonel Han Tao and many officers and he got Peng Chi and Ling Chen to persuade them to join the bandits. Colonel Han Tao agreed to this, as he was destined to be one of the seventy-two leaders at Liang Shan Po.

General Huyen Sho had escaped but having lost all his men he was very despondent as he rode by himself. He realized that he could not return to the capital. He thought, "I never expected to be in such an awful predicament. Where can I go now? The only place is Ching Chou where my old friend Prefect Mujung may assist me. He may arrange the matter with the government, and then I may be able to find means of getting my revenge for this defeat."

He traveled in that direction for two days, and then in the evening he came to an inn by the roadside. He was both hungry and thirsty so he tied up his horse, and entered the inn. He sat down, placed his whip on the table, and ordered food. The waiter said that they had only wine, but if Huyen Sho would give him the money he would go into the village and buy some meat and food.

Huyen Sho did so, and asked him to buy some mutton. He also asked him to give his horse some fodder. He would stay there for the night, and go to Ching Chou in the morning.

"Sir, we have no beds here either," replied the waiter.

"That does not matter as I am an old soldier, and can sleep anywhere," said Huyen Sho.

The waiter went to buy the food, and Huyen Sho went to look after his horse. He then sat down outside the inn waiting for the waiter to return. Soon the waiter came, and Huyen Sho sat down for his evening meal. He told the waiter who he was, and said that he would depart for Ching Chou Fu the following day.

"Sir, I will tell you something. Not far from here is Tao Hwa Shan where there are some bandits named Li Chung, nicknamed Tiger Hunter, and his company. There are about five hundred men in that band, and they are always raiding the surrounding villages. In fact they come here often so that to-night you must be wary."

"That will not upset me," said Huyen Sho, "I should not be afraid even if all of them came. You just take care of my horse."

As Huyen Sho had now finished his supper, the waiter prepared a temporary bed for him. That day he had been very melancholy, and in addition he had drunk rather a lot of wine so that he lay down to sleep without taking off his clothing. About 4 a.m. he was awakened, and heard the waiter complaining at the back of the inn. He jumped up, and taking his two whips he went to the door, and called out, "Why are you complaining like that?"

"I came out to feed your horse," replied the waiter, "and saw that a part of the fence had been broken down. I found that your horse had been taken away. I saw a torchlight about a mile away, and it must have been the man stealing your horse."

"What place is in that direction?"

The waiter said it was Tao Hwa Shan, and Huyen Sho insisted upon his going with him to find the road. After they had gone a mile the light in front vanished.

"This is a great disaster to me," said Huyen Sho, "as that horse was presented to me by the emperor himself."

"Sir, we cannot do anything further to-night, so we must go back. To-morrow you can go on to Ching Chou Fu, and there get soldiers to recapture the horse for you."

So they returned to the inn, but Huyen Sho could not sleep. Early the next morning he asked the waiter to accompany him, and carry his armor. They both set out for Ching Chou Fu where they reached after dusk.

Early the next morning General Huyen Sho went to the yamen of the Prefect Mujung who was surprised to see him, and said, "I have heard that you went to attack the bandits at Liang Shan Po. How is it that you come here?"

General Huyen Sho told the prefect what had happened, and the latter said, "It was evidently not your fault that your army was defeated and destroyed, but was due to the vile strategy of the bandits. In this district there are many bandits. I want to use you against the brigands at Tao Hwa Shan, and there you can recover your horse as well. After that I shall ask you to clear the bandits from the Two Dragons Mountain, and also the White Tiger Mountain. Then if successful I will report the whole matter to the emperor, and reëstablish your command in the army,

Then you can take your revenge on the bandits at Liang Shan Po. What do you say to my proposal?"

"I am deeply grateful for Your Excellency's kind consideration, and shall be much pleased to undertake the task," replied General Huyen Sho. "I will pledge my life to repay you."

The prefect gave him a room in his quarters, and supplied food and clothing. The waiter returned to the inn. After about three days General Huyen Sho got three thousand troops from Prefect Mnjung, and advanced upon Tao Hwa Shan.

The bandits at Tao Hwa Shan were delighted at having captured a general's horse, and they celebrated the event with several days' feasting. One day a bandit scout reported that a great many soldiers were approaching. The second leader in command Chou Tung offered to meet the army, and he took about a hundred men, went down the mountain to meet the opposing army.

General Huyen Sho upon seeing the bandits, halted his soldiers and rode forward. He called out to the brigands, "Robbers, be quick to surrender:" Upon hearing this challenge Chou Tung arranged his men, and then riding forward engaged General Huyen Sho in conflict. After about seven bouts, however, Chou Tung realized his own weakness, and retreated giving his men orders to retire to the stronghold on the mountain. General Huyen Sho seeing the bandits retiring, remembered his previous experience, and he ordered his army to stop pursuit.

Upon seeing Li Chung, Chou Tung explained what had happened, and asked what must be done if the soldiers advanced upon the stronghold. Li Chung said, "We must get assistance from Lu Ta, Yang Chih, and Wu Sung who are famous heroes at the Two Dragons Mountain. I will write a letter at once, and send it by messenger. I will tell them that we will compensate them for any losses, and amply reward them for a success."

"I know there are many heroes there," said Chou Tung, "but I am afraid that the leader Lu Ta has an old grudge against us."

Li Chung laughed at this, "Lu Ta is a very straightforward man, and he may not treat us like that. I think that he will come and assist us when the position is fully explained by our messenger." He wrote the letter forthwith, and sent two men with it.

The letter reached the Two Dragons Mountain within two days, and the leaders had a conference at the headquarters. The messenger explained that General Huyen Sho had been defeated at Liang Shan Po, and was now endeavoring to retrieve his fortunes by attacking Tao Hwa Shan and other brigand's strongholds.

After listening to the full statement Yang Chih spoke, "We are independent and each protects his own stronghold. But it is true that if Huyen Sho destroys the Tao Hwa Shan stronghold it will be our turn next. We should therefore go with all our men, and fight together in this common cause."

This was agreed to, and that day five hundred bandits set out for Tao Hwa Shan.

When Li Chung at Tao Hwa Shan heard of the arrival of the reënforcements he marched to meet them with three hundred men. General Huyen Sho being informed of this movement assembled his men on the main road. When the two forces met he rode forward to challenge Li Chung to single combat. Li Chung was a descendant from military ancestors, and he rode forward to keep up his reputation. After about ten bouts, however, he knew that General Huyen Sho was more than his equal, and therefore retired. Huyen Sho, however, pursued him up the mountain as he was confident of victory. Chou Tung, however, seeing this gave orders to his men to throw stones at General Huyen Sho, and this hail of stones forced General Huyen to retire also. As he rode back, however, he was surprised to hear loud shouts from the rear of his own army. He then saw there was a large cloud of dust under which a troop of bandits were advancing. He rode forward, and saw that in front of the bandits rode a big fat priest (Lu Ta) who shouted out, "You fellows have been defeated by the heroes at Liang Shan Po, so how dare you come here to disturb us?"

"I will first kill you bald-headed donkey," replied General Huyen Sho. "That will appease my anger."

Lu Ta advanced flourishing his iron priest's staff, and was met by the general. They fought for about fifty bouts without either gaining an advantage, and at last General Huyen recognized that he had a skillful opponent. Gongs were sounded on both sides as a signal for an interval of rest for both combatants. After a brief rest General Huyen Sho dashed forward again, shouting, "Come on, you priestly thief."

Lu Ta was on the point of returning to fight when Yang Chih called out, "Brother, take a rest and I will engage this man." He then urged his horse forward, and met General Huyen Sho. They fought for about fifty bouts without either gaining any advantage, and then General Huyen thought, "This is the second man I cannot beat. But where do they come from? They do not look like brigands."

Yang Chih seeing the skill of his opponent turned his horse to retire. General Huyen did not pursue him, and also retired.

Lu Ta spoke to Yang Chih, "We have just come and cannot encamp so close to this opposing army. Let us withdraw about seven miles, and come again to-morrow." This was agreed to, and the bandits retired.

General Huyen Sho in his tent felt disappointed, as he had expected to deal with these bandits just as one breaks a piece of bamboo, but he had actually met his equals. He must be ill-fated to get such results. But what could he do just then? However a messenger came from Prefect Mujung ordering him to bring the troops back to guard the town. The brigands from White Tiger Mountain had arrived and were threatening the town. General Huyen gave orders immediately for a general retreat, and that night all the troops arrived near Ching Chou Fu.

The next day when Lu Ta, Yang Chih, and Wu Sung led their bandits to the foot of Tao Hwa Shan, they were very surprised to find that the troops had all gone. It was not long however before Li Chung and Chou Tung arrived, and invited the three leaders to go to their stronghold on Tao Hwa Shan. There a feast was prepared, and matters discussed.

When General Huyen Sho reached Ching Chow Fu he saw a large body of men was approaching outside the town. They were the brigands from the White Tiger Mountain under the leadership Kung Ming and Kung Liang. These two leaders had had a dispute with a wealthy man whom they had killed, and had then escaped to White Tiger Mountain where they assembled about five hundred bandits. Because of this murder the Prefect Mujung had arrested Kung Ping, the uncle of Kung Ming, and had put him in prison. Kung Ming therefore took the brigands against Ching Chou Fu to try to release his uncle from prison.

When General Huyen Sho arrived with his army he at once led them against the bandits. Prefect Mujung having been informed of the arrival of the troops had taken up his position in a tower gate to watch the battle. General Huyen Sho rode out in front of the army, and his challenge was accepted by Kung Ming. The general soon found that his opponent was not very skillful, and soon succeeded in unhorsing him, and taking him prisoner. Upon seeing this Kung Liang gave orders for all the bandits to retreat.

Prefect Mujung sent orders for the troops to pursue the brigands, and this was done, capturing about a hundred of them. The other brigands were scattered in all directions, and at last Kung Liang found himself alone, and slept that night in an old temple he came across.

Prefect Mujung was much pleased that Kung Ming had been captured, and sent him to prison to join his uncle. The prefect rewarded the troops, and then sat down with General Huyen Sho to hear the news of the Tao Hwa Shan expedition. General Huyen Sho said, "The bandits at Tao Hwa Shan were cornered like a tortoise in a jar, but a strange thing happened. Another body of brigands arrived to attack us. They were led by a big fat priest, and a sallow complexioned man with both of whom I fought, but without success. Their military skill was quite unusual, and they were quite capable of defending themselves."

"I know that priest," said Prefect Mujung; "he is Lu Ta, who was previously a major in the army, but afterwards became a priest and then a bandit. The other leader is Yang Chih who was also previously an officer in the army. There is also another leader Wu Sung, an ex-army man also, who is famous for having killed a tiger on Ching Yang Ridge. They are now at the Two Dragons Mountain, and although we have tried to dislodge them, our troops have failed, and have always been defeated."

"I also have heard of those men," said General Huyen Sho, "and certainly they are equal to their reputation. But I am here now, and will see to it that those men are captured."

The next morning when Kung Liang was riding in a forest, he met a body of bandits in charge of Wu Sung. He dismounted, saluted, and inquired after his health. The two exchanged compliments and related what had happened on both sides.

At last Wu Sung suggested that Kung Liang and his men should join with the bandits of Tao Hwa Shan in an attack on the government troops. Kung Liang agreed to this, and was taken and introduced to Lu Ta and Yang Chih.

When discussing the proposed attack on Ching Chou Fu by the combined bandits from the three mountains Yang Chih said, "The town is strongly fortified, and has a general like Huyen Sho in charge of the defense it will not be easy for us to take. But I have a plan that I think will succeed." He then explained how to take the town, and they were highly pleased with his proposal.

> Tiles are broken; town in flames;
> Pity the people of Ching Chow.
> Smashing fists and crushing blows,
> Admire the bandits and heroes.

CHAPTER 57

THE BANDITS FROM THE THREE MOUNTAINS ATTACK CHING CHOU; ALL THE HEROES CAST THEIR LOT WITH LIANG SHAN PO

YANG CHIH said that it would be better if they had the support of the brigands at Liang Shan Po, and he suggested that Kung Liang should go to Sung Chiang to ask for his assistance.

"That is a good idea," said Lu Ta. "I very often hear of the fame of Sung Chiang, but so far I have not met him. I have heard of him so much that I am almost made deaf with hearing his name. I hope our brother Kung Liang will go, and bring that famous man to join us. We will proceed with our attack on Ching Chou Fu in the meantime."

Kung Liang agreed, and handed over all his men to Lu Ta. He then departed for Liang Shan Po.

Lu Ta then sent to his stronghold to summon all the 200 bandits upon hearing of the news from Ching Chou Fu. Li Chung also got all his 500 men from Tao Hwa Shan. When these bandits arrived they joined to attack Ching Chou.

Kung Liang was allowed to pass the outposts upon reaching Liang Shan Po and was conducted up the mountain. There he explained his mission to Sung Chiang, and the other leaders, who unanimously agreed to join in the attack upon Ching Chou Fu. The bandits were soon ready, and Sung Chiang divided them up into five companies in charge of twenty leaders. They left the mountain the same day, and duly joined the other bandits in the neighborhood of Ching Chou Fu. There all the leaders were introduced, and were pleased to meet each other.

Sung Chiang introduced the question as to how they were to attack the town, and Yang Chih spoke, "Before you arrived we had attacked the town about five times without gaining any advantage. The defense of Ching Chou Fu evidently depends upon one man (General Huyen Sho), and if we can capture him, his army would disappear like snow when hot water is thrown on it."

Wu Yung laughed and said, "To use force against such a man is useless. We must use strategy."

"How could that be done?" asked Sung Chiang.

Wu Yung explained a trick he had thought of, and Sung Chiang was delighted as he considered the plan excellent.

Early the next day all the bandits surrounded the town with much noise of gongs and drums. Inside the town the Prefect Mujung upon hearing of this sent for General Huyen Sho. "Evidently," he said, "these men have now got the bandits from Liang Shan Po to assist them, and we are surrounded. What shall we do?"

These brigands are skilled in fighting on water," replied Huyen Sho, "but now they are out of their element and far away from their stronghold. I will capture them one by one. I request you to go to the gate tower, and watch me defeat them."

General Huyen put on his mail armor, mounted his horse, and led about one thousand men out the gates to meet the bandits.

Out of Sung Chiang's forces Chin Ming rode forth armed with a spiked mace and he cursed the enemy. "You covetous and malicious thieves of the people. You have ruined my family, and to-day I come for revenge."

Prefect Mujung on the wall recognized the man as ex-general Chin Ming, and shouted, "You were an official appointed by the emperor, and were well treated. So why are you now a rebel? If I capture you I will have you hacked into a thousand pieces. General Huyen, please arrest that man."

General Huyen at once galloped forward towards Chin Ming who also advanced. They met, and were well matched. After about fifty bouts neither had gained any advantage.

Mujung being afraid that General Huyen would not succeed in single combat had a gong sounded as a signal for the general to return inside the gate. As General Huyen retired, Chin Ming also withdrew without pursuing his opponent. Sung Chiang issued an order for all the bandits to withdraw about five miles from the town.

When General Huyen had dismounted inside the city he spoke to Prefect Mujung, "I wanted to defeat Chin Ming. Why did you give the order for a retreat?"

"I saw that you had not succeeded after many attempts, and fearing that you would be tired, I thought it better that you should have a rest. That man Chin Ming was previously in charge of the troops here, but he and an officer Hwa Jung deserted. You must not treat them lightly."

"You need not worry," said General Huyen, "as I can easily defeat that fellow. While we were fighting I noticed his weak spots. If he comes to-morrow I will certainly overcome him and kill him."

"In that case we must open a way through these bandits and get three messengers through. One can go to the capital, and beg for assistance there, and the other two can go to the towns in the neighborhood, and ask them to help us."

"Your proposal is excellent," replied General Huyen Sho.

The prefect wrote his dispatches accordingly, and selected three reliable men to act as messengers. General Huyen retired to his quarters, undressed and was soon asleep. Early the next morning before dawn he was awakened by a messenger knocking at his door. The man reported, "Just outside the North Gate there is a mound, and three horsemen are there overlooking the town. One on the right we recognize as Hwa Jung, the one in the middle is dressed in red, and another one is dressed like a Taoist priest."

"That priest will be Wu Yung, and the one in red will be Sung Chiang," remarked General Huyen. "They must not be disturbed at present. Let one hundred cavalry be mustered at once, and I will capture these three men." He quickly dressed, mounted, and led his cavalry to the North Gate. The gate was opened, and the drawbridge was lowered quietly. General Huyen and his men rode forth towards the mound. The three brigand leaders were still there looking towards the town, but as soon as the troops were near they turned their horses and rode away. General Huyen galloped after them, but as the men reached a clump of dead tree they halted. As General Huyen approached, his horse tripped and fell into a hidden pit. At the same moment there were many loud shouts from bandits who had lain in ambush at that spot. He was seized, and bound with ropes; and taken off as a prisoner in next to no time. As the troops came forward Hwa Jung shot arrows, and killed several men at the head. The cavalry, seeing this, swung round and retreated in great confusion. When Sung Chiang returned to his camp the executioners led the prisoner to meet Sung Chiang who ordered that the prisoner should be set free. He then conducted him into his tent, requested him to be seated, and then saluted him with both hands.

"What is this done for?" asked General Huyen Sho.

"How dare I, Sung Chiang, to disobey the imperial court? It is only the corrupt officials who force us to seek refuge at Liang Shan Po. We will wait until the emperor pardons us. I do not expect that we would give much trouble to you and have offended you, and I therefore beg you to forgive us this time."

"I am a prisoner," replied General Huyen, "and quite ready for death. Why do you treat me in this polite manner?"

"We have no desire to injure you," said Sung Chiang. "Heaven knows that our intentions are good." He again saluted, and begged General Huyen to forgive him.

"Is it your idea to ask me to go to the capital and put your case before the emperor and beg for a pardon?" asked General Huyen Sho.

"How could you go?" said Sung Chiang. "There is still the Minister for War, Kao Chiu, in office. He is a mean fellow; always forgets meritorious deeds, and never overlooks a minor fault. As you have been defeated after great expenditure of money he will undoubtedly seek to punish you. Moreover, your three assistants, Colonels Han Tao, Peng Chi, and Ling Chen, have already joined us. If you have no objection to join us, I will retire, and offer you my position as second in command here. If in the future the emperor pardons us you can still be of service to the court."

General Huyen Sho for some time did not reply to this, and was evidently undecided. He saw that Sung Chiang was treating him with great respect, and that there was some force in his arguments.

At last he sighed, and kneeling replied, "If I agree to your proposal you must not think me disloyal to the emperor, because your generosity obliges me to comply with you. I will gladly 'hold your whip and stirrup,' and will never return."

Sung Chiang was much pleased at this, and introduced General Huyen to the other leaders as one of their band. He then asked Li Chung to return the horse stolen from General Huyen, and this was done. They then discussed how they were to rescue Kung Ming who was still in prison. "There is only one way," said Wu Yung "General Huyen must get the town gate open by some deception, and the rest will be easy. That will complete the estrangement between General Huyen and the Prefect."

Sung Chiang addressed General Huyen Sho, "We do not wish to loot the town, but only get inside, and release Kung Ming and his uncle who are still in prison there. If it was not for that I would not ask you to get the town gate open by deception."

"As you have treated me with great hospitality," replied General Huyen, "I must do as you suggest."

About ten of the leaders disguised as soldiers and accompanied General Huyen Sho on horseback. They reached the town moat in the evening, and General Huyen called out, "Open the gate! I have just escaped with my life." The gatekeepers recognized the voice of General Huyen, and at once reported the matter to the prefect.

The Prefect Mujung had been distressed at the capture of General Huyen, but when he heard this report he was delighted, and mounting his horse rode to the gate. In the dark he saw eleven horsemen, and could not make out who they were. He however called out, "General Huyen, how did you escape?"

"The bandits seized me, and took me as a prisoner to their stronghold," replied General Huyen. "There, however, was an old attaché of mine, and he secretly helped me to escape, and also gave me my old horse, and has accompanied me here."

The prefect hearing this gave orders for the drawbridge to be lowered and the gate opened. Then the ten brigands were inside the gate, and Chin Ming struck at Prefect Mujung and killed him on the spot. The other leaders soon scattered the guard. A fire was at once set in the city and Sung Chiang and the other brigands outside, immediately advanced, and were soon all inside the town. Sung Chiang immediately gave orders that the people were not to be troubled, and deputed a part of his men to seize the government granary and treasury. Another party attacked the prison, and soon rescued Kung Ming and Kung Ping and their relatives. The fire was extinguished. The members of the prefect's family were all killed, and his residence were looted. When it was daylight, Sung Chiang ordered that all civilians whose houses had been burnt should be compensated. The loot was placed on about five hundred carts, and sent to Liang Shan Po. The bandits then held a great feast in the town, and afterwards Sung Chiang invited all the brigands from the other three mountains to join together at Liang Shan Po, and this they agreed to. It took several days before they all assembled at Liang Shan Po. Altogether this adventure brought twelve new leaders to Liang Shan Po.

After a time Lu Ta spoke to Sung Chiang about the bandits at Shao Hwa Shan, at Hwa Yin Hsien under the leadership of Shih Chin, and he asked to be allowed to visit his old friends there. He said perhaps he could induce them to Liang Shan Po.

Sung Chiang agreed to this, and appointed Wu Sung to accompany Lu Ta. The two leaders set off on their journey, but shortly after they had gone, Sung Chiang thought that there might be risks on the way, and therefore dispatched Tai Tsung, the Flying Prince, to follow them.

Upon reaching Shao Hwa Shan, Lu Ta and Wu Sung were stopped by a sentinel bandit who asked what their business was. Wu Sung said they wished to see Shih Chin, and a messenger was at once sent up the mountain to report the matter. Within a short time they saw the leaders Chu Wu, Chen Ta, and Yang Chun coming down the mountain to meet them, but Shih Chin was not with them. When they had been introduced, Lu Ta asked where Shih Chin was, and Chu Wu without replying invited them to come to their headquarters when matters could be discussed. But Lu Ta objected to this, "If you have anything to say, say it at once. I came to see Shih Chin, but he is not here. I am not going further until you explain the position."

"We three were in charge of the stronghold, and then were joined by Shih Chin who became our chieftain," said Chu Wu. "Everything went smoothly until one day he went down the mountain, and happened to meet an artist named Wang I who was traveling with his daughter. Sometime before he (Wang I) had been sick, and had then taken a vow that if he recovered he would paint a special screen for a temple in that neighborhood.

"One day while doing this work the Prefect Ho came to the temple to burn incense before the god. He had been struck by the beauty of Wang I's daughter, and had sent a go-between to ask her to become his concubine. Wang I objected to this, and then the prefect sent his soldiers to take the girl by force. A false charge was made against Wang I, and he had been banished to a distant prison. On the way as a prisoner he passed this spot, and so met Shih Chin to whom he told this story. Shih Chin was so annoyed that he attacked the escort of two soldiers, and killed them. He then went himself into the town to kill the prefect, but was arrested and placed in prison, but I," continued Chu Wu, "have no plan to solve this problem."

"This fellow, the prefect, is without decency," said Lu Ta. "Why is he so brutal? I will go and kill him myself."

"Let us first go to our stronghold to discuss this question," said Chu Wu.

Lu Ta wanted to go at once, but Wu Sung seizing hold of the priest's iron staff pointed to the sky, "Elder brother, you can see that the sun is almost touching the top of the trees, and it will soon be dark."

Lu Ta saw this, but although still angry, he agreed to go up the mountain with them.

A feast was arranged, but Lu Ta refused to join the others. "As long as our younger brother Shih Chin is absent, I will not eat or drink anything," he said. "I will sleep here for one night, but to-morrow I will go into the town, and kill that fellow."

"Do not be reckless," said Wu Sung. "To-morrow we must go to Liang Shan Po, and ask Sung Chiang to help us to attack Hwa Chou," said Lu Ta.

"I am afraid that Shih Chin will be killed before the men come from Liang Shan Po," said Lu Ta.

"Even if you killed the prefect," said Wu Sung, "you would not then be sure of releasing Shih Chin from prison. I object very strongly to your going."

"Elder brother," interposed Chu Wu, "what Wu Sung says is quite right. Please keep cool in this matter."

"It is you indolent people that involves our younger brother Shih Chin?" replied Lu Ta. "Now he is in prison, and yet you drink wine and eat food here as though nothing unusual had happened." He then left them, and went to bed. He was up early the next morning, and went away without speaking to any one.

As soon as this was found out, Wu Sung considered that there would be immediate danger, and Chu Wu at once sent two bandits as spy.

When Lu Ta reached the town, he asked a man on the street where the yamen was. He was told to cross a bridge and then go east. Upon reaching the bridge, however, there were many men there who said, "You cannot pass this way as the prefect is coming." Lu Ta thought, "I come here to look for this man, but there he is coming straight into my arms. He deserves death!" Soon the prefect came along in his winter sedan chair, and was attended by his guard on both sides. Lu Ta seeing this realized that he could not carry out his plan. He thought if he made an attempt he might fail, and would only be laughed at.

Just at the moment the prefect looked through the window of the chair and noticed Lu Ta take a step forward and then withdraw as if undecided about something, so when he reached the yamen he told a messenger to go, and bring the big priest to see him. The messenger soon found Lu Ta, who was surprised but pleased when he heard the message. Upon reaching the yamen he was asked to lay aside his sword and iron priest's staff, and was then asked to go into the prefect's quarters to dine there. Upon reaching the room, the prefect told his attendants, "Arrest that thief!" And Lu Ta was arrested as a prisoner.

> By flame, the moth is lured,
>   Its wings are quickly burnt;
> By bait, the fish is caught,
>   Its struggles end in death.

CHAPTER 58

WU YUNG'S DECEPTION IN THE GOLDEN BELL AFFAIR; SUNG CHIANG MAKES A ROW AT WESTERN SACRED MOUNTAIN

LU TA was very angry at being arrested in the yamen, and said, "You oppressor of the people and ravisher of women! How dare you arrest me! I wish to die along with Shih Chin. I shall not mind that. Only Sung Chiang will punish you for my death. I will tell you something. No enmity cannot be abolished. If you hand over to me Shih Chin, and the daughter of Wang I, and then you resign from your position then our enmity will vanish. I see from your face that you are lustful, and have no right to be a prefect. If you do these three things, however, Buddha will look upon you with mercy, but if you miss this opportunity you will live to regret it. Now let me go to see Shih Chin, and then give me an answer."

The prefect was very angry at this, and said, "As I suspected, you came to assassinate me like Shih Chin. That fellow! You want to see him! Take this fellow to prison, and I will deal with him later on. He is evidently a bird of the same feather with Shih Chin. Put a strong cangue on him, and see that he is well locked up." This was done, and the prefect wrote a dispatch to his superior mandarin asking for instructions.

This affair was soon known all over the town, and one of the brigand spies hearing of it, rushed off at once to Shao Hwa Shan to report it. Wu Sung was surprised at the news and said, "How can I now face the other leaders when Lu Ta has been taken prisoner?" While he was thinking the matter over another spy arrived, and reported that a leader named Tai Tsung had just come from Liang Shan Po, and was waiting at the foot of the mountain to see Wu Sung. The latter immediately went down the mountain, and conducted Tai Tsung up to their stronghold where he introduced him to Chu Wu.

Tai Tsung was surprised to hear the news about Lu Ta and Shih Chin, and said, "I must not stop here! I will go back at once to Liang Shan Po, and ask Sung Chiang to send his men to rescue the two brothers."

"I will wait here until you return," said Wu Sung. "Please come back quickly with assistance."

Tai Tsung put on his charmed greaves, and flew off. It took him three days to travel from Shansi province to Liang Shan Po in Shantung. When Ch'ao Kai and Sung Chiang got the news, arrangements were made for 7,000 cavalry and infantry to depart at once with sixteen leaders under the command of Sung Chiang. Tai Tsung was sent off to report to Shao Hwa Shan in Shansi province that help was coming. The bandits duly reached their destination, and the leaders were taken up the mountain to discuss matters. Chu Wu reported that Lu Ta and Shih Chin were still in prison, and the prefect was now waiting a decree authorizing him to execute the prisoners.

Sung Chiang asked whether there was any proposal as to how the prisoners could be rescued.

Chu Wu said, "Hwa Chou is a very big town, and the moat is very deep. It is a difficult town to take. If there is a coup d'étate inside the town we might succeed."

"To-morrow we must go and inspect the town and its defenses," said Wu Yung. "Then we can discuss matters. We must not however go in the daytime because the prefect will take care, and will be on the lookout for us. We must start to-morrow afternoon so as to reach the town after sunset. There will be a full moon to-morrow."

This was agreed, and the next afternoon five leaders started off on horseback, and reached the town about 8 p.m. They dismounted near a hillock where they could overlook the town. It was a bright moonlight night, with a cloudless sky. In the distance they could clearly see the Western Sacred Mountain, Hwa Shan. Sung Chiang saw that the town was well situated for defense, and was also well protected.

Wu Yung suggested that they should return to their headquarters, and discuss matters again. They all remounted, and rode off. Sung Chiang felt very depressed at the prospect. Wu Yung suggested that they should have scouts around the town to spy, and notice what was going on, and this was done.

Two days later one of these scouts arrived at Shao Hwa Shan, and reported that there was an official who was coming from the capital conveying a bell for the temple on the Western Sacred Mountain as offered by the emperor. He had crossed the Yellow River, and was now traveling along the Wei River towards Hwa Chou.

"Elder brother, do not be disappointed," said Wu Yung. "I think we can make something out of this." He then summoned Li Chun and Chang Shun, and told them his plans.

Li Chun, however, pointed out that they did not know the district well, and therefore must have a guide to go with them. Yang Chun offered to accompany them. This was agreed to, and the three men left the mountain.

The following day Sung Chiang with seven leaders and about five hundred men also left the mountain. Upon reaching the ferry across the Wei River they had got ten boats there, Wu Yung divided the leaders placing Hwa Jung and three others on the bank with the men, while Sung Chiang, Chu Tung, Li Ying, and himself were on the boats. Li Chun, Chang Shun, and Yang Chun were in hiding near the landing place. They waited there all that night, but early the next morning they heard the sound of gongs and drums, and soon an official boat hove in sight. It was flying a yellow flag on which was written that the official named Hsü was proceeding by Imperial Order to the Western Sacred Mountain to burn incense and offer sacrifices.

Li Ying and Chu Tung took their spears, and stood behind Sung Chiang, while Wu Yung sat on the bow of his boat. Their boats blocked the river so that the official's boat had to stop. The men on the boat shouted, "Who are you? How dare you obstruct the river, and delay a mandarin?"

Sung Chiang held out an official ivory tablet such as is used by men on imperial business, and bowed. Wu Yung on his boat called out, "The hero Sung Chiang from Liang Shan Po wishes to interview Mr. Hsü."

An officer came forward on the boat, and replied, "This is a boat conveying imperial envoy Hsü to the Western Sacred Mountain there to offer sacrifices and burn incense. How can you bandits stop our passage?"

Sung Chiang still retained his stooping posture, while Wu Yung spoke, "Our hero wishes to state a case to His Excellency."

The officer replied, "What kind of man are you? How dare you be so reckless as to wish to speak to His Excellency Hsü!" The men on both sides of him, however, asked the officer not to speak so loudly.

Sung Chiang still retained his attitude while Wu Yung spoke, "We request your official to disembark here, and we will discuss an important matter on the bank."

"Stupid talk! His Excellency is on imperial business. How can he talk with you?"

Sung Chiang now stood up and said, "If His Excellency will not meet me I am afraid that my men will startle him."

Chu Tung now took his spear at the top of which was a flag, and he waved this. Hwa Jung and the other leaders seeing this signal brought all their men to the river bank. The sailors on the boat seeing this took cover, and the officer went into the cabin, and reported the matter to His Excellency Hsü who came on deck and took his seat there.

Sung Chiang again saluted, "I am afraid that I have been very disrespectful."

"Why have you stopped my boat in this way?" asked His Excellency.

"We dare not hinder you," replied Sung Chiang, "but I request you to disembark here, when I will disclose an important matter."

"I am on a special mission from the emperor," said His Excellency Hsü, "and have nothing to say to you. How can a high dignitary do as you wish?"

"If Your Excellency will not disembark," said Wu Yung, "I am afraid that our men will come here to fetch you."

Li Ying now waved a flag at the top of his spear, and immediately Yang Chun, Li Chun, and Chang Shun rowed their boats towards the official boat. His Excellency was surprised at this. Li Chun and Chang Shun unsheathed their swords and as the boats got near they leapt across, seized two of the minor officers and threw them into the river.

"Don't do such silly things," called out Sung Chiang. "His Excellency will be upset."

Li Chun and Chang Shun upon hearing this dived into the water, rescued the two men, and brought them safely on to the boat again.

"You two go away as you have frightened His Excellency," said Sung Chiang. "We will talk matters over, and request His Excellency to disembark."

"Hero!" said His Excellency Hsü. "What have you to say? You can tell me here."

"This is not a place to discuss matters," said Wu Yung. "We should prefer that you come to our stronghold on the mountain. We have no bad intentions, and if we deceive you may the spirits of the Western Sacred Mountain punish us."

As His Excellency Hsü saw no way of escape, he left his boat and went up the river bank. A man came from the forest with a horse, and His Excellency Hsü mounted it. The leaders also mounted, and they all set off for Shao Hwa Shan. The incense, bell, etc. were taken off the official boat, and conveyed up the mountain. Li Chun and Chang Shun with about a hundred men were left in charge of the boats.

Upon reaching the stronghold the leaders assembled in the main hall on both sides with His Excellency Hsü in the seat of honor in the center. Sung Chiang gave four salutations to His Excellency, knelt down, and said, "Previously I was a clerk in the magistrate yamen at Yun Cheng Hsien, but I was persecuted, and compelled to escape to Liang Shan Po where I joined the heroes there. We are quite ready and willing to help the emperor when needed. Just now two of our leaders have been unjustly sent to prison by the prefect of Hwa Chou. We wish to borrow the incense, bell, etc. and so get entrance into the town. We will relieve you of all responsibility in this trick. We hope that you will agree to our proposal."

"If you use my things in this way," replied His Excellency Hsü, "I shall be blamed."

A GOLDEN BELL TRICK

"When you return to the capital you may throw all the blame on me," said Sung Chiang.

His Excellency Hsü glanced round at the armed bandit leaders, and saw that there was no means of escape so he agreed.

Sung Chiang again saluted, and offered wine to His Excellency. The leaders then exchanged clothing with His Excellency Hsü and his followers. When all had been satisfactorily arranged the bandits in their new disguise left the mountain, and embarked on the official boat. But instead of going towards Hwa Chou they proceeded towards the Western Sacred Mountain. Tai Tsung went in advance to the temple on the mountain, and informed the head priest of the arrival of an Imperial Commissioner. The priests came down the mountain, and met the boat upon arrival. The presents were carried in front, many being carried by the priests' servants to the temple. Wu Yung said that His Excellency had not been well on the journey so a closed sedan chair was provided in which the false commissioner was carried up the mountain. He was assisted out of the chair upon reaching the temple.

Wu Yung again spoke to the head priest, "We have brought many presents from the emperor which are for the spirits of this mountain. But how is it that the prefect of Hwa Chou is not here to receive us respectfully?"

"I will send a man to report your arrival," said the head priest, "and he will soon be here."

Soon after this, however, a deputy from the prefect arrived with about seventy soldiers, and much fruit and wine for the Imperial Commissioner.

The bandit who was acting the part of the Imperial Commissioner had certain likeness, but he had not the intelligence and learning, and therefore could not speak like an educated mandarin. Therefore he pretended to be sick so as to avoid conversation, and sat silently on the bed. But the prefect's deputy saw all the genuine imperial presents and the official dresses, and had no suspicion. When introduced to His Excellency, he could not hear what the false commissioner was saying. But Wu Yung asked why the prefect had not come personally, and the deputy explained how the brigands had been attacking the town, and how the prefect were afraid of leaving the town, and had sent him as deputy. He said, however, the prefect would come later on. The deputy then ordered wine to be served to all the men who had brought the presents.

Wu Yung went, and got the key, and opened the box containing the bell. He took the bell out, and hung it on a framework. It was made by the best workmen at the capital, and looked very fine with its precious stones inlaid. Underneath the bell was a lamp with a red silk shade. It was intended that this bell should be hung in front of the idol in the temple. It was a fine piece of craftsmanship such as only the emperor could obtain.

After inspection by the deputy and the priests Wu Yung locked it up again in the box. He then took out the official letters, and handing these to the deputy asked him to convey them to the prefect who could fix a lucky time for his visit to the temple to offer the sacrifices.

The deputy and his followers then took their leave and returned to Hwa Chou to report the matter to the prefect.

"What a cute plan," thought Sung Chiang. "The prefect is sure to be deceived." As there was nothing else to do he took a stroll round the temple admiring the building which really was of exceptional rarity and beauty. As he returned to the main hall he was informed that the prefect was coming. He told Hwa Jung, Hsu Ning, Chu Tung, and Li Ying (now dressed as imperial soldiers) to take up their positions on both sides of the hall, and four other leaders with Tai Tsung to take up their positions on both sides of the supposed Royal Commissioner.

The prefect brought with him about three hundred soldiers as an escort. They dismounted at the temple gate and entered. Sung Chiang and Wu Yung saw that all the men were armed so Wu Yung called out, "As an Imperial Commissioner is here these soldiers must not come inside." The soldiers therefore halted, and the prefect went forward by himself. Wu Yung then said, "His Excellency requests the prefect to go into his room for an interview." The prefect entered the room, and saluted the brigand on the bed in the disguise of an imperial commissioner.

"Prefect, are you not conscious of your fault?" asked Wu Yung.

"I did not know that His Excellency had arrived, and beg him to excuse me," replied the prefect. "After the first dispatch from the government about these presents I got no further dispatch as to when you would arrive."

"Seize him," ordered Wu Yung, and immediately the four leaders standing at the side unsheathed their swords, and seizing the prefect cut off his head.

"Proceed with your work," called out Sung Chiang, and immediately all his men attacked the prefect's escort. They were taken by surprise, and most of them were killed on the spot. Some tried to escape but were met at the gate by other bandits and were soon finished. Not a single man of the three hundred soldiers escaped death. Even civilians who had followed the soldiers to see the ceremony were also killed.

Sung Chiang had all the imperial presents transferred to the boat, and set off for the town. He saw that fire had broken out in several parts of the town, as his men had got inside. He himself went straight to the jail, and released Lu Ta and Shih Chin. Lu Ta got his priest's staff, and joined in the uprising. The daughter of Wang I had previously committed suicide by jumping into a well. The brigands secured much loot, and conveyed this on carts to their boats. When all was ready they returned to Shao Hwa Shan.

The offerings were duly handed over again to His Excellency Hsü. Sung Chiang also presented him with much gold and silver, and gave much also to his guard. After a feast His Excellency Hsü and his men went down the mountain, and again embarked on their boat.

His Excellency Hsü proceeded to Hwa Chou, and there he saw the enormous amount of damage that the bandits had done. He also went to the Western Sacred Mountain, and saw the large number of dead bodies lying about. He then got the recorder in the town to write a full account of the disaster, throwing the full blame on Sung Chiang and his brigands. He then returned to the capital to report the affair.

The bandits and leaders at Shao Hwa Shan agreed to join those under Sung Chiang at Liang Shan Po. They all left for that place where they celebrated their victory and alliance by the usual feast.

After this, however, there was a dinner provided by Shih Chin and three other leaders. At that dinner Ch'ao Kai spoke, "I have something to tell you about what happened while Sung Chiang and his men were at Hwa Chou. One day Chu Kwei came, and reported that at Mang Tan Shan in Hsuchow there are about three thousand brigands under the leadership of a man named Fan Jui, nicknamed the Devil of Disorder. He can control the wind and rain, and uses his men with great skill and strategy. He has two assistants—Hsiang Chung and Li Kun, who are famous for throwing swords which would kill men at a hundred paces. These three are sworn brothers, and they have the intention of attacking Liang Shan Po and getting control here. When I heard of this I was very angry."

Sung Chiang was also annoyed at this report and said, "How dare they be so impudent? I must go and setttle the matter."

At this point Shih Chin stood up and said, "We four brothers from Shao Hwa Shan have so far done no meritorious deed here, although we have been admitted to your band. We are willing to take our men to attack these robbers."

Sung Chiang was much pleased at this offer, and it was agreed to. The men and horses were got ready, and they left the mountain with Shih Chin, Chu Wu, Chen Ta, and Yang Chun.

It took them three days to reach Mang Tan Mountain. When Shih Chin saw the place he remembered that it was near there that Liu Pang of the Han dynasty had killed a snake. They soon reached the foot of the mountain, and an outpost went to report their arrival. Shih Chin arranged his men in ranks. He donned his armor, and rode to the front on a brown horse. He was armed with a sword with a double blade. He was accompanied by the other three leaders.

They had not waited long when they saw a large number of men descending the mountain with two leaders in front— Hsiang Chung and Li Kun. When they had arranged their men in ranks these two leaders without any parley rode forward to attack Shih Chin. They threw their flying swords, and Shih Chin found that he could not get near his two opponents so he gradually fell back. The other leaders also retreated about ten miles. Yang Chun's horse was wounded and abandoned. Half of their men had deserted. Shih Chin held a conference with his comrades, and they all agreed that help must be requested from Liang Shan Po. While they were talking, one of their scouts arrived, and reported that on the northern road there was a large body of cavalry coming towards them. Shih Chin galloped forward to see who they were, and recognized the flags of Liang Shan Po. In front rode Hwa Jung and Hsu Ning, and Shih Chin rode forward to meet them. He told them how Hsiang Chung, and Li Kun threw flying swords, and had driven him back without being able to even strike a blow. That day the Liang Shan Po forces encamped in the same spot with Shih Chin's forces.

The next morning they were all ready for marching forward when another scout arrived and reported that there was a large body of cavalry coming along the north road. Shih Chin and the other leaders rode forward to reconnoiter, and were pleased to find that they were about three thousand brigands under the leadership of Sung Chiang, Wu Yung, and Kung-Sun Sheng.

They then had a discussion, and Wu Yung was in favor of them remaining in camp that day. Sung Chiang was impatient, and wished an immediate attack. Kung-Sun Sheng pointed out that on the mountain there were blue lanterns and he thought that this indicated that the bandits there used magical spells. He advocated that they should withdraw all their men to some distance, and he would find a plan to capture the three leaders Hsiang Chung, Li Kun, and Fan Jui.

This was agreed to and all the men withdrew about six miles.

    The king of devils joins the bandits;
    The wounded chief surrenders to Liang Shan Po.

CHAPTER 59

KUNG-SUN SHENG CAPTURES A WIZARD; CH'AO KAI IS WOUNDED BY AN ARROW

KUNG-SUN SHENG explained his strategy. He said, "At the time when the Han dynasty was declining, General Chu-ko Liang worked out his plans by means of stones. He formed a square, and divided each side into two. Each of these eight sections had eight companies so that there were altogether sixty-four companies. His headquarter was in the middle of the square. There were four "heads" or advance companies, and they could turn either to right or left, and lead the whole square. The result was that the whole square moved as one body (like a tiger) just according to the conditions faced. When an enemy was approaching the two leading companies separated, and opened the square. When the enemy was inside the wings he was in the coils of an encircling snake. I will adopt the same method, and when our three opponents are in our midst they will find no means of escape. I will have a concealed pitfall ready, and we will slowly drive them towards it until they fall into it. There they can be easily arrested by men with hooked sticks."

Sung Chiang was pleased, and approved of the suggested plan. He issued orders placing Kung-Sun Sheng in charge of the forthcoming encounter, and dividing the bandits into eight parts.

The following day the brigands started on their march with much beating of drums and gongs, and when nearing Mang Tan Mountain they heard the sound of gongs. There were about three thousand bandits under the command of the three leaders. The two wings were in charge of Hsiang Chung and Li Kun, with Fan Jui in the center. Fan Jui was without any skill as a general, and depended on his black arts for success. Upon seeing the opposing large army from Liang Shan Po arrayed in the form of a square, he was quite pleased, and said to himself, "You (Sung Chiang) have arranged your men well, but you will soon be caught by my ruse. So he sent orders to the other two leaders on the wings that when a strong wind arose they must advance with five hundred men rushing forward with their swords. Those leaders upon receiving this order put on their shields, and armed themselves with spears and swords which could be hurled a long distance, and awaited the wind to be started by Fan Jui. The latter was seated on his black horse with a copper mace in his left hand, and with a sword in his right hand. He was muttering a spell, and then called out, "Quickly." Immediately a strong wind raged, hurling loose stones and sand about. The sky darkened, and the sunlight was obscured. Upon seeing this Hsiang Chung and Li Kun gave orders and their five hundred men rushed forward.

Upon seeing the enemy advancing, Sung Chiang gave the signal, and the front part of the square opened out on both sides. The five hundred men rushed into the square, and were fired upon from the remaining three sides with arrows. Most of them could not face this, and beat a hasty retreat. Only fifty men were left with the two leaders Hsiang Chung and Li Kun. They dashed first one way and then another without a way out, Kung-Sun Sheng standing on a high mound had controlled the wind, and wherever the two leaders went they found the fierce wind with them hindering their movements. The two leaders could not see their followers, and were nonplused by the wind and darkness. At last their horses fell into the hidden trap, and there they were seized by men with hooked sticks, who took them to the camp at the base.

Sung Chiang now dashed forward on his horse, and was followed by all his men. Fan Jui, seeing the advancing body of men, realized that his plan had failed, and at once retreated up the mountain with the remainder of his men— about half of the original force. Seeing this Sung Chiang gave orders for the pursuit to stop, and returned to the camp at the base with all his men.

Upon seeing the two prisoners he unloosened their bonds, and offered them wine saying, "I hope you two heroes will excuse me. This has happened only owing to our fighting in opposite forces. I hope that you will now join us at Liang Shan Po, and help us to seek justice. I am sorry that I have not had the opportunity before of meeting you and making this offer."

The two leaders kotowed and replied, "We have heard of your celebrated name for a long time, but we have not had the fortune of meeting you. We now know for certain that you are a very just person. Had we known before of your goodness we would not have been your opponents. To-day we are your prisoners, and expected to die, and never expected to be treated in this way. If you do not kill us we shall certainly be under a great obligation to you. As we have left Fan Jui, he will now be helpless without us, and if you would allow us to return we would explain to him who you really are, and probably get him also to join your force."

"I agree to your proposal," said Sung Chiang, "and both of you may go. I will trust you, and will expect you both to come here to-morrow, and report the result of your journey."

They both kotowed again, "We realize that you are really great. If Fan Jui will not listen to our pleadings, then we will seize him and bring him here by force."

Sung Chiang was very glad, and invited them to dine with him. He then gave them new clothes, good horses, and sent two men to accompany them on their trip. On their horses the two leaders meditated on Sung Chiang's generosity. Upon reaching Mang Tan Mountain the outposts were astonished upon seeing the return of their leaders, and sent the information up the mountain. Upon reaching the camp Fan Jui received them, and after explaining how they had been kindly treated by Sung Chiang and then released, Fan Jui agreed that they could no longer oppose "The Will of Heaven," but must go and join forces with such a just man.

The following day they set out for Sung Chiang's headquarters, where they were gladly welcomed. Their men and everything were duly brought to Liang Shan Po, and the two bands of bandits were now united.

On the day that Sung Chiang and the new adherents were arriving at Liang Shan Po, and were on the point of crossing the lake when a man saluted him. Upon being inquired for his name the man replied, "I am Tuan Ching-chu, but because of my light-colored hair the people call me 'Golden Haired Dog.' I am a Cho Chou man, and get a living by stealing horses. This spring I stole a horse at Chiang Kan Ridge, and it was pure white without a single hair of any other color. It was very swift, and was well known as Jade Lion. It previously belonged to a prince of the Tartars. I have heard of your great reputation so I decided to present it to you. On the way, however, I was attacked at the village Tseng T'ou Shih where the horse was taken from me. I told them that it was your horse, but they only cursed you so badly that I dare not to go into details. I came to inform you of the matter."

Sung Chiang saw from the man's appearance that he was not a ruffian, and replied, "As matters are like this I request you to come to our stronghold where we can discuss the case."

They then crossed the lake by a boat, and upon reaching the mountain all the leaders were summoned to attend the Assembly Hall where dinner was served. There Tuan Ching-chu again recited how the horse had been stolen, and Sung Chiang dispatched Tai Tsung, the Flying Prince, to the village Tseng T'ou Shih to find out where the horse was. Within five days Tai Tsung returned, and reported that in the village there were about seven thousand strength with many horses and about fifty carts. The headman named Tseng was a Tartar, and he had five sons. They had great influence there, and would not allow any opponent to exist. They declared they would crush Liang Shan Po. The stolen horse was now in the possession of a drill teacher there named Shih Wen-kung. There was a very detestable poem recited on the streets of that village. It was as follows:

> Startle all the spirits,
>   Capture all the brigands;
> Arrest Ch'ao Kai and Sung Chiang,
>   Put them all in prison.

> Strong and mighty are we,
>   Tseng has many tigers;
> They are known throughout the empire,
>   There are none their equal.

"There is not a single person who does not sing that, and I found it unbearable."

Ch'ao Kai was very angry and said, "Those animals have no sense of decency. I must go myself. If I do not capture them I shall not return. I only want five thousand men, and about twenty leaders to accompany me. The others will stop here under Sung Chiang to guard our stronghold."

That day Ch'ao Kai selected his twenty leaders, and they left the mountain with their men divided into three contingents. Sung Chiang and the other leaders descended the mountain, and while they were drinking a parting cup there arose a strong wind which blew Ch'ao Kai's flag pole into two parts. When they saw this they were all astounded.

Wu Yung remonstrated with Ch'ao Kai. "It is evident that the wind disapproves of our military preparations, and I therefore think that it would be better to delay our expedition for some time."

"It is nothing unusual for the wind to do such a thing," said Ch'ao Kai. "The weather is favorable, and if we do not go now it will only enable them to prepare their defenses, and that might lead to our defeat. I ask you not to obstruct me in this matter as I intend to proceed at all costs."

Wu Yung saw that it would be useless to urge delay, and Ch'ao Kai ordered his troops to cross the lake. Sung Chiang and his men returned to the mountain, but Tai Tsung was dispatched to watch the proceedings and report results.

Ch'ao Kai and his men duly reached the vicinity of the village of Tseng T'ou Shih without any trouble, and encamped there. The following day he and the leaders mounted their horses and went to survey the land. They had stopped at a certain place, and while looking round they saw a large body of men emerge from a forest. In front of them rode a man who was Tseng Kwei, the fourth son of the head Tartar of the village. When he got near he shouted, "You brigands are from Liang Shan Po, and are outlaws. For a long time I have the idea to capture you, and now Heaven has given me that opportunity. You had better dismount at once, and become my prisoners."

Ch'ao Kai was highly provoked at this insolent speech, but

before he could reply one of his leaders dashed past him on horseback. It was Lin Ch'ung, the Leopard's Head. He engaged with Tseng Kwei for about twenty bouts, and then the latter realized that he had an opponent whom he could not overcome so he withdrew to the forest. Lin Ch'ung did not pursue him.

Ch'ao Kai ordered that his fellow leaders should return to camp where they held a meeting to discuss matters. Lin Ch'ung suggested that they should attack the village the following day, and then they would see how the enemy fought. This was agreed to, and the next morning their five thousand men took up their position on an open ground in front of the entrance to the village. Soon they heard the guns in the village fired, and a large number of men emerged from the village, led by seven men on horseback. These leaders wore mail armor. In the center was Shih Wen-kung, the teacher, riding the stolen white horse, and armed with a halberd, and bow and arrows. A drum was beaten three times, and at this signal the villagers opened their ranks to allow several prisoner's carts to pass through. (These were fashioned with dragon's heads in front.) Pointing to the carts one of the seven leaders, Tseng Tu, shouted, "You rebels! Do you see these carts? We do not wish to kill you, but only take you alive as prisoners so that we can send you to the Eastern Capital. That is how we, the Five Dragons, wish to display our skill. You had better submit at once."

Upon hearing this Ch'ao Kai was very angry, and dashed forward. He was immediately followed by all his twenty leaders and the whole of their men. The two armies met, and a fierce struggle ensued. The villagers could not repulse the attack, and slowly fell back towards their village. Lin Ch'ung and Hu Yen-shao saw that the ground near the village was uneven, and suspecting a trap they ordered a general retreat. On both sides there had been many casualties.

Upon reaching their camp Ch'ao Kai felt very sad, but his leaders said, "Brother, set your mind at ease, and do not grieve too much about our many losses to-day. You must not forget that our brother Sung Chiang have had many defeats. We shall be victorious before we go back."

But Ch'ao Kai still remained depressed.

For the next three days the brigands challenged the village to fight, but the villagers did not show themselves. But on the fourth day two priests came to Ch'ao Kai's camp, where they said, "We are from the Fa Hwa Temple to the east of the village of Tseng T'ou Shih here. We have been frequently disturbed by the Five Tigers, sons of the Tseng family, who have demanded money from us. We know all their defenses, and are willing to show them to you so that you will relieve us of their trouble."

Ch'ao Kai was pleased to hear this, and invited them to be seated and take refreshments. But Lin Ch'ung exhorted Ch'ao Kai, "Do not listen to these men, as this may be only a plot."

"I think we can depend upon them as they are both priests," replied Ch'ao Kai. "We men of Liang Shan Po are always willing to assist people in distress, and now that we are here, we must not miss this opportunity. These priests have no grudge against us, so why should they try to deceive us? You should not be so suspicious, and hinder our affairs. There is no reason why we should not win the next time. This evening we must try again."

"As you have decided to do so," said Lin Ch'ung, "let us divide our men in half, and I will take one half into the village, while you remain in charge of the other half outside."

"If I do not go into the village I am afraid our men will hold back," replied Ch'ao Kai. "You had better take charge of our men outside the village."

"Whom do you want to accompany you?" asked Lin Ch'ung.

"I want ten leaders and two thousand five hundred men." He then named the ten leaders.

This was agreed to, and after the evening meal they set out. No bells were allowed on the horses, and each man carried a gag in his mouth so that nobody should utter a word. It was growing dark, and they followed the two priests to the Fa Hwa Temple outside the village. Ch'ao Kai saw that it was a very old temple. He dismounted, and entering the building saw that there was nobody inside. So he asked the priests how it was that the place was so empty. The priests replied that most of the priests had long since left the temple on account of the trouble caused by the Tseng family. There was only the abbot left, with a few acolytes, and they lived in the room near the pagoda. They said that Ch'ao Kai and his men had better stay there till the third watch (11 a.m.) when the priests would take them to the village.

"Where is the stronghold of the village?" asked Ch'ao Kai.

"There are four camps in the village, and the Tseng brothers are in the northern one. If you can get the northern camp the others will give no trouble," replied the priest.

"At what time can we go?" asked Ch'ao Kai.

"Just now is about the second watch (9 p.m.), and it would be better to go about 11 p.m."

Just then the drums in the village signaled the time as the second watch. But after some time the drums were not beaten again, and the priests thought that that watchmen had gone to sleep. So they decided to start off at once, and the priests led the way. Ch'ao Kai gave the order for an advance, and his leaders and their men silently followed him. They had gone about two miles when Ch'ao Kai missed the two priests who had been acting as guides. So a halt was called. They searched all around in the dark, but could not find the road. There were no houses there. The men were getting nervous so Huyen Sho shouted an order for a general retreat. They had only gone about a hundred steps when they heard drums beaten on all sides around them in the dark. Soon there were sounds of men shouting, and torches were lit all around them. Ch'ao Kai and his men had not gone much farther when they met a body of men who discharged arrows at them. One of these hit Ch'ao Kai in the face, and he fell off his horse. Five of the leaders lifted Ch'ao Kai on to his horse again, and retreated. Lin Ch'ung who had half the men in reserve saw the light, and heard the drums, and at once ordered an advance of his men. The fight continued during the night. Orders were not given for a general retreat to their camp until daybreak.

In camp Ch'ao Kai was bleeding badly from the wound in his face, and Lin Ch'ung applied a medicine to the wound. They examined the arrow, and found on it the name of Shih Wen-kung. They did not notice however that it was a poisonous arrow. A cart was obtained, and in this Ch'ao Kai was sent back to Liang Shan Po with an escort.

The leaders left behind held a conference. The general opinion was that the mishap to Ch'ao Kai's flag when they started on the expedition was an omen, and now that Ch'ao Kai was wounded they had better stop operations against the village and wait until Sung Chiang's order for withdrawal. They were still in a nervous condition when a scout arrived, and reported that a large body of men with numerous torches was advancing towards the camp by five different roads. Upon going outside they saw torch-lights on the hills all around their camp. Lin Ch'ung suggested that they must not fight again in the dark, and this being agreed to, orders were issued for camp to be struck, and an orderly retreat to be undertaken. As the opposing army came up a general rear-guard fight took place as the bandits retreated step by step. They retreated about twenty miles before the army of the Tsengs stopped pursuit. Now the leaders saw that they had only about six hundred men left, all the rest having been captured, wounded or killed. They went on towards Liang Shan Po where they duly arrived.

There they found that Ch'ao Kai was much worse, his body having swollen considerably, and he was no longer capable of either eating or drinking. Sung Chiang stayed by the bedside attending to his chief, and about midnight the latter spoke, "Do not be surprised at what I am going to say. I wish that the person who captures the man who shot me with that arrow, should become chieftain of our men in my place." As soon as he had said this he died. All the leaders heard Ch'ao Kai's will. After Ch'ao Kai's death the leaders decided to ask Sung Chiang to become their chieftain. A general meeting took place in the General Assembly Hall with Lin Ch'ung in the chair. He opened the proceeding, "In the state and family a single day cannot pass without an emperor or master respectively. Ch'ao Kai has gone to Heaven, so that our affairs are now without a chieftain. We think that you, our elder brother, Sung Chiang, should now fill the vacant position, and as to-morrow is a lucky day we propose to install you as our chieftain."

Sung Chiang replied, "Upon his death-bed our chieftain Ch'ao Kai told me that he wished the post be given to the man who would capture Shih Wen-kung. The death-dealing arrow is still there so how can we forget his dying command? We have not yet avenged the injury so how can we make any other arrangement?"

"Nobody has yet captured the enemy and carried out Ch'ao Kai's command," said Wu Yung, "but still we cannot remain any longer without a chieftain. There is nobody here equal to you so we cannot appoint anyone else. We are all intimately known to you, and nobody would object to your order. We request you to occupy the post at least temporarily, and we can talk the matter over again at some future date."

"Your arguments are well reasoned," replied Sung Chiang, "and I will agree to your proposal. But should any one of you capture Shih Wen-kung that man must be our chieftain."

"Elder brother," interposed Li K'wei, "you need not talk of being chieftain here, because you would like to be emperor of the Sung dynasty if you could."

Sung Chiang was angry and said, "If you talk of that again I shall have your tongue cut off."

"I did not ask you refuse to be our chieftain," replied Li K'wei. "I said you would be an emperor and yet you want to cut off my tongue!"

"This man does not understand how affairs should be conducted," said Wu Yung. "We need not regard his saying, but proceed with our business."

Wu Yung and Lin Ch'ung stepped forward, and assisted Sung Chiang to the chair placed in the central position, and there he took his seat.

The leaders on both sides saluted their new chieftain, and then also took their seats.

Sung Chiang spoke, "To-day I temporarily occupy this position, and beg for your support. We must be united, and work together as one body. We have all been appointed our work by Heaven. Now our forces are very great, and I propose to divide same into six parts so that we can live in six strongholds. I propose to rename this hall as the Loyalty and Justice Hall. On the four sides of it will be four big fortresses. Behind it will be two small fortresses. In front will be three strategic barriers with a fortress on the lake and two fortresses on the shores." He then divided the leaders into six parts, and gave them their respective new positions. Everything worked smoothly under the new arrangements, and during the hundred days of mourning for Ch'ao Kai all new buildings were completed.

One day a traveling priest was passing near Liang Shan Po, and the leaders asked him to stay at their stronghold and assist in the funeral prayers for Ch'ao Kai. His name was Ta Yuan, and he came from the Dragon Flowery Temple in the Northern Capital, Ta Ming Fu. One day Sung Chiang asked him for the news of the Northern Capital, and in reply the priest said, "Sir, have you not heard about the Jeweled Chilin at the Northern Capital?"

"I am so forgetful of affairs," replied Sung Chiang. "It is true that in Ta Ming Fu there is an official named Lu Tsun-i who has a nickname, Jeweled Chilin. He has a very good reputation. His military skill is good, and in use of spear is unexcelled in the empire. If we could get him to join us I should feel satisfied."

Wu Yung laughed at this and said, "Elder brother, how is it that you have not more confidence in your present staff? If however you want him here it is easy to get him to come."

"He is the leading literary scholar of the Northern Capital," replied Sung Chiang. "How can we induce him to come here?"

"I often thought of bringing him here," said Wu Yung, "but owing to other affairs I forgot about him. I will find a means of getting him to join us."

"Your reputation as a Clever Star rests upon a firm foundation," said Sung Chiang. "But how can you induce him to join us here?"

Wu Yung then explained his plans in detail.

>   A hero leaves his comforts,
>   Meets dangers face to face.

CHAPTER 60

WU YUNG SCHEMES TO GET HOLD OF THE JEWELED CHILIN; CHANG SHUN UPSETS A BOAT AT GOLDEN SAND BANK

"I rely on my small tongue," said Wu Yung, "to go to the Northern Capital and get the Jeweled Chilin to join us here just as easily as I take an article out of my pocket. But it would be necessary that a man of strange appearance should accompany me there."

Li K'wei heard this, and said, "Elder brother, I am willing to go with you."

"You keep quiet," said Sung Chiang. "I shall need you if there is any incendiarism, murder, looting, to be done. But this requires artfulness, and your nature is not suitable for such work."

"But am I not an ugly strange person?" said Li K'wei. "Why not make use of my strange appearance?"

"I do not dislike you," said Sung Chiang, "but if you go to the Northern Capital and they found out your name, your life would be in danger."

"Never mind that," said Li K'wei, "I think that Wu Yung will see that I am suitable."

"You must listen to my three conditions," said Wu Yung. "If you do not agree to them then you must stay here."

"Three conditions will not stop me," replied Li K'wei. "If there were thirty conditions I would agree to them."

"The first condition," said Wu Yung, "is that you should abstain from wine because when you take it you have a violent temper. Second condition, you must dress as a Taoist acolyte, and obey my orders implicitly. The third is difficulty. From to-morrow you must not speak a single word, but act like a dumb person. If you will observe these three conditions you may go with me."

"The first two I can observe, but the third is very hard," said Li K'wei.

"If you open your mouth mischief is bound to happen," said Wu Yung.

"I shall have to do it," said Li K'wei. "I can keep my mouth closed by having a copper cash on my tongue."

There was general laughter at this. It was agreed to let Li K'wei go, and that evening a farewell banquet was held in the Loyalty and Justice Hall.

Early the next morning Li donned the priest garb, and left the mountain with Wu Yung. For five days these two traveled along the road to the Northern Capital, Ta Ming Fu, and rested each night at inns on the way. Li K'wei kept his word, but found it very difficult at times to keep quiet when he had lost his temper. Upon reaching the capital they stayed at an inn, and one evening when Li K'wei was in the kitchen cooking food he lost his temper and struck one of the servants. The servant went and complained to Wu Yung of this. Wu Yung offered apologies, and gave the servant ten strings of cash in compensation.

The next morning after breakfast Wu Yung called Li K'wei and said, "You have begun to annoy me with your temper. Let us have no more of this. To-day you must accompany me and keep out of mischief. If there is any trouble to-day you may endanger my life. I will now give you a secret signal. When I wag my head you must not move."

They both then left the inn and went into the city. Wu Yung was dressed as a priest, and carried a small bell; Li K'wei was dressed as an acolyte, and carried a stick over his shoulder to which was attached a piece of paper with a text written on it, "Tell fortunes, and give advice on any matter for one ounce of silver."

At that time there were many soldiers in Ta Ming Fu because in the country around were many bandits and thieves. It was also the headquarters of Grand Secretary Liang, the commander in chief of the armies north of the Huang Ho. Wu Yang and Li K'wei came to the city gate where there was an officer of the guard. Wu Yang saluted him, and the officer asked, "Sir, where are you from?"

"My name is Chang Yung," replied Wu Yung, "and this is my assistant named Li. I am a fortune teller."

An inspector of passports was looking at Wu Yung's paper, when a soldier remarked, "This acolyte has the appearance of a thief." Li K'wei was angry and would have hit the fellow, but Wu Yung wagged his head, and so Li K'wei curbed his temper and hung down his head.

Wu Yung offered apologies for his assistant's quick temper, and then all being in order they went their way. As he went along the street Wu Yung rattled his bell and sang a ballad:

> Kan Lu a mandarin, when young
>   Tsu Ya when old;
> Unlucky Yen Hui died in youth,
>   Peng Tzu when old;
> Fan Tan was always poor from birth,
>   Shih Chung was rich.
>
> Some men just prosper, smiling,
>   Seem destined for the best of fate;
> For others, graves are yawning,
>   Unlucky and unfortunate.
>
> From me nothing is hidden,
>   Of life and death or poverty;
> Beware of fatal omen,
>   Consult me now, avoid delay.

Having finished this he rang his bell again. He was soon followed by a crowd of boys who laughed at him. When he reached Lu Tsun-i's house he walked backwards and forwards there, singing the funny song, and ringing his bell, and being ridiculed by the crowd of boys.

Lu Tsun-i heard the noise, and asked a servant what it was about.

"It is very funny!" said the servant. "There is a fortune teller who asks for an ounce of silver to tell one's horoscope. He is accompanied by a strange-looking acolyte who is very uncouth, and his antics amuse the people."

"As he asks for so much he must be a well-educated man," said Lu Tsun-i. "You go and ask him to come here."

The servant went and asked Wu Yung to come to his master. "What is your master's name?" asked Wu Yung. The servant told him, and then Wu Yung agreed to go. Upon reaching the room the servant gave Li K'wei a chair on the veranda and asked him to wait there. He then lifted the door curtain, and showed in Wu Yung who saluted Lu Tsun-i.

"What is your honorable village and name?" asked Lu Tsun-i.

"I am Chang Yung, and my nickname is Heaven's Mouth, and I am a Shantung man. I am familiar with the book on 'Nativity and Fate,' and can foretell the future. My fee is one ounce of silver."

Lu Tsun-i asked him to enter a smaller room at the back, and there sat down.

The host ordered tea, and also an ounce of silver to be given to Wu Yung. He then asked Wu Yung to tell his fortune.

Wu Yung asked for the date, hour, etc. of his birth, but Lu Tsun-i said he did not want to know much of his good fortune but whether any mishap would happen to him. "This year I am thirty-two years old, and was born in the last month of the year."

Wu Yung shook his box, and throwing out the cash exclaimed, "How strange!"

Lu Tsun-i was startled and asked, "Is it auspicious or inauspicious?"

"I cannot be straight with you," replied Wu Yung, "because you would not like it."

"If I have gone astray I hope that you will tell me," said Lu Tsun-i, "and never mind what I say."

"In the near future," said Wu Yung, "you will meet some bloody disaster, and you will be killed. Your family possessions will all be lost."

Lu Tsun-i laughed at this and said, "I am afraid that you have made a mistake. I was born in this town, and have always had plenty of money. In our family we have never had a lawbreaker, nor have we had a criminal. Our women-folk have always been chaste. Moreover my affairs have always been well done; nothing irregular, and no ill-gotten gain. How could I now get into some bloody disaster?"

Wu Yung changed his countenance, handed back the money he had received, and said, "Everywhere people like to be flattered. Enough! I speak the truth and yet my words are taken in an ill purpose. I must go now."

"Do not be annoyed at what I said," replied Lu Tsun-i. "I was only jesting. Please tell me exactly what you think will happen."

"It is always hard to believe unpleasant truths," said Wu Yung.

"I ask you to conceal nothing from me, and I will hear the worst," said Lu Tsun-i.

"Your fate has been propitious up to now," said Wu Yung, "but this year there will be a change for the worst. Within a hundred days your body will lose its head. Your fate has been fixed by Heaven, and there is no way of escape."

"Is it not possible to avoid this trouble?" asked Lu Tsun-i.

Wu Yung again shook the cash in his box, and throwing them out examined them with apparently great care. He said, "It appears that if you went from here about three hundred miles to the southeast you might get out of the reach of this coming disaster. You might still have some trouble there, but it would not be so serious."

"If you help me to escape this coming disaster I will recompense you liberally," said Lu Tsun-i.

"I will express your fate in four lines of poetry which you may write down on the wall," said Wu Yung, "and when things happen to you, you will realize the accuracy of my prognostication."

Lu Tsun-i summoned a servant to get a writing brush, and wrote on the white wall of the room the following stanzas as Wu Yung dictated:

> On bank a gallant hero strolls,
>   His boat is hidden in the reeds;
> The end is destined by fate
>   No sorrow if he takes rest.

After Lu Tsun-i had written this Wu Yung picked up his box and was about to depart but Lu Tsun-i requested him to wait a little. Wu Yung, however, said he had some business to attend to, but he would come again some other day. Lu Tsun-i accompanied him to the door, and both Wu Yung and Li K'wei departed. Upon reaching the inn they packed up their baggage, paid their bills, and left at once. When they were on the road again, Wu Yung said, "That business is finished. We can now quickly go back to Liang Shan Po, and await there for the arrival of Lu Tsun-i."

When Wu Yung had left, Lu Tsun-i kept going over what he had said. He kept looking at the sky and was restless. One day he sent for all his employees to discuss matters. His chief steward was named Li Ku, and was a Tung Ching (Eastern Capital) man. Previously he had come to the Northern Capital to see a friend, but as that man had left he found himself stranded. One winter day he was starving, and Lu Tsun-i saw him, and took pity on him, and gave him employment. He had proved his abilities in his work, and very soon he was promoted. Step by step he had become chief steward, and managed all the affairs of the estate. Under him were about fifty servants.

When all the employees had assembled Lu Tsun-i did not notice another confident steward so he asked where he was. Just as he spoke a big man presented himself. He was about twenty-five years of age, but had a moustache. He had broad shoulders, but a slim waist. He wore a white silk gown, and had a hat shaped like a melon. He had a red decorated belt, and wore yellow leather boots. A metal ring was hanging at the back of his head, and a flower was stuck in the side of his hat. He was a native of the town, and had been succored by Lu Tsun-i as he had neither father nor mother. His skin was quite white, and had been tattooed all over with numerous designs. He played well on the flute and the guitar, and was also good at singing and acting. In fact there was hardly anything he could not do, and do well. He knew all dialects, and spoke them fluently. He also knew the expressions used in every trade and profession. A skilled archer and good at all games, he was always a successful champion in whatever he took up. His name was Yen Ch'ing, and he was known by his nickname Beau. He was the confident of his master Lu Tsun-i. It was he who now entered the room along with Li Ku, the steward.

When he saw them enter Lu Tsun-i spoke, "The other day I had my fortune told, and within a hundred days I shall meet a bloody disaster. In order to avoid that fate I must go about three hundred miles to the southeast. The likely place I know is Tai Shan in Tai An Chou, Shantung, where there is a temple dedicated to the Supreme God, who controls the births, deaths, and calamities of the people. I will go there and offer incense to redeem my sins. I can take refuge there until this threatening danger has passed by. While there I can buy and sell things, and also see the views. Li Ku, I want you to get ten carts for me, and load them with suitable goods for sale there. You can accompany me on this trip. You can hand over to-day all my household affairs to Yen Ch'ing who will take your place. I want to start in three days from now."

"Sir, I am afraid that you are making a mistake," replied Li Ku. "There is a saying, 'Divinations can be forged in any form.' You better not believe what fortune tellers say. If you remain here there will be no fear of any danger."

"My life is decided by fate," said Lu Tsun-i. "Do not hinder my movements, because if the calamity happened it would be too late for regret."

"Sir, will you please listen to me," interposed Yen Ch'ing. "If you go to Tai Shan you must pass close to Liang Shan Po, and there the brigands are very powerful under a leader named Sung Chiang. Soldiers have failed to suppress the brigands. If you must go to offer incense at Tai Shan, it would be better if you waited here until the affairs in that quarter are more settled. You need not believe what that fortune teller told you. It may be that he was sent by the brigands to delude you, and so get you into their net. I am sorry that the other day I was not here and did not see the man. I could have found out his game after asking him a few questions."

"Do not talk nonsense," said Lu Tsun-i. "Who can cheat me? I do not care a rap for those fellows at Liang Shan Po because they are hardly worth a straw, and I myself could easily arrest them. Since my youth I have practiced all kinds of military drill, and am well known everywhere as a skilled fighter."

When he had finished speaking his wife came from behind the screen and said to him: "Husband, I have been listening to all you have said. There is an ancient saying, 'One mile away from home, and things are not like home.' Do not listen to what the fortune teller said. Stay at home and look after our own affairs instead of going to places where you will meet with danger. It would be better to prepare another room where you can purify your heart and diminish the passion. Live there in solitude and nothing will of course happen to you."

"You woman do not understand affairs," replied Lu Tsun-i. "I have decided what I must do, and it is useless for you to interfere."

"I will go with you. I will not boast of my skill," said Yen Ch'ing, "but if on the way we are attacked by brigands I will stand by you. I can defeat fifty such men myself."

"I do not understand trading matters," said Lu Tsun-i, "and that is why I want Li Ku to accompany me. You can stay behind and take care of the house."

"In the last few days I have been suffering from some foot trouble," said Li Ku, "and I cannot very well go with you."

Lu Tsun-i was angry at this, and said, "'Maintain troops for a thousand days, and use them only one day,' I want you to accompany me, and yet you offer excuses. If anyone places obstacles in my way I shall have to land out with my fist."

Li Ku was afraid, and looked helplessly at the wife who seeing the position withdrew behind the screen. Yen Ch'ing even did not care to say another word. All the servants took their leave. Li Ku smothered his annoyance, and left the room to make arrangements for the journey. He got ten carts and fifty men to pull them.

Three days later all was ready, and after sacrificing to the home gods they took leave of all the household who assembled to see them off. After the first day Lu Tsun-i arranged for Li Ku and two men to go in advance, and make arrangements for the party to stay in the inns.

On the journey Lu Tsun-i enjoyed the scenery and the pleasure of traveling. He said that if he had stayed at home he would have missed all this.

They had traveled for several days without any untoward incident happening. One morning, however, as they were about to leave, a waiter of the inn spoke to Lu Tsun-i, "Sir, I have something to tell you. You are only seven miles from Liang Shan Po, and your road will take you close to that place. The chieftain of the brigands there is Sung Chiang, and though he does not wish to injure travelers yet you must go quietly on your way without any anxiety."

Upon hearing this Lu Tsun-i had a box unlocked, and taking out four white flags wrote seven characters on each, "The Generous Lu Tsun-i of the Northern Capital." He then displayed these on sticks, and stuck them on the carts. His men upon seeing these flags were downcast as they were afraid. The inn waiter also was surprised and asked, "Are you a relative of Sung Chiang at Liang Shan Po?"

"No!" replied Lu Tsun-i, "I am a wealthy man from the Northern Capital; I come here to capture that fellow."

"Don't speak so loudly here," said the waiter, "because I do not want to be implicated in your affairs. I am not joking. If you had a thousand men with you, you could not capture any brigands here."

"Shut up!" said Lu Tsun-i, "I expect that you are in league with them."

The waiter covered his ears and ran away. Lu Tsun-i's men were now almost frightened out of their wits. Li Ku knelt down, and said, "Master, have pity on us. If you would let us go home alive, it will be very kind of you."

"What are you talking about!" said Lu Tsun-i. "Should an eagle be afraid of a sparrow? I have been well trained in physical drill since my youth, and I have never yet met a man who could defeat me. To-day I shall perhaps have an opportunity of showing off my skill. I have placed on the top of that cart a sack of ropes. While I kill the men with swords you can pick them up and bind them on the barrows. Then we can cart them off to the capital, and the emperor will reward us for our enterprise. If any of you are unwilling to go with me I will kill you on the spot."

Without any further objection all the carts moved forward, but the men were very mortified at being forced to go. Lu Tsun-i tied his sword to one of the flag sticks on a cart. As they approached Liang Shan Po the road became steeper, and the men took each step with fear. Lu Tsun-i urged them forward.

About 10 a.m. they saw in the distance a forest in which were monstrous trees. As they got near the forest they heard a whistle. Li Ku and two men were in front as usual, and upon hearing this they looked round for a hiding place. Lu Tsun-i gave orders for the carts to be placed at one side of the road. This was done, and the men took cover under the carts. Lu Tsun-i shouted out, "As I capture these brigands I want you to bind them with the ropes." As he was saying this he saw about five hundred men coming round the corner of the forest. Many gongs were also sounding behind him, and turning round he saw another body of five hundred men also approaching. A shell in the forest was fired off, and at the same time a man leapt out of the forest close to him. The man carried an ax in each hand, and shouted, "Do you recognize the fortune teller's acolyte?"

Lu Tsun-i was startled. He replied, "I have always had a desire to capture you brigands, so I intentionally come here to meet you. Tell Sung Chiang to come here at once, and pay respects to me. If he delays his arrival I shall kill the whole lot of you."

Li K'wei laughed at this and said, "Sir, our fortune teller predicted that you would be in danger, so I request that you come and join us as a leader."

Lu Tsun-i was angry at this, and seizing his sword advanced. Li K'wei did the same, holding his two axes aloft. After three bouts of fighting, however, Li K'wei jumped apart, and retreated to the forest. Lu Tsun-i followed him, but Li K'wei hid himself from place to place as Lu Tsun-i came near. At last Li K'wei saw a chance, and escaped entirely into the forest. Lu Tsun-i looked round, but could not see a single man near that spot. As he was returning, however, he heard men behind him, and someone called out, "You need not go away. You surely will recognize me."

Lu Tsun-i looked round, and saw a big priest with a large iron staff in his hand. "Where are you from?" he asked.

The priest (Lu Ta) laughed and replied, "I am the priest Lu Ta. I have been instructed to come and request you to take refuge at our stronghold."

Lu Tsun-i was more angry still and cursed, "You baldheaded donkey! How dare you talk in this impudent way!" He then advanced with his sword in hand, and Lu Ta stood on defense ready to receive the attack. After three bouts, however, Lu Ta ran away with Lu Tsun-i in pursuit. They had not gone far when Wu Sung armed with two swords stepped out of the trees, and faced Lu Tsun-i. He said, "Sir, if you will follow me there will be no bloody disaster."

But Lu Tsun-i would not listen to this, and attacked Wu Sung. After three bouts, however, Wu Sung also ran away.

Lu Tsun-i laughed at this, and called out, "I am not going to run after you, because evidently you fellows are of no importance."

He had hardly finished saying this when he saw a man at the foot of the hill who called out to him, "Lu Tsun-i, you need not boast! Have you not heard of the saying, 'Man fears falling into a trap; iron fears being cast into the fire.' Our commander-in-chief has a plot, and however you try to get away where there is no means of escape."

"Who are you, fellow?" shouted out Lu Tsun-i.

The man laughed and replied, "I am Liu Tang, the Red Haired Devil."

Lu Tsun-i reviled him, "You little thief! Don't you also run away." He advanced and fought three bouts with Liu Tang who was then joined by another brigand, Mu Heng, the Invulnerable One, and they both attacked Lu Tsun-i. But after three bouts another voice was heard, and these two withdrew a few steps. Turning round Lu Tsun-i found his third opponent, Li Ying, the Striking Hawk. He was now almost surrounded, but as he advanced each man retreated in turn. He did not pursue them as he was feeling quite warm, but returned to the spot where he had left his men, and the ten handcarts, but there was not a single one left. He therefore climbed a small eminence, and looked all round. In the distance he saw both his carts and men in charge of a party of brigands. His steward Li Ku was bound with ropes. Lu Tsun-i was extremely annoyed at this, and seizing his sword he started off to try to catch up with them. On his way, however, he met two leaders of the brigands who shouted, "Where are you going?" One was Chu Tung, the Beautiful Whiskers, and the other was Lei Heng, the Winged Tiger.

"You brigands!" replied Lu Tsun-i, "go at once, and return me those carts and men."

Chu Tung stroked his beard, and with a smile replied, "Do you not understand yet? Our wise leader has often said, 'In our galaxy of stars, some come, but none go!' As you cannot get away from here you better join us as a leader."

Lu Tsun-i was again angry, and advanced to attack them. They fought for about three bouts, and then the two leaders retired. When he saw this Lu Tsun-i thonght that he must pursue them before he could get back his carts and men. But as he ran round the hill, his two opponents had disappeared. Up the hill, a number of drums were beating, and looking there he saw a yellow flag bearing four characters, "Executor of Heaven's Wish." Under a large red silk umbrella stood Sung Chiang with Wu Yung and Kung-Sun Sheng on either side. Behind them stood about seventy leaders who all saluted him, and called, "Sir, how are you?"

Lu Tsun-i paid no attention to this and simply cursed them.

"Sir, do not be angry," interposed Wu Yung. "Our commander Sung Chiang has wished to meet you for a long time, and he sent me to your house to get you to come to our mountain. He wants you to join us here and not remain an outsider."

Lu Tsun-i replied, "You are only brigands, and how dare you try to deceive me!"

Hwa Jung fixed an arrow in his bow, and called out, "Lu Tsun-i, don't be too confident in your skill, just watch my arrow." He then shot the arrow which took the red tassel off Lu Tsun-i's cap. Lu Tsun-i was startled, and beat a retreat down the mountain. He saw thousands of men to the east and west, so he went towards the north. It was now evening, and he felt both tired and hungry. Mists were covering the ground, and there was no moonlight. He could not find even a small path in the increasing darkness. He tried several times, but was always forced to stop by some obstacle. He soon found himself in tall reeds, with water on all sides. He stopped, and gazing towards Heaven he said, "Because I would not listen to advice, so now I am in trouble." While in this flight he saw a fisherman rowing a boat among the reeds. The man called out to him,

"How brave you are! This is close to Liang Shan Po, and it is now nearly midnight. Why have come to such a place?"

"I have lost my way," said Lu Tsun-i, "and cannot find a resting place. Please help me."

"There is a market village about ten miles from here," replied the fisherman, "but the road is hard to follow unless you have been that way before. You could, however, get there easily by boat, and that way would only be about two miles. If you will pay me ten strings of cash I will take you there on my boat."

"If you will convey me there," said Lu Tsun-i, "and find me an inn, I will pay you liberally."

The fisherman brought his boat to the side, Lu Tsun-i stepped on board, and the man pushed off. They had gone about two miles when they heard another boat approaching. On that boat they soon saw two men, one of whom was stripped naked, and was punting the boat along with a pole. The other man at the stern was sculling. The first named man was singing:

> For books a hero has no need,
> As brigand bold his life's secured;
> With crossbow tiger fierce is shot,
> By baited hook the fish is lured.

Lu Tsun-i was afraid, and dared not utter a sound. He just then saw another boat emerging from among the reeds on his left, on which were also two men just as in the first boat. One also began to sing:

> I'm not of violent nature,
> But Chilin in my boat,
> I'm sure of being victor,
> Take brigands by the throat.

Lu Tsun-i now realized his danger especially as he saw a third boat sculled by one man who also began to sing:

> On bank a gallant hero strolls,
> His boat is hidden in the reeds;
> The end is destined by fate,
> No sorrow if he takes rest.

When the song was ended the men on the three boats all saluted Lu Tsun-i, and called out "ngo." They were the three brothers Yuan, Lu Tsun-i being unaccustomed to swimming asked the fisherman to take him to the bank at once. But the fisherman only laughed, and replied, "Above is the blue sky; below is the green water. I was born at Hsun Yang River, but afterwards went to Liang Shan Po, I am Li Chun, the Muddy Water Dragon. If you, Lu Tsun-i, do not submit now, your end is very near."

Lu Tsun-i was surprised at this, but said, "Then one of us two must die." He took his sword, and thrust it at Li Chun who seeing this evaded the blow by turning a back somersault into the water. Soon the boat began to move round in a circle, and Lu Tsun-i's sword had been thrown into the water. Just then he saw a head emerge from the water, and it said, "I am Chang Shun, the White Fish." He seized hold of the rudder, and kicking the water, he overturned the boat, and threw Lu Tsun-i overboard.

A plot to capture the phœnix and dragon,
A trap to hold an extraordinary man.

CHAPTER 61

BY SHOOTING AN ARROW FROM AMBUSH YEN CH'ING SAVES THE LIFE OF HIS MASTER; SHIH HSIU JUMPS FROM AN UPPER ROOM AND SAVES LIFE ON THE EXECUTION GROUND

WHEN Lu Tsun-i was thrown overboard he was rescued by Chang Shun, who brought him to the bank, where there were many men with torches who seized Lu Tsun-i, disarmed him, removed his wet clothes, and were going to bind his hand with ropes. Just then Tai Tsung appeared, and called out, "Do not injure Lu Tsun-i in any way!" He took some new embroidered clothes from a man, and handed them to Lu Tsun-i. A sedan chair was there, and Lu Tsun-i was asked to take his seat in same. In the distance were about forty men with red silk lanterns illuminated and beating drums who were to conduct Lu Tsun-i to the mountain. With them were Sung Chiang, Wu Yung, Kung-Sun Sheng, and all the other leaders. When near, the chair was set down, and Lu Tsun-i got out. The leaders all dismounted, and knelt down. Lu Tsun-i also knelt down, and said, "I am your prisoner, and request a quick dispatch."

Sung Chiang laughed and replied, "Sir, I request you to be seated in the chair."

Lu Tsun-i did this, and all the leaders again mounted their horses. They then all moved off up the mountain, and upon halting before the Loyalty and Justice Hall Sung Chiang pressed Lu Tsun-i to enter the hall. There was a blaze of lanterns on all sides. In the hall Sung Chiang addressed Lu Tsun-i, "I have heard of your fame for a long time, and to-day I am gratified to be fortunate enough to meet you. I am afraid that we have annoyed you just now, and I ask you to forgive us."

"I was instructed by our commander," said Wu Yung,

"to go to your house as a fortune teller, and by some means get you to come and join us here."

Sung Chiang requested Lu Tsun-i to occupy the second seat of honor, but the latter only laughed, and said, "At home I had no conduct deserving capital punishment, and now here I do not think of living. You want to kill me, then kill me at once. Do not joke with me."

Sung Chiang laughed, "How dare I joke with you? Your virtue is abundant, and we have been longing for a long time to meet you. So we thought out a plan to get you to come here, and now we will obey your orders."

"Stay!" said Lu Tsun-i. "For me to die is easy, but to follow your wishes is very difficult."

"We had better discuss matters further to-morrow," said Wu Yung.

Food and wine were now brought in, and they all sat down. Lu Tsun-i saw no way of avoiding this so he ate and drank with the rest, and then was conducted to a bedroom.

The next day a feast was prepared, and Sung Chiang pressed Lu Tsun-i to join them. When they entered the hall Lu Tsun-i was pressed to take the premier seat. During the feast Sung Chiang stood up, filled Lu Tsun-i's cup with wine, and then said, "Last night we spoke rather abruptly, and now ask you to forgive us. Though our stronghold is small, and is not a suitable place for a great man, yet I ask you look at that inscription, 'Loyalty and Justice,' and become our commander-in-chief, and I will make room for you."

"Tut, tut!" exclaimed Lu Tsun-i. "You are wrong. I have committed no fault! Whether I live or die, I shall still be loyal to the Sung dynasty. My eating and drinking with you would be of no significance, but if you talk about 'Loyalty and Justice,' I could not bear it, and my blood would be spattered all over the place."

"If you are unwilling to join us," said Wu Yung, "we cannot force you to do so. We might detain your body, but we could not keep your spirit. Only it has been very difficult for us to get you come here. If you will not join us, we hope that you will stay with us for at least a few days."

"As you cannot stay me here why should you not let me leave at once?" asked Lu Tsun-i. "I am afraid that my people at home will be very much upset at not hearing of me."

"That can be easily arranged," said Wu Yung. "We can send your steward Li Ku back with your carts and goods so that you can rest here for a few days." He then summoned Li Ku, and upon his arrival asked him, "Have you got all your goods and carts?"

"There are none missing," replied Li Ku.

Sung Chiang sent for some silver, and distributed it among Li Ku and his subordinates.

Lu Tsun-i then spoke to Li Ku, "You know all my trouble. I want you to tell my wife everything, and urge her not to be downcast. If I am not killed here I will certainly come back."

"The men here like you," said Li Ku, "so that it won't matter if you stay here for one or two months." He and his men then withdrew.

"Sir, I hope that you will make yourself at home here," said Wu Yung. "I will go and see that Li Ku departs without any difficulty." He then left the hall, mounted his horse, and went down the mountain to wait for Li Ku. When he met him he said, "Li Ku, we have settled every thing with your master, and he has agreed to occupy the second seat in our assembly. While he was at home he wrote on the wall of a room a poem of twenty-eight characters, seven in each line, and along the top of the four lines are four characters, 'Lu Tsun I Rebel.' The poem is as follows:

> 'On bank a gallant hero strolls,
> His boat is hidden in the reeds;
> A long sword he holds,
> To kill the traitorous ministers.'

"To-day your master has arrived here, but you do not understand the reason. He asked us to kill all you men so that nobody would know where he was, but that would represent us heroes at Liang Shan Po as being nujust. So you can now return and tell his people that he will never come back."

Li Ku and his men saluted. Wu Yung got a boat, and the party was rowed across the lake. Wu Yung took leave of them, and they departed on their way to the Northern Capital (Ta Ming Fu).

The next day another feast was held in the Loyalty and Justice Hall, and there Lu Tsun-i spoke, "As you have not killed me yet my stay here seems very long. To-day I must take my leave of you."

"I have no ability," said Sung Chiang, "but to-day I am aware of your greatness. To-morrow I will arrange a private feast for us two then we can discuss matters fully. I must ask you not to decline the invitation."

The next day Sung Chiang gave the feast, and the day afterwards Wu Yung also had a special private feast for Lu Tsun-i. Then Kuang-Sun Sheng did the same, and he was followed by all the other thirty leaders so that Lu Tsun-i had a special feast every day for a whole month. At last Lu Tsun-i decided to depart at all costs, and Sung Chiang agreed to this. He arranged for a parting feast, and drank wine with Lu Tsun-i. But the other leaders complained because Lu Tsun-i would not also drink wine with them. They used the proverb, "Why is the brick thick and the tile thin," i.e., why do you treat him intimately and treat us coldly?

Li K'wei also called out, "I went through a lot of trouble in my journey to and from the Northern Capital to induce him to come here, but now he would not drink a parting cup with me. Let me fight with him to settle the affair."

Wu Yung laughed at this, but pointed out to Lu Tsun-i how much he was liked. At last Lu Tsun-i agreed to stay five days more. But after that he was again induced to stay until nearly another month had passed. It was then near the end of autumn, and the days were getting cold. At last Lu Tsun-i spoke personally to Sung Chiang about his departure, but the latter only laughed, and said, "This can be easily arranged. I will accompany you across the lake to-morrow." The next day Lu Tsun-i put on his sword and clothes for journey, and all the bandit leaders came down the mountain to see him off. He accepted from them only enough money to cover his expenses on the way.

Lu Tsun-i had no adventure on his journey, and duly reached the Northern Capital (Ta Ming Fu). As it was evening when he arrived he decided to pass the night in an inn just outside the gate. The next morning he entered the city, and happened to meet a man who had a tattered turban and shabby clothes. Upon seeing Lu Tsun-i he began to cry. Upon looking at the man closely he recognized him as his employee Yen Ch'ing, and therefore asked him what was the matter.

"This is no place to talk," replied Yen Ch'ing. So they both went off the road to a quiet corner where Yeh Ch'ing said, "Sometime after you had gone Li Ku returned and told your wife that you had joined the brigands at Liang Shan Po, and had become the second in command. So they both went to the yamen, and made an accusation against you. They then went away and lived together. As I objected to that arrangement they dismissed me, and then prevented me from getting other employment so that I have been reduced to begging for a bare living. I knew that you would not join the brigands, and therefore waited here for your return. Now if you will take my advice you will at once return to Liang Shan Po, because if you stay here there will be danger for you."

"My wife is not the kind of woman who would do such a thing," replied Lu Tsun-i.

"As you have no eyes at the back of your head," said Yen Ch'ing, "how could you know what has happened here. Previously you were so engaged in your military drills that you had no time for your wife's favors, and it was at that time that your wife had Li Ku as her lover. They now live together as man and wife, and if you interfere there it will lead you to trouble."

Lu Tsun-i was angry and said, "Our family has been in this town for five generations, and I am well known here. I know Li Ku dares not do this kind of thing. I think you may be deceiving me for some reason. I will go myself to make inquiries at my home, and then I will deal with you."

Yen Ch'ing cried again, and seized hold of Lu Tsun-i's clothes, but the latter kicked him, and getting free he hurried off towards his home.

Upon arriving there all the servants were surprised to see him. Li Ku hurried forward, saluted, and requested him to enter the main hall. Lu Tsun-i asked for Yen Ch'ing, and Li Ku replied, "That is a long story, and you had better not ask about him just now. You just take a rest and then I will tell you all about him."

Just then Lu Tsun-i's wife stepped from behind the screen, and he spoke to her: "How do you do, wife? Now can you tell me about Yen Ch'ing?"

His wife replied, "You need not ask, as that is a long story. You may take a rest and then I will tell you all about him."

Lu Tsun-i was now very suspicious, and wanted to pursue his inquiries about Yen Ch'ing. But Li Ku said, "Please change your clothes; then worship your ancestors' tablets; get your breakfast, and then we can discuss matters fully." He then went and ordered the food.

As Lu Tsun-i sat down to eat there arose a great noise at the gates, and about two hundred yamen runners entered. They seized Lu Tsun-i, bound him, and took him off to the yamen beating him on the way with their staves. The commander-in-chief of the garrison, Liang, the grand secretary, took his seat on the bench. Lu Tsun-i was taken in front of the bench, and the yamen runners stood in ranks on both sides. Li Ku and Lu Tsun-i's wife had also arrived, and they knelt down at one side.

Liang, the grand secretary, addressed the prisoner in a loud voice: "How is it that you, a highly respected citizen of Ta Ming Fu, the Northern Capital, went and joined the brigands at Liang Shan Po, and became second in command there? Do you now return to the Northern Capital to devise schemes to attack us with the brigands? What explanation have you to offer?"

"I was rather stupid," replied Lu Tsun-i. "One of the brigand leaders, Wu Yung, came to my house in the disguise of a fortune teller. He instigated me to go to Liang Shan Po, where I was kept as a prisoner for two months. By lucky chance I escaped and returned home here, really I have had no bad intentions. I request that you go into this matter fully."

"It is useless for you to say you have no bad intention," said the Grand Secretary Liang. "If you were not on very intimate terms with the brigands how could you stay there for two months? The accusation against you was made by your own wife and your steward Li Ku. It cannot be false."

"Master," said Li Ku, "if I were you I would make a full confession. On the wall of a room at your house we found a rebellious poem so that it is useless trying to hide anything."

"We do not wish to injure you," said Lu Tsun-i's wife, "but we are afraid of being implicated. There is a saying, 'If one man rebels, his family is exterminated.'"

Lu Tsun-i felt deeply wronged, knelt down, and denied the accusation.

"Master, do not deny the charge," said Li Ku. "If you now speak the truth you may get off more easily than if you speak falsely. If you do not confess very soon they will force a confession by torture."

The wife also said, "Husband! If there was nothing definite you would not be here, and if you speak the truth it will be easier to get your release. If you have done this, my own life will be endangered. Your flesh is sensitive, but the bamboo has no feelings. If you confess you will only be punished according to the law."

As Li Ku had bribed all the officials high and low, so the clerk of the court Chang addressed the bench, "This is an obstinate man, and he will not confess without torture."

"That is so," said the Grand Secretary. He then gave an order for the accused to be beaten.

The court runners seized the prisoner, forced him on the ground, and beat him on the buttocks with the bamboo until blood flowed freely. Lu Tsun-i fainted several times. He could not endure this torture, and at last said, "My fate is evidently to meet with an untimely death so I will now confess."

The clerk of the court wrote down his confession, and afterwards the accused had a cangue fastened round his neck, and was sent to the prison.

Most of the public present considered that the prisoner had merely confessed in order to escape further torture.

In the prison Lu Tsun-i was in charge of a jailer Ts'ai Fu, nicknamed, the Iron Arm, who had his younger brother, Ts'ai Ching, nicknamed the Flower, as his assistant. Ts'ai Fu was the chief executioner, and never took two strokes, his younger brother always wore a flower in his cap-hence the nicknames. Ts'ai Fu told his younger brother to take the prisoner to a cell, as he wished to go home. This was done. As Ts'ai Fu left the prison he was accosted by a man at the door who was crying and also carrying a can of food. Ts'ai Fu recognized him as Yen Ch'ing and asked what he was doing. Yen Ch'ing knelt down with his tears falling to the ground like pearls and beans. He said, "Elder brother, I ask you to have pity on my master Lu Tsun-i as he was innocent, although now a prisoner. I have been begging for food, and have now brought a little for him. Do not refuse me." He could not control his sorrow or say another word, but burst into tears.

Ts'ai Fu replied, "I know about the case. You can go inside and give the prisoner the food."

Yen Ch'ing saluted, and entered the jail.

Ts'ai Fu went on his way, but soon met a tea boy who called out, "There is a guest in our tea house who wishes to speak to you." Ts'ai Fu went upstairs with the man, and found Li Ku waiting for him. After saluting each other Li Ku spoke, "You know all about my affairs so I will not attempt to deceive you. To-night I want you to extinguish his life. I wish to present you fifty ounces of silver for this. If the officials make inquiries I will 'square' them."

Ts'ai Fu laughed and said, "Have you not noticed the stone tablet on the wall of the court with the inscription, 'It is easy to deceive persons, but difficult to deceive heaven.' You may deceive yourself, but you may be sure that I shall know all about it. You have got hold of his wealth, and also his wife, and now you offer me a bribe to kill him. If I commit a crime I shall suffer for it when it is discovered."

"You think fifty ounces are too small, so I will double that amount," replied Li Ku.

"Li Ku," said Ts'ai Fu, "'you cut off the cat's tail, and then mix it with the cat's food.' Lu Tsun-i is a very wealthy man, and your offer is not enough. I might do it, however, for five hundred ounces."

"I have the money here," said Li Ku, "and I will hand it to you, if you will kill him this very night."

Ts'ai Fu took the money, hid it in his clothes, and then said, "You come early to-morrow morning for the corpse."

Li Ku thanked him, saluted, and took his departure. Ts'ai Fu went on his way, and upon reaching his home was met at the entrance by a man, who was good looking, well dressed, with a jeweled belt, and embroidered silk shoes. They saluted each other, and then Ts'ai Fu asked for the man's name and business.

"Let us go inside and then we can talk," replied the man.

They did so, and took their seats in a small private room.

"Do not be alarmed at what I say," commenced the man. "I am a Heng Hai Hsien man, and my name is Ch'ai Chin. I am a descendant of the emperor of Ta Chou, and I am known as the Small Whirlwind. I am just and upright and distribute wealth in good cause. By a misfortune I committed a crime, and therefore had to fly for safety to Liang Shan Po. Our commander there is Sung Chiang who instructed me to come here, and watch carefully the affairs of Lu Tsun-i. Who could know that the venal officials, avaricious subordinates, an adulterous wife, and a fornicating villain would join together to injure an innocent man. You hold the life of the innocent man in your hand. I have come to see about this matter, and have scorned the danger I run in doing so. If the prisoner survives we shall never forget your virtue. If the slightest error occurs in this matter then when the heroes of Liang Shan Po enter this city they will kill everyone, whether good or bad, young or old. We have heard that you are a very upright man, so I will present you a thousand ounces of silver. If you wish to arrest me please do so, and I will not resist you."

Ts'ai Fu while listening to this was covered with goose flesh, and was so paralyzed that he could not utter a word.

So Squire Ch'ai Chin continued, "Sir, do not hesitate, but give me an immediate answer."

"I request you, sir, to go back," replied Ts'ai Fu. "I will arrange matters as you wish."

"As you agree to do this I will see that you are duly recompensed," said Squire Ch'ai Chin.

He then took the money from his companion who was standing outside the gate, and handing it to Ts'ai Fu took his leave.

Ts'ai Fu was undecided what to do in view of what Squire Ch'ai Chin had said. He however returned to the jail, and told his younger brother what had passed. His brother said, "You generally have no difficulty in deciding what to do, and as this is only a small matter where is the difficulty? There is a saying, 'In killing a man we must see his blood, in saving a man, we must save him out of trouble.' As we have a thousand ounces of silver we can make presents to our superior and inferior men in his name. Both Liang, the grand secretary, and clerk Chang are fond of bribes, and they can be bought to spare the life of Lu Tsun-i. We can easily arrange for him to be banished to another place, and so avoid trouble from Liang Shan Po."

"What you say is just what I think," said Ts'ai Fu. "Take Lu Tsun-i and put him in a decent cell, and see that he has good food and wine. You can also tell him what has happened."

The money was duly distributed among the various officials, and the matter was explained to them. The following day as Li Ku got no further news he went to Ts'ai Fu's house to find out the reason. Ts'ai Ching, the younger brother, was at home, and he told Li Ku, "We wanted to get rid of the prisoner as you proposed, but unfortunately we got orders from Liang, the grand secretary, that the prisoner's life must be saved. So you had better go to the grand secretary and bribe him. As soon as he issues orders to us our work will soon be done."

Li Ku sent another man to bribe the officials, and an intermediary reported that the grand secretary declined to have anything to do with killing the prisoner. But perhaps after a few days the prisoner might commit suicide.

Clerk Chang had been bribed by Ts'ai Fu, so he put up the case purposely. Ts'ai Fu also urged him that something should be done at once, and Clerk Chang consulted Liang, the grand secretary, as to how the case should be dealt with. "They had a clear accusation, but there was little proof of the crime. Though he stayed at Liang Shan Po for some time, there was no evidence that he was really a bandit. We can beat him, and then banish him to some place about three hundred miles away. What do you think of that?"

Liang, the grand secretary, agreed to this proposal, so sentence was made that Lu Tsun-i was to receive forty blows with the bamboo, to have a smaller cangue, and be banished to Shan Men Tao.

This was done, and Lu Tsun-i was placed in charge of an escort of two men, Tung Chao and Hsueh Pa. Now these men were the same who had tried to kill Lin Ch'ung when on his journey of banishment but were prevented by Lu Ta. Upon receipt of the signed order they took charge of Lu Tsun-i, and placed him temporarily in a small room while they went home to get their traveling kit ready. Li Ku heard of the new arrangement, and sent a messenger to request Tung Chao and Hsueh Pa to come, and see him before starting off. They duly met Li Ku in an inn where they all sat down in a private room to eat some food and drink wine. After drinking three cups of wine Li Ku spoke to them, "I will be straight with you. Lu Tsun-i is my enemy. He has no money now, and on this long journey to Shan Men Tao you will have to pay all the expenses yourself. It will be at least three months before you can get back. Just now I have only these two ingots of silver to give you. If however, when on the way you kill the prisoner, and upon your return you show me the skin bearing his brand mark, then I will give each of you fifty ounces of silver. Then you can bring a report back that the prisoner died on the way and I will fix matters up all right for you at the yamen."

Tung Chao and Hsueh Pa looked at each other, and then Tung Chao replied, "I am afraid this is hard for us to do."

But Hsueh Pa said, "Our friend Li Ku is a well-known man, has a good name, and perhaps we can do this thing for him. If there is any difficulty he can arrange matters for us."

"I am not ungrateful, and I can certainly compensate you well," said Li Ku.

So Tung Chao and Hsueh Pa took the money, went home for their baggage, and departed that night with the prisoner.

They placed their baggage on Lu Tsun-i's cangue. They treated the prisoner very harshly on the way. Towards evening of the second day they had gone about five miles, and they stopped at an inn, just on the outskirts of a forest. They were shown by the waiter into a room at the back, and Hsueh Pa spoke to Lu, "We are minor officials so how can we wait upon you. If you want a meal you must go and cook it yourself."

So Lu Tsun-i went into the kitchen, and getting some fuel from the waiter he lit the fire. The waiter also gave him clean rice to boil. But as Lu Tsun-i had been brought up in a wealthy family he did not know how to cook food. The fire he had lit soon went out, and upon his blowing the embers to revive the flame he got the ashes in his eyes. Tung Chao was annoyed at the delay, and cursed him. When the rice was cooked Tung Chao took it all away, and Lu Tsun-i dared not even ask for some. When they had finished there was a little left which they gave to Lu Tsun-i, but it was cold. Hsueh Pa now told Lu Tsun-i to boil some water to wash their feet. When he had done this Lu Tsun-i went into a room and sat down. When they had finished they filled a tub full of very hot water, and summoned Lu Tsun-i to come and wash his feet. When he had taken off his shoes they seized his legs, and thrust both feet into the boiling water. He shrieked with the pain.

Hsueh Pa said, "We wait upon you but you are so fastidious." They took a chain and fastened Lu Tsun-i to the door. They then went to sleep.

About 3 a.m. they got up, and called for the waiter to get their breakfast ready. When they had dined they picked up their bundles to leave the inn. Lu Tsun-i saw that his feet were all scalded, and he could not walk. Outside it was raining heavily, and the path slippery. Lu Tsun-i attempted to walk, but fell down. Hsueh Pa took a stick and thrashed him. Lu Tsun-i struggled on, while they cursed him. They had gone about three miles like this when they came to a forest, and Lu Tsun-i said, "I cannot really go any further, and I hope you will take pity on me and allow me to rest here." They agreed to this, and they all entered the forest. It was now daybreak, and there were no people about. Hsueh Pa said, "We got up very early this morning, and as we are a bit tired we will rest here. We would like to sleep, but are afraid that you will try to escape."

"Even if I had wings I could not get away just now," said Lu Tsun-i.

"We will not trust you," said Hsueh Pa, "and will tie you up."

He took a hempen cord from around his waist, and tied Lu Tsun-i to a pine tree. He then asked Tung Chao to act as sentry some distance away, and to cough if he saw anyone coming.

"Brother, please get it done as quickly as possible," said Tung Chao.

Hsueh Pa took his stick, and said to Lu Tsun-i, "You must not think ill of us but your steward, Li Ku, asked us to kill you on the way. In any case you would soon have died at Shan Men Tao, so it would be better if you died here. When you get to the Hades do not blame us."

Lu Tsun-i wept, but did not speak a word. Hsueh Pa lifted the stick to strike Lu Tsun-i on the head when Tung Chao at his post heard a noise, and assumed that the deed had been done. He hurried back to see the result, and there Lu Tsun-i was still tied to the tree, but evidently none the worse. Hsueh Pa, however, was lying at the foot of the tree, and his stick was some distance away. "How strange!" said Tung Chao. "You must have over-exerted yourself, and so have fainted." He stooped down to raise his companion, but could not move him. He now saw blood issuing from Hsueh Pa's mouth, and looking more closely he saw an arrow sticking in Hsueh Pa's breast. He was startled at this, and quickly looking round espied a man sitting in a tree. At the same moment the man shot an arrow which struck Tung Chao in the neck, and he fell down dead.

The man jumped down from the tree, and taking his sword cut the cord binding Lu Tsun-i to the tree. When Lu Tsun-i opened his eyes he saw that the man was Yen Ch'ing, his servant, and exclaimed, "You! Surely we are both dead, and are now both spirits."

"I have followed you all the way from the town," said Yen Ch'ing, "because I thought that they would try to murder you. But I have succeeded in killing them. See, here they are."

"You saved my life," said Lu Tsun-i, "but you have killed those yamen runners so that I am now implicated in a serious crime. Where can we go?"

"Sung Chiang certainly did you an injury when he tricked you into leaving your home, but now there is no other place than Liang Shan Po for us to go to."

"But I am still suffering from the beatings I got in the prison, and my feet were scalded so how can I walk, or go anywhere?" said Lu Tsun-i.

"We cannot delay matters, so I will carry you on my back." Yen Ching was feeling very perturbed, he kicked the corpses aside and then took Lu Tsun-i on his back, and started off in an easterly direction. But after going about three miles like this Yen Ch'ing felt tired, and therefore he stopped at an inn for the night.

Now it happened that some travelers passing near the forest saw the two corpses, and told the alderman at the next village, who reported the matter to the officials at Ta Ming Fu, the Northern Capital. When the coroner arrived he recognized Hsueh Pa and Tung Chao. The officials duly issued an order for the arrest of the murderer within a fixed time. Upon examining the arrows it was found out that they belonged to Yen Ch'ing, so another proclamation was issued giving description of that man, and also Lu Tsun-i, and ordering their immediate arrest.

Lu Tsun-i and Yen Ch'ing were now staying at an inn. The waiter at the inn heard of the murder, and as everybody was talking about it, he had suspicions about them. So he went to the village, and told the alderman there who sent a report at once to the nearest yamen runners.

As Yen Ch'ing had no dish for the meal so he took his bow and arrows and went out to shoot some birds. As he was returning to the inn he heard a hubbub in the village so he hid in some trees to see what was happening. Soon he saw a large number of yamen runners with a cart on which Lu Tsun-i was bound a prisoner again. Yen Ch'ing's first desire was to rush out, and rescue Lu Tsun-i, but he realized that this would be useless as he was not well armed. So he thought, "The only way now is for me to go to Liang Shan Po, and beg Sung Chiang to come and rescue Lu Tsun-i."

So he started off at once, and traveled all that night. He was very hungry, as he had not a cash to buy food. He crossed a ridge, but as the trees were very dense he could not find his way very well, so he lay down among the bushes and slept there. At daybreak he was aroused by a magpie chattering in a tree just over his head. He thought, "If I shoot that bird I can take it into a village, and get it cooked." When he got up, the magpie, seeing him, began to chatter again. He took his bow and an arrow, and prayed to Heaven, "I have only one arrow, but this shot must hit the bird if my master is to live. If my master's fate is death then this shot will fail." He fixed the arrow and addressed it. "Dart, do not fail!" He pulled the string, and the arrow flew and hit the magpie's tail. The bird flew away towards the foot of the ridge with the arrow sticking in its tail. Yen Ch'ing ran in the direction the bird had gone, but instead of seeing the magpie he ran into two men. The first man wore a cap, in the shape of a pig's snout and had two rings hanging from the cap at the back of his head. He wore a brown silk gown and an engraved metal girdle. His cloth boots came up to his knees. He carried a long staff. The second man wore a big Fanyang cloth cap and a tea-colored gown. His belt was red, and contained pockets for money, etc. He had leather boots. He carried a bundle on his back, a small stick in his hand, and a sword in his belt. Yen Ch'ing passed two men close by before he could stop. He looked round and thought, "Why should I not attack these man, and take their money, and so have enough to take me to Liang Shan Po?" He stuck his bow in his clothes, and turned on the men. The two men, however, seeing his action went on as before. Yen Ch'ing pursued them, and upon catching up, struck one in his back with his fist and knocked him down. The other man, however, took his stave, and swinging it struck Yen Ch'ing on the leg so that he fell down. Before he could get up the other man put his foot on Yen Ch'ing's back, drew his sword to kill him. At this, Yen Ch'ing called out, "Good sir. I do not mind death, but I ask you to have pity on me, as there would be no man to carry the news." The man stayed his hand, and asked what the news was.

"Why do you ask for news?" asked Yen Ch'ing.

The man seized hold of Yen Ch'ing's arm, and seeing the tattoo marks asked, "Are you not Yen Ch'ing, the employee of Lu Tsun-i?"

Yen Ch'ing was face to face with death so he thought, "As these men know me I had better tell them the whole truth." He replied, "Yes, I am Yen Ch'ing."

The man said, "It was very lucky that we did not kill you. Do you not recognize us? We are from Liang Shan Po. I am Yang Hsiung and this man is Shih Hsiu. We were deputed to come here, and find out what has happened to Lu Tsun-i. Wu Yung and Tai Tsung will come very soon."

Yen Ch'ing then told them all that had happened.

Yang Hsiung said, "As that is the position I must go at once to Liang Shan Po with Yen Ch'ing, and ask for instructions. Meanwhile Shih Hsiu had better go to Ta Ming Fu and watch what happens there."

Shih Hsiu agreed to this, and gave Yen Ch'ing some of their spare food, and also his bundle. They went their separate ways.

When Shih Hsiu reached Ta Ming Fu it was just dark, and as the gates were closed he could not enter that night so he slept at an inn outside the gate. Early the next morning after breakfast he entered the city, and found the people very depressed about something. When he reached the market place he asked an old man whether there had been any trouble. The man replied, "Stranger! Do you not know about the case of Lu Tsun-i? To-day he is to be beheaded about noon so that you can see the affair."

When Shih Hsiu heard this his blood ran cold. He went to the place of execution, and entered an inn overlooking the ground. There he sat down and ordered wine and food.

The waiter asked, "Are you alone, or have you invited others to join you here?"

Shih Hsiu was now very angry and shouted, "Bring me large bowls of wine and plenty of food. Don't ask question!"

The waiter was startled at this gust of temper, but hurried off, and soon brought the refreshments. Shih Hsiu quickly ate a hearty meal, but just as he had finished he heard a row down below. Looking out of the window he saw that all the shops were closing doors. Just then the waiter entered, and asked if he had had enough and said, "An execution is taking place so would you please pay now and leave."

"What should I be afraid of?" asked Shih Hsiu. "You get off at once before I hit you."

The waiter beat a hasty retreat. Soon afterwards drums and gongs were sounded in the street below, and looking out again Shih Hsiu saw Lu Tsun-i being taken to the execution ground which was just in front of the inn where he was. The head jailer Ts'ai Fu was there with his big sword, and also his brother Ts'ai Ching who spoke to Lu Tsun-i, "You must understand that it is not us who do not try to help you, but you have done wrong. Over there is a temple, and we have prepared there a proper seat for your soul to rest there in peace."

The crowd standing round now called out, "It is well afternoon now." So Ts'ai Ching took off the cangue, and held the prisoner's head in position. Ts'ai Fu raised the sword to strike the deadly blow. The clerk held aloft the sentence and read it aloud. The yamen runners applauded.

Shih Hsiu now drawing out his sword shouted out, "All the brigands from Liang Shan Po are here," and jumped down to the ground. Upon hearing and seeing this Ts'ai Fu and Ts'ai Ching deserted. Shih Hsiu killed every man within reach, and in no time ten men lay on the ground. He seized Lu Tsun-i, and took him off down the south street. Shih Hsiu did not know the roads, and Lu Tsun-i was too dazed to notice anything.

As soon as the news reached Liang, the grand secretary, he ordered all the city gates to be closed, and dispatched large numbers of soldiers to search the whole city for the escaped prisoners.

How could any hero escape from a city under such conditions?

> A man cannot burrow through earth without claws;
> Nor fly into the sky without wings.

CHAPTER 62

SUNG CHIANG'S MEN ATTACK TA MING FU; KUAN SHENG DISCUSSES THE CAPTURE OF LIANG SHAN PO

IT was not long before the yamen runners found Lu Tsun-i and Shih Hsiu, and took them bound to the yamen. Having been brought before Liang, the grand secretary, Shih Hsiu glared at him and abused him, "You slave do the work of the slave's slave. But very soon my elder brother will arrive here with troops, attack and destroy the whole town. You will then be cut into three parts. He asked me to come here and inform you of your fate."

Many of the yamen runners were afraid, as Shih Hsiu said this several times. When Liang, the grand secretary, heard of this he could not speak for some time. He then ordered that large cangues be placed on the prisoners, and that they be sent into the prison for those about to be executed. He also instructed Ts'ai Fu to guard them well as they must not escape again. Now Ts'ai Fu wished to be on good terms with Liang Shan Po so he placed the prisoners in quite decent cells, and gave them excellent food, so that they had nothing to complain of.

Liang, the grand secretary, also instructed his assistant to suitably compensate the relatives of the persons who had been killed by Shih Hsiu. There were at least seventy men who had been killed. A great many had been injured. They were given medical attendance and medicine free

The next day the people found that anonymous placards had been secretly posted all over the town so they at once took some to the grand secretary who found them read as follows: "I, Sung Chiang, commander in chief, at Liang Shan Po hereby proclaim to all the officials at Ta Ming Fu that

Lu Tsun-i is the greatest hero in the whole empire. I invited him to come to see me, and act with me as the Apostle of Heaven. How dare you, corrupt officials, accept secret bribes and oppress the people. I sent Shih Hsiu to report this to you, but you have also arrested him. You must not execute those two prisoners, but at once arrest the adulterer and the adulteress who have caused this trouble. Should you execute my brothers, I shall come with large armies and take full revenge on you. I shall make no discrimination, but kill everybody. I will root out the lawbreakers, and Heaven will approve of my administration of justice. I chat and smile at this small affair, but I will come dancing to the beating of drums. Just men and decent women, filial sons and obedient grandsons, orderly citizens, and honest officials need have no fear of us. I issue this for your information."

As the grand secretary read this, his color changed, and he was quite nonplused to know what to do. He, however, sent for his assistant Wang to discuss the matter with him. Wang was a weak person, and when he had heard the details he said, "The imperial troops have tried several times to exterminate those brigands at Liang Shan Po, but have failed every time; so what can we do as we are so weak? If the brigands attack us there will be no time to get more troops, and we shall soon be defeated. So I think it would be wiser for us not to execute the prisoners. Then we must report the matter at once to Ts'ai, the royal tutor; and secondly we must assemble our troops outside the town so as to be prepared against the attack. If we do this I do not think there will be much danger, and the people will not suffer from an attack outside the town."

Liang, the grand secretary, agreed to this and sent for the head jailer, Ts'ai Fu. When he arrived the grand secretary said to him, "Those two prisoners are evidently very important persons, and I am afraid that if roughly treated by you they might die. You must therefore treat them well."

When Ts'ai Fu heard this he was much pleased as it agreed with what he had already done. He returned to the jail and told his brother about the new order.

Liang, the grand secretary, next sent for his two generals to discuss matters with them. When they heard the news General Li Cheng said, "I think this place is too far from Liang Shan Po, and the brigands will never get here. So why should you worry about this impudent notice? I have not much ability, but still I hold this important post. I have received imperial favors, but so far have not been able to show my gratitude in a practical way. I am willing to do my utmost for my master, and will take the troops and encamp outside the town. If the brigands come I will never let them go back alive."

The grand secretary was much pleased at this, and presented the general with much silk and satin.

The following day General Li Cheng held a conference of all his officers, and there one of his officers, So Ch'ao, the Rash Scout, stepped forward. Li Cheng addressed him, "Sung Chiang and his brigands will soon be here to attack Ta Ming Fu. I want you to take command of some troops, and establish a camp about twelve miles from the town. I will come and join you there with more men."

So Ch'ao having received his orders took his troops the following day to a place called Flying Tiger Gully, and there established a camp. General Li Cheng established another camp about three miles nearer the town at a village called Ash Tree Mound. Around these camps hidden pits and traps were made, so that the positions seemed impregnable. The officers and men felt quite secure, and calmly awaited the arrival of the brigands.

The proclamation issued from Liang Shan Po was composed by Wu Yung, and was posted on every bridge and on every road. Tai Tsung kept the leaders at Liang Shan Po well informed as to the developments at Ta Ming Fu. At a conference of leaders Sung Chiang spoke to Wu Yung, "You had a good plan to inveigle Lu Tsun-i to our hold, but now he is in trouble. Our strong brother Shih Hsiu has also been arrested. Have you any suggestion as to how we can save their lives?"

"Brother, do not worry," said Wu Yung. "If we embrace the present opportunities, we can not only save those two lives, but also seize much loot at Ta Ming Fu. To-morrow is a very lucky day, and I want you to give me half of our forces to proceed to Ta Ming Fu."

This was agreed to, and men were appointed for the coming expedition. But Li K'wei interposed, "It is a long time since my two axes joined in a fray, and as they have just heard of this expedition they are naturally very glad. So please let me lead five hundred men in this expedition. Previously I was told to remain dumb on an expedition, but now I want to vent my anger."

"Younger brother," said Sung Chiang, "this is a very serious and important affair, and we must not forget that Liang, the grand secretary, is the son-in-law of Ts'ai, the imperial tutor. The government troops will be in charge of two great generals, Li Cheng and Wen Ta, who are brave and the equal of ten thousand men. We cannot treat them lightly, although I do not doubt your bravery and fierceness."

"Elder brother, you know that I am outspoken so you expected me to be silent," said Li K'wei. "Now I should be only too pleased to kill our enemies, so why not let me go?"

"In that case," said Wu Yung, "you had better go in advance. You can lead a vanguard of five hundred men and conduct your own fighting. You can start to-morrow."

That evening Sung Chiang talked over the details of the expedition with Wu Yung, and Pei Hsuan wrote out the various orders, and dispatched them to the various leaders.

It was just the end of autumn, and the country was very suitable for campaigning. The horses were well fed and were in good condition. The men had rested for some time, and were quite ready for some more fighting. They got their arms, saddled the horses, and left the mountain in four divisions the next day.

So Ch'ao at his camp near the Flying Tiger Gully received a report from his scout that the brigands were now only ten miles away, and were quickly advancing. He sent the news to General Li Cheng who sent all his cavalry to support So Ch'ao. They were duly placed in position by So Ch'ao.

The following day breakfast was taken at daybreak, and then they all went to meet the brigands. The brigands were approaching, and as they got near it was seen that Li K'wei was in front of them. When near, he shouted, "Do you recognize your grandfather, the hero of Liang Shan Po?"

General Li Cheng on his horse laughed at this, and spoke to So Ch'ao, "I have heard of the men of Liang Shan Po, but this is a very dirty lot, and we need not take any notice of them. Now general, let us take that fellow."

So Ch'ao also laughed, and replied, "It is beneath me. There is somebody else!"

Near them was a lieutenant named Wang Ting who heard this, and without waiting for an order he galloped forward to fight with Li K'wei, and was followed by his hundred cavalrymen. When Li K'wei's foot soldiers saw the cavalry they turned and fled in all directions. As the cavalry pursued the men So Ch'ao saw a large body of brigands advancing on both flanks so he signaled an order for the cavalry to retire.

General Li Cheng however asked, "Why not let them capture those brigands?"

"I am afraid there may be an ambush, and our cavalry might fall into a trap," replied So Ch'ao.

But General Li Cheng did not agree with this, and ordered the soldiers to advance. As General Li Cheng advanced he saw that the main body of the brigands was led by a girl on horseback. On the flag he read the name of the commander, "Miss Hu, the Pure One." The men were of all sizes — some big and some small, so that they looked disorderly.

Li Cheng turned to So Ch'ao, "What is the use of this ill-assorted rabble? You take some men to fight that lot, while I will capture some of the other brigands."

So Ch'ao whipped his horse and dashed forward. When the girl Miss Hu saw him coming she turned her horse round, and galloped off, followed by her men and her lady Amazons. General Li Cheng ordered his men to spread out and attack the retreating brigands. He had not gone far when he saw large bodies of brigands approaching, shouting and waving their arms. He therefore ordered a retreat, but when this movement was being done, he found brigands on both his flanks. The girl Miss Hu and her followers returned, and were now attacking his army in the rear. His men could not stand the attack on three sides, and they soon broke into disorder, and galloped off in all directions. As he neared his camp he found his way blocked by Li K'wei and his men. General Li Cheng signaled for a charge, and his men bore down on Li K'wei's body of men, and dividing it cut their way through. Upon eaching their camp he realized that he had lost a good number of his men. The brigands however did not advance any further, and so the battle came to a halt.

When Liang, the grand secretary, heard of the defeat he immediately ordered General Wen Ta to take the reserve of soldiers to support General Li Cheng. Upon reaching the camp Li Cheng met Wen Ta, and after discussing the position asked for the latter's opinion.

General Wen Ta laughed and replied, "It is only like a painful sore, and is of no importance." They however discussed their plans for the following day, and came to an agreement.

Early the next morning rations were served to the troops, and after breakfast orders were issued for a general advance, and they had just got moving when the brigands appeared in the distance also marching towards them. General Wen Ta gave orders for the troops to halt, and open out, and for bows and arrows and spears to be ready. The brigands also halted, but a horseman rode forth with a red flag bearing the characters "Chin Ming." He pulled up his horse just in front of the imperial troops, and shouted out, "Let covetous and corrupt officers from Ta Ming Fu listen to me! For a long time I have planned to attack your town, but deferred doing so because I did not wish to injure the common people there. But if you will now release Lu Tsun-i and Shih Hsiu, and hand over the adulterer and adulteress we will at once retire, without any further fighting. If, however, you are stubborn and will not listen to this proposal then tell me so at once."

General Wen Ta was angry at this, and turning round to his men asked, "Who will volunteer to go out and attack that fellow?"

Before he had finished saying this So Ch'ao galloped forward to fight. Halting he called out to Chin Ming, "You were previously in the imperial army, and you were not ill treated. So why are you now a brigand instead of being a loyal man? To-day I will capture you, and cut you up into small pieces."

At this Chin Ming was wild with rage, and raising his spiked mace, dashed forward. So Ch'ao did likewise. Their horses took their riders, temper, and were also keen for the fray. The assembled troops cheered at the sight. The two fought for about twenty bouts without either gaining any advantage. Among the brigands was the leader Han Tao who shot an arrow which struck So Ch'ao in the shoulder, and as the latter could no longer wield his battle-ax he turned his horse and retreated.

Sung Chiang seeing this signaled the order for a general advance, and then began a great battle. Blood was flowing over the ground like water. The imperial troops gave way, and being again defeated retreated to their camp. They further retreated to the second camp at the Flying Tiger Gully. There Wen Ta found that he had lost about one third of his men.

Sung Chiang halted his men at the first camp, and discussed matters with Wu Yung who said, "The troops have been defeated a second time so that their morale will be weak just now. We must seize this opportunity for a further attack, before they have had time to recover." Sung Chiang agreed to this, and issued orders at once for a general attack that very night.

General Wen Ta was resting, and meditating in his tent that night when a soldier reported to him that there was a big fire on the east. General Wen Ta immediately mounted his horse, and riding forward he saw all the hills and plains to the east were lit up. Looking round he now saw that to the west of his camp it was also ablaze with lights. He returned to camp, and saw that the brigands were advancing on both sides. He was very much upset, and had no definite plan of defense. The brigands approached with great noise. The imperial troops were restless, and were evidently on the point of decamping, but they were now quite surrounded. General Wen Ta had decided to cut a way through with his men, but just then the brigands opened fire upon them. He could not control his men any longer as they were in great disorder. He therefore spoke to General Li Cheng to get a few men together, and then with a sudden rush they broke through the cordon of brigands, and so escaped. This remnant of the imperial troops reached Ta Ming Fu just after daybreak.

When Liang, the grand secretary, heard of the disaster he felt as though he had lost two of his three souls. He hurriedly ordered all the remainder of his troops to rescue. When the defeated troops had all entered the town he ordered that all the gates be closed, and the wall strongly defended.

The following day the brigands approached and encamped outside the East Gate.

The grand secretary summoned a conference of all officials to discuss means of defending the town. At the meeting General Li Cheng spoke, "The brigands are just outside the town, and we are in great danger. If we are not careful the town will soon be taken. Sir, you should write a personal note to Ts'ai, the imperial tutor explaining our position, and asking for immediate relief. Send this by a very trusty and confidential servant this very night. Secondly, you should dispatch urgent letters to all the surrounding towns asking for support. Thirdly, you should issue a proclamation in this town appealing to every man to join in the defense of the town. They must prepare logs of wood and stone to hurl at the enemy; arm themselves with crossbows and stiff bows; get bottles of powder and lime dust, vile smelling manure; and take guard both night and day. It we do this at once we may be able to hold out for some time."

"I can write all the dispatches you refer to," said the grand secretary, "but who can face the danger outside and get through?"

Lieutenant Wang Ting volunteered to do this, and that night he left with the confidential dispatches. He was successful, and reaching the nearest town he delivered the messages, and had them sent to all the surrounding towns. He himself went on to the Eastern Capital with the important dispatch.

On the other hand, Sung Chiang divided his men and besieged the town on three sides, but he left the South Gate open intentionally. He also ordered for supplies to be sent from Liang Shan Po as he was uncertain how long the attack would last. He was however determined to continue his attack until both Lu Tsun-i and Shih Hsiu were rescued.

Every day General Li Cheng and Wen Ta led some of his soldiers outside the town to skirmish with the brigands but could not succeed.

Wang Ting quickly reached the Eastern Capital and delivered the confidential dispatches to Ts'ai, the royal tutor. The latter was astonished at the news, and questioned Wang Ting closely. Wang Ting told the whole story of Lu Tsun-i, and explained in detail how the imperial troops had been defeated by the brigands.

The royal tutor then told him to go and take rest after his tiresome journey, while he would discuss the matter with the other ministers. Ts'ai Ching then summoned all the ministers to assemble in the privy chamber to discuss urgent matters. It was not long before all were assembled, and then Ts'ai Ching, the royal tutor, explained what had happened at the Northern Capital (Ta Ming Fu). He asked "What can be done to relieve the town and defeat the brigands?"

The ministers looked at each other in a helpless air, but nobody spoke. A man however stepped forward from behind the seat occupied by the commander of the infantry. He was Hsuan Tsan, captain of the bodyguards. His face was dark, and had a snub nose. His hair was curly, and his moustache was red. He was very tall, and was armed with a steel sword. During a war against a Mongol tribe he had distinguished himself as a skillful bowman, and the prince was so pleased with his skill that he had been given the prince's daughter in marriage. But the girl had not loved him, and as she had died after a short term of married life he had fallen into disfavor with the prince who had given him a minor military position as captain in a cavalry regiment. For this reason he gained the nickname of "Disgraceful Son-in-law." He now addressed Ts'ai Ching, the royal tutor, "When I lived at home I knew a man named Kuan Sheng, who is a descendant of the famous general of the Three Kingdoms, Kuan Kung. His manner and form carries a close resemblance to his ancestor and always carries a long-handled sword. Because of this he is called, Kuan Sheng, the Big Sword. He is in charge of a police force at Pu Chou in Shansi province, and is well known for his military skill. Nobody can beat him, and he is quite fearless. If presents were made to him and he was promoted to some responsible position in the army, I think he could exterminate the brigands and make the country safe."

Ts'ai Ching was much pleased at this suggestion, and at once commissioned Hsuan Tsan, the Disgraceful Son-in-law, to send a dispatch to Kuan Sheng and bring him to the Eastern Capital (Kaifeng) without delay.

We need not go into many details, but will just say that Hsuan Tsan duly carried out his orders, and quickly reached Pu Chou. He was gladly welcomed by Kuan Sheng who had not seen him for a long time. When Hsuan Tsan had delivered his message Kuan Sheng was highly delighted at the news. He then introduced him to his best friend, Hao Ssu-wen, and told him the story of Hao's birth. "Hao Ssu-wen's mother dreamt that a star (Ching Mu Han) descended and entered her womb. Soon afterwards a son was born once he was called Hao Ssu-wen, with the nickname Ching Mu Han. He is well skilled in military drill, but so far has no opportunity of proving his ability, and lives an insignificant life here." Kuan Sheng proposed to take Hao Ssu-wen with him to fight against the brigands. This was agreed to, and they set out that night for the Eastern Capital. Their arrival was reported to Ts'ai Ching, the royal tutor, who invited them to enter. They all three entered the hall and saluted. Ts'ai Ching was pleased with Kuan Sheng's appearance, and asked for his age. Kuan Sheng replied that he was thirty-two years old. Ts'ai Ching then explained the position at the Northern Capital (Ta Ming Fu) and asked if he had any suggestions to make.

"I have long heard," said Kuan Sheng, "that those brigands occupy Liang Shan Po and make disturbances in the surrounding country. For the first time, however, they now leave their base far behind so I think we can easily defeat them. However, it would be useless to rescue Ta Ming Fu with a large force. I beg you to give me ten thousand soldiers to capture Liang Shan Po first, and by cutting off their base we can early arrest the brigands.

Ts'ai Ching was very much pleased at this, and said, "That is the same method that was used in rescuing the Kingdom of Chao by besieging the capital of the Kingdom of Wei. I agree with your plans." He then summoned the privy councilors, and explaining the plan got three armies placed under the command of Kuan Sheng. An immediate start took place, and the armies went straight to Liang Shan Po

> When dragons leave their home i'th sea;
>   They cannot fly i'th clouds;
> When tigers come down to the plain,
>   Of what use are their claws;
> While yearning for the harvest moon,
>   The pearls in the tray are stolen.

CHAPTER 63

HUYEN SHO LURES KUAN SHENG IN THE MOONLIGHT; SUNG CHIANG ARRESTS SO CH'AO IN A SNOWSTORM

AT TA MING FU the bandits attacked the town every day, but the government troops inside dared not sally forth for combat. So Ch'ao had not yet recovered from the arrow wound, and could not take part in the fighting.

Sung Chiang was disappointed at the delay in taking the town, and one night he was sitting in his tent reading by candlelight the Divine Books he had received from the Taoist Goddess, when his orderly entered and said that Wu Yung wished to see him.

When Wu Yung entered he said, "We have been besieging this town for a long time, and it is strange that no troops have come to relieve the town. We know that three horsemen left the town, and I expect they carried dispatches asking for help. As Liang, the grand secretary, is son-in-law to Ts'ai Ching, the royal tutor, the latter must send relief at once. But as no troops have arrived here it is possible that they have gone to Liang Shan Po, and are adopting the military strategy as used in saving the Chao by besieging the capital of the Wei. In that case, what shall we do? That is a possibility which we must not overlook. Would it not be better if we quietly sent some of our men back?"

Just then Tai Tsung, the Flying Prince, came in and spoke, "A large army of imperial troops have arrived at Liang Shan Po, in charge of General Kuan Sheng. Our leaders there cannot decide as to what should be done, but they ask you at least to send some men back to relieve the assault."

"Though this is the position," said Wu Yung, "we must not send all our men back at once. To-night we can order our foot soldiers to start off on the return journey. The cavalry must be left here, and be so divided up that the enemy will not notice our reduced numbers. If the imperial troops in the town find out our position they would renew their attacks with greater vigor."

"What you say is quite true," said Sung Chiang. He gave orders that Hwa Jung should take charge of five hundred men and encamp on the left of the Flying Tiger Gully, while Lin Ch'ung should encamp on the right-hand side of the same village with another five hundred men. Huyen Sho should post his artillery about three miles from the town, and in case of any attack from the government troops he must at once open fire. All the other men must disperse, and return individually to Liang Shan Po, and were not to fight with any imperial troops they might meet on the way. This movement took place secretly in the night, and by about 10 a.m. the following morning most of the brigands were quietly making their way towards Liang Shan Po.

But the troops inside the town discovered the movement of the brigands, and Liang, the grand secretary, was duly informed of this, and he summoned his two generals for a conference.

"I think that this movement indicates that the imperial troops are attacking Liang Shan Po," said General Li Cheng, "and this has forced the brigands to withdraw their men from here. We must embrace this opportunity to attack them and capture Sung Chiang."

Just at this point a messenger arrived with a dispatch from the royal tutor at the Eastern Capital stating that an attack was being made upon Liang Shan Po, and that if the brigands withdrew from Ta Ming Fu the troops in the town should immediately attack them. Liang, the grand secretary, therefore ordered his generals to pursue the brigands.

The imperial troops shortly afterwards left the town for an assault, but when they had only gone a short distance they were fired upon by artillery at their rear. At this generals Wen Ta and Li Cheng were surprised and called a halt. Looking back they saw numerous flags flying, and heard many drums and gongs sounded as though there were many brigands there. While they were still wondering what to do they were attacked from two sides by the brigands in charge of Hwa Jung and Lin Ch'ung. General Li Cheng was afraid of a trap, and gave orders for a retreat to the town. The attack was so fierce, however, that the troops were just able to reach the town gates in the nick of time.

The brigands who were on their way to Liang Shan Po found their roads blocked by imperial troops, and could not reach their destination. So Sung Chiang collected them together in a secluded place, and sent a messenger secretly to Liang Shan Po informing them where he was, and giving orders for a joint attack to be made from both sides.

At Liang Shan Po Chang Heng and Chang Shun were in charge of a fort on the bank of the lake. When Sung Chiang's order was made known Chang Heng spoke to his brother, "We have been here a long time, but so far have had no chance of doing anything. Now General Kuan Sheng's army is approaching by three roads to attack us. How would it be if we attack his camp and capture the general himself? Then our reputation would be much enhanced."

"We are only in charge of this fort," replied Chang Shun, "and if we do not get help from the other leaders we should be in great disgrace if we lost."

"If we are so circumspect, what day can we achieve a meritorious deed?" said Chang Heng. "You need not take part in this. I will do it by myself this very night."

Chang Shun remonstrated with his brother without effect. That night Chang Heng took fifty boats, with five men on each armed with bamboo poles, spears, and swords, and clad in light short clothing. It was a cold frosty night with very little moonlight. The boats were taken across the lake and the men disembarked.

It was about 11 p.m. and General Kuan Sheng was reading a book in his tent. One of his scouts entered, and reported that many boats had just come across the lake, and that the men were now making their way through the reeds and grasses towards the camp. General Kuan Sheng smiled at this, and turning to his adjutant spoke quietly some secret word.

Chang Heng and his two hundred and fifty men made stealthy progress through the reeds towards Kuan Sheng's camp and removed sundry obstacles placed there as part of the defenses of the camp. In the camp they saw the general's tent, well lighted by lamps, and the general himself reading a book and stroking his beard. Chang Heng saw no soldiers about, so he ran forward with his long spear in his hand. He had not gone into the tent when a gong was sounded, and there was such an outburst of shouting that it seemed as though both heaven and earth were falling to pieces. Chang Heng was alarmed, and turned to retreat. But it was too late. He was seized, and also all his men were surrounded and captured. They were all taken before General Kuan Sheng who laughed when he saw them. "You rabble of brigands! How dare you visit me like this?" He ordered Chang Heng to be placed in a prisoner's cart and the rest to be put under guard.

At Liang Shan Po Chang Shun went to the headquarters where the leaders were assembled, and told them what had occurred to his brother.

Upon hearing this Yuan the Seventh was excited, and said, "We are all in the same boat, and we must at once rescue our elder brother. Why did you not rescue him yourself? I and my brothers must go at once to rescue him."

"It was done without any orders," said Chang Shun, "and therefore I dared not go with him."

"If you wait for orders from our commander-in-chief before you act then you will be too late to save your brother," said Yuan the Seventh.

Chan Shun and the three brothers Yuan thereupon embarked their men, and about 3 a.m. a hundred boats were filled with men and went across the lake.

The scouts of the imperial troops seeing this fleet with armed men immediately informed Kuan Sheng. He laughed, and said, "These slaves are stupid." He turned and whispered orders to his adjutant again.

The brigands disembarked, and as they approached the camp they saw many lights burning, but not a single man. The brothers Yuan were startled, and decided to retreat. But gong was sounded, but immediately soldiers sprang forth from hiding places on all sides. The brigands were quite surrounded, and Chang Shun being near the boats dived into the water at once. He and about four others escaped in this way, but all the others were taken prisoners.

Upon the news of the disaster reaching Liang Shan Po, Liu Tang ordered Chang Shun at once to make his way by swimming to Sung Chiang's secluded camp. Upon arriving there Chang Shun told the news, and Sung Chiang discussed with Wu Yung how they could repel General Kuan Sheng's army.

"To-morrow we must have a trial of strength with these imperial troops," said Wu Yung.

While they were talking of their plans the sound of drums was heard, and Wu Yung was surprised as it indicated that General Hsuan Tsan was approaching to attack the secluded camp. Sung Chiang marched all his men out to meet the attack, and met then the imperial troops. He turned to his men, and asked, "Who will go for single combat?" In response Hwa Jung spurred his horse forward to engage in combat with General Hsuan Tsan. That general was ready, and they engaged in a fight. After about ten bouts, Hwa Jung decided on a change of tactics. After delivering a blow with his sword he wheeled round and retreated. He now took his bow and arrow, and turning in his saddle shot at General Hsuan Tsan who was pursuing him. The general saw the movement, and lifting his sword caught the flying arrow with it. Hwa Jung saw that he had failed, so immediately took another arrow, and shot it at the general who was now quite close. This time the general saw the arrow, and bent down on his horse, and the arrow just missed him. But the general realized the great skill of Hwa Jung, and decided to run no further risks. He turned his horse, and went back to his men. Hwa Jung seeing this also turned and pursued the general. Again he shot an arrow, but this struck the brass plate on the general's back and did no damage. Now the general rushed back to his camp and reported the feat to Kuan Sheng.

General Kuan Sheng ordered his attendant to bring his fiery horse. He rode forth with his big sword in his hand. Sung Chiang saw the fine martial bearing of the man, and turning round called out, "He is indeed a great hero!" Lin Ch'ung hearing this expression was annoyed, and called out, "We brothers, since we joined at Liang Shan Po we have taken part in many fights, and so far have never been daunted in any contact. To-day we are not to be despised." So saying he whipped his horse and rushed forward to fight.

General Kuan Sheng seeing this called out, "You brigands, it is not worth while for me to fall on you. I want Sung Chiang to come forward, and explain why he has rebelled."

Sung Chiang hearing this called Lin Ch'ung to return, and then rode forward himself. He halted in front of General Kuan Sheng, and saluting said, "I am now waiting for your questions."

"You were a clerk in a yamen," shouted General Kuan Sheng, "how dare you rebel in this way?"

"The imperial affairs are in disorder," replied Sung Chiang, "and corrupt officials are in power; loyal men are ignored; and covetous men are employed. This results in the suffering of the people. We are the agents of Heaven, and have no personal aims."

Kuan Sheng shouted, "It is clear that you are a brigand. Which Heaven has appointed you? My troops carry out the Son of Heaven's wish, but you have only fine words on your side. If you don't dismount at once, I will have you cut into many pieces."

Upon hearing this Chin Ming was angry, and dashed from the rear on horseback. At the same moment Lin Ch'ung did the same. Kuan Sheng, however, stod his ground, and fought with the two. The three horses circled round like a small whirlwind. Sung Chiang called to the gongs to summon the two leaders to come back, and when they returned Chin Ming protested, "We could have captured that man. Why did you stop us?"

Sung Chiang replied in a loud voice, "We are honest and upright, and we do not like to see two men attacking one. It is not fair. If you had captured him you could not capture his mind. He is a loyal and devoted official, and the spirits of his ancestors must be very proud of him. If we could win him over I would immediately resign in his favor."

Both Chin Ming and Lin Ch'ung could say nothing against this. That day nothing further was done, and both armies retired to their bases.

Upon reaching his camp General Kuan Sheng doffed his mail armor and sat down in silent meditation, "I would have been defeated by those two men, but when they were on the point of seizing me Sung Chiang summoned them to return I wonder why he did that?" So he sent for both Chang Heng and Yuan the Seventh (the prisoners) and then asked them, "Sung Chiang previously was only a clerk in a magistrate's yamen so why do you men serve him so faithfully?"

Yuan the Seventh replied, "Our leader Sung Chiang is famous in Shantung and Hopei (north of the Yellow River) as the protector. You do not know honest and upright men, and therefore cannot recognize such men when you meet them."

General Kuan Sheng bowed his head, but did not speak except ordering the prisoners to be taken back. That night he was restless, and as he could not sleep he got up, and strolled round his camp in the moonlight. It was a cold night, and hoarfrost covered the ground. Shortly an orderly came and said that a general had arrived and wished to speak to him.

"What is his name?" asked General Kuan Sheng.

"He would not tell me that," said the orderly. "He is however unarmed and without mail armor."

"In that case you can admit him," said the general.

In a short time the man was brought to his tent. General Kuan Sheng trimmed his lamp so as to get a clear view of the man, and thought the face was familiar. He, however, asked for his name.

"Can we talk together privately?" asked the man.

General Kuan Sheng laughed at this and said, "I am commander-in-chief of these hundred thousand soldiers, and we are all united together with one mind. If we were not of one mind how could I command them? They are all familiar with my affairs, and I keep no secrets from them. You can talk to me without any hesitation."

"I am Huyen Sho," said the man, "and was previously a general in the imperial army, and was once appointed to attack the brigand at Liang Shan Po. They captured me by a ruse, and all my army was annihilated so that I dared not go back. Yesterday I heard that you had arrived here, and I was much pleased. This morning you were attacked by Chin Ming and Lin Ch'ung, but Sung Chiang summoned them to return as he was afraid that they might wound you. He had the idea that at some time he might surrender to you but the others would not agree with him. Just now I have had a secret conversation with Sung Chiang, and discussed how we might make all the others surrender to you. So if you are willing we can suggest a plan. To-morrow night you my come to our camp by a small by-path, lightly armed, to capture Lin Ch'ung and the other bandits. By this not only you will gain great credit, but Sung Chiang and I may also redeem our guilt."

General Kuan Sheng was much pleased at this, and invited Huyen Sho to drink wine with him. Huyen Sho talked very much of the honesty and justice of Sung Chiang, and dwelt upon his hard luck which had forced him to become a brigand.

The next day General Kuan Sheng spoke to Huyen Sho, "As you have a certain plot for this evening, it would be better if I attacked and defeated the brigands to-day."

Huyen Sho donned his mail armor, and rode to the front of the imperial army. When Sung Chiang saw him he cursed him, "We never treated you unfairly why did you desert us last night?"

"Previously you were only a petty officer so how could you undertake a big affair now," replied Huyen Sho.

Sung Chiang did not reply to this insult, but ordered Huang Hsin to engage in single combat with Huyen Sho. The two fought for about ten bouts, and then Huyen Sho hit Huang Hsin a severe blow with his bludgeon and knocked him off his horse.

General Kuan Sheng was much pleased at this, and ordered a general attack. But Huyen Sho said this was not advisable because Wu Yung was full of tricks which he would use if his men were hard pressed. General Kuan Sheng agreed and ordered a retreat to their camp.

Upon reaching the camp generals Kuan Sheng and Huyen Sho drank wine in the former's tent, and there the general asked about the opponent who apparently had been killed.

"That man was previously a lieutenant-general in the imperial army," replied Huyen Sho. "He joined the brigands at the same time as Chin Ming and Hwa Jung. He is at variance with Sung Chiang about many questions and perhaps that is why Sung Chiang to-day ordered him to attack me so that he (Huang Hsin) would get killed and be removed out of his way."

General Kuan Sheng was pleased to hear this. He issued orders that generals Hsuan Tsan and Hao Ssu-wen at eleven o'clock that night should lead five hundred cavalry as a reserve on an attack on Sung Chiang's camp. At the appointed time everything was ready. The iron accouterments on horses and men had been taken off so that less noise would be made. Each man had a small gag in his mouth to prevent any talking. Huyen Sho mounted his horse and led the way.

It was a bright moonlight night. They had traveled for about an hour, and upon turning round a mountain they encountered a party of about fifty mounted brigands who called, "Are you not Huyen Sho's men?"

Huyen Sho told the men not to speak, but just follow him. He then whipped his horse, and galloped forward followed by General Kuan Sheng and his men. They had soon passed round another ridge of the mountain, and then Huyen Sho halted, and pointed to a red lamp burning in the distance on the mountain.

"Where is that red lamp burning?" asked the general.

"That is in Sung Chiang's camp," replied Huyen Sho.

They proceeded on their way, but when fairly near the red camp a bomb was fired, and General Kuan Sheng galloped forward and called his men to follow him. But when they reached the red lamp they found nobody there, and even Huyen Sho had vanished. General Kuan Sheng was startled and realized that he had been deceived. He turned round and ordered a retreat.

But now gongs and drums were heard on all sides. The path was soon lost, and the general saw his men scattering in all directions so that soon he had only about ten men with him. As they turned the spur of the mountain another bomb was fired, and he now saw a large body of armed brigands blocking his way. He was soon surrounded by men armed with hooked poles, and with these they caught hold of his clothes and pulled him off his horse. They seized his sword and horse, bound his arm, and pushed him forward towards their camp. Lin Ch'ung and Hwa Jung led another attacking party, to cut off Kuan Sheng's reserve forces in charge of Lieutenant-General Hsuan Tsan who fought for about twenty bouts in the bright moonlight. At the end Hsuan Tsan was almost exhausted, and turning his horse tried to escape. But the Girl Amazon Miss Hu had been watching this at one side, and she now threw her red silk lasso, caught Hsuan Tsan, and brought him off his horse. He was seized by the men around, and was also taken to the brigand's camp as a prisoner.

We will now see what had happened to the brigands led by Chin Ming and Sun Li against the reserve force of the imperial troops under Lieutenant-General Hao Ssu-wen. When they met on the road Hao Ssu-wen reviled the brigands, "If you brigands obstruct my progress you will certainly die. If you wish to live then withdraw at once."

Chin Ming was angry at this speech, lashed his horse, and dashed forward for single combat. They fought for a long time, and then Sun Li went forward to assist Chin Ming. When Hao Ssu-wen saw he had two opponents he was undecided what to do and was off his usual guard. Chin Ming seized the opportunity, and knocked Hao Ssu-wen off his horse, who was immediately seized by the brigands.

Li Ying led other brigands to the camp of the imperial troops, where they overcome the guard, released Yuan the Seventh and Chang Heng, and took away all the stores, fodder, and accouterments.

It was near daybreak when all was finished, and Sung Chiang ordered all to start for Liang Shan Po. Upon arriving there all the leaders assembled in the Loyalty and Justice Hall where the three captured generals were brought. Sung Chiang came forward to meet the generals, and released them himself. He conducted General Kuan Sheng, and made him sit in his own chair. He then bowed, and saluted the general and said, "We ruffians have offended your dignity, and beg for your pardon."

Huyen Sho now stepped forward, bowed, saluted, and then addressed the general, "I acted under orders from my commanding officer whom I dared not disobey. I hope that you will forgive me for deceiving you."

General Kuan Sheng looked round on all the assembled leaders, and realized that they were all actuated by upright principles. He turned round and spoke to his two lieutenant generals, "We are prisoners here. What can we do?"

"We will follow your orders," they replied.

"We are too disgraced to return to the capital," said General Kuan Sheng to Sung Chiang. "Let us have an early death."

"Why do you talk like that?" asked Sung Chiang. "If you do not despise our lowly calling perhaps you might join us to carry out the heavenly wish. But if you are unwilling to do so, then we will not detain you here, but allow you to return to the capital."

"Many people have said that you are loyal and just, but now I know that that remark is true," said General Kuan Sheng. "In this life if the emperor treats me well, I will support him; if a friend treats me well, I will support him too. Now as I am undetermined I will stay here in the capacity of a small soldier."

Sung Chiang was much pleased, and ordered a feast to be prepared in honor of the general. He also ordered all the prisoners to be brought to Liang Shan Po, and to be well treated. Those soldiers who wished to return home were allowed to do so, and presented with money for traveling expenses. A man was also sent to take the family of General Kuan Sheng to join him at Liang Shan Po.

During the aforementioned feast Sung Chiang remembered that Lu Tsun-i and Shih Hsiu were still in the prison at Ta Ming Fu (Northern Capital) so he shed tears. Wu Yung then spoke to Sung Chiang, "Brother, do not be downhearted. I have a plan of rescuing our brothers. To-morrow morning we may dispatch men to assist in the final attack on Ta Ming Fu."

Upon hearing this General Kuan Sheng stood up and said, "I have not yet had the opportunity of recompensing you for your generosity, please allow me to take charge of this movement."

Sung Chiang was much pleased, and agreed to this. Kuan Shen's troops were now enrolled as brigands, and were placed in charge of Hao Ssu-wen and Hsuan Tsan who were under General Kuan Sheng. They were to be the vanguard in the new attack on Ta Ming Fu.

In the Northern Capital Liang, the grand secretary, was now dining with So Ch'ao. It was a dull day with a strong wind blowing   A scout entered, and reported that General Kuan Sheng and all his troops had been captured, and moreover had all joined the brigands. They were now all advancing towards the Northern Capital (Ta Ming Fu).

When Liang heard this he was astounded, and dropped the wine glass he was holding at the moment.

"I was wounded by an arrow from the brigands, and now must have my revenge," said So Ch'ao.

Liang, the grand secretary, filled up a glass with wine, and presented it to So Ch'ao saying, "Take the troops to encounter immediately."

It was now the middle of winter, and the weather was very cold with strong winds. The hoofs of the horses were frozen and the mail armors were as cold as ice when they left the town.

Sung Chiang had taken up his position on a mound where he could watch the pending battle.

The brigands under Kuan Sheng soon faced the troops under So Ch'ao. The latter did not recognize Kuan Sheng, but his officers told him that fact. So Ch'ao did not make any remark, but dashed forward on his horse, Kuan Sheng also did the same, and the two fought.

After about ten bouts Lieutenant-General Li Cheng saw that So Ch'ao was getting the worst of the combat so he galloped forward to assist him. But Hsuan Tsan and Hao Ssu-wen on the other side, seeing this move, also came forward to assist Kuan Sheng. Now the five horses were so close together that it was hard to follow individual movements. Sung Chiang seeing this from his mound ordered a general advance, and the brigands attacked the imperial troops, and drove them back towards the city. When they were close to the gates Sung Chiang signaled for a cessation of hostilities.

The following day was very cloudy and it seemed going to rain. So Ch'ao led his troops outside the city, and Wu Yung ordered the brigands to put up a trifling defense. If pressed they were to retire. Thus So Ch'ao won a slight victory, but ordered a retreat. That evening the clouds were heavier and quite low, and a big wind also sprang up. This was soon followed by a heavy fall of snow. Seeing this Wu Yung ordered a party of men to proceed to a defile in the hills near the town where a narrow road passed through, and there make pitfalls which, when finished, were to be covered over with earth. This was done. It snowed all night, and next morning the snow was deep enough to reach to the horse's knees.

In the morning So Ch'ao went to the city wall to view the enemy. He noticed that owing to the snow the horses moved with difficulty, and were in some disorder. He therefore ordered three hundred of his cavalry to start a sudden raid. The mounted brigands upon seeing the cavalry scattered in all directions.

Sung Chiang had ordered Li Chun and Chang Shun to leave off their mail armor, and go out for single combat. They opposed So Ch'ao, but soon threw away their spears and bolted after their men. So Ch'ao was hasty, and pursued these men who induced So Ch'ao towards the concealed pitfalls. The narrow path was on the bank of the river, and upon reaching that part the two men dismounted and jumped into the river as though to escape from So Ch'ao. In the water Li Chun called out, "Brother Sung Chiang, get away quickly!" and So Ch'ao hearing this dashed forward along the road towards the point where he thought Sung

Chiang was, and fell into one of the pitfalls, and at once brigands were on the scene from all sides. Even So Ch'ao had had six arms and three heads he could not have got away.

> White sheets of snow like silver,
> As pure as broken jade,
> Concealed a cunning pitfall,
> As good as man e'r made.

CHAPTER 64

CH'AO KAI APPEARS IN A DREAM;
WHITE FISH HAS HIS REVENGE

So CH'AO'S soldiers did not follow his mad dash, but returned to the city and reported the matter to the Grand Secretary who was much upset by the news. He gave orders for all soldiers to stand on defense, but not go outside the city. He realized now that he could not execute Lu Tsun-i or Shih Hsiu without aggravating Sung Chiang for another attack. As the imperial troops had been defeated he saw disaster facing him. He sent an urgent messenger to the Eastern Capital reporting the position and appealing for help.

So Ch'ao was taken to the brigand's camp as a prisoner, and was brought before the assembled leaders in Sung Chiang's tent. Sung Chiang was much pleased at seeing him, dismissed the guard, untied the prisoner's bonds, and then addressed him, "You will have noticed that among our leaders here more than half have previously served in the imperial army. If you do not disdain us we request you to join us to execute heavenly wish."

Yang Chih now stepped forward, and greeted So Ch'ao as an old friend. They talked and wept together at this meeting.

Since this was the position So Ch'ao accepted Sung Chiang's proposal. Sung Chiang was very glad at this, and ordered a feast to be prepared to celebrate the occasion.

On following day the attack on Ta Ming Fu continued, and was repeated for several days without any success. One night when Sung Chiang was sitting in his tent in a melancholy mood, suddenly a very cold wind sprang up, and his lamp was almost extinguished by the icy blast. Looking up he saw in the dim light the form of a man who looked very like his late commander Ch'ao Kai. The figure did not enter his tent, but spoke, "Younger brother, what are you doing here?"

Sung Chiang was startled, but standing up, he replied, "Elder brother, where have you come from? I am very sorry that since you left I have not been able to avenge your death. Just now we have urgent business here so that I have not been able to sacrifice to you for some time. To-day your spirit has appeared, and I am quite prepared to be reproved for my faults."

"Brother, you do not understand," said Ch'ao Kai. "We were bosom friends, so I have now come to help you. There is a propitious star (Ti Ling Hsing) in Kiangnan which will relieve you of your load of trouble. Of many plans sometimes the best and only one is to leave. Why do you not clear out at once? What keeps you here? If a calamity is approaching how can you avoid it? By that time you must not blame me for giving you no help."

Sung Chiang wished for further information and took a step forward. He asked, "Spirit of my Elder Brother! I beg you to speak clearly and truthfully."

"You need not speak any further," said Ch'ao Kai. "Arrange your affairs and depart without any delay. I must go now."

The figure vanished, and Sung Chiang thought he had only had a dream. But he sent for Wu Yung to come and see him at once. Upon the latters arriving Sung Chiang told him of his dream.

"We cannot doubt that Ch'ao Kai's spirit has actually conveyed that message to you," said Wu Yung. "It is very cold here, and our men cannot stand these hard conditions very long. We must send them all back to Liang Shan Po. We can come again in spring and attack this town with greater chances of success."

"What you say is quite true," said Sung Chiang. "But Lu Tsun-i and Shih Hsiu are still in prison, and they are expecting us to save them. I am afraid that they will be executed if we leave now. What shall we do?"

They talked the matter over for a long time, but came to no decision.

The following day Sung Chiang was feverish, and also had a splitting headache. He felt very tired, and did not get up. The leaders came to see what was the matter, and Sung Chiang told them that he had a pain in his back. Upon examining the spot they found a big red swelling. Wu Yung said, "I have read in a medicine book that the poison in these swellings can be kept away from the heart by a diet of green beans. We have no doctor on our strength, so that is the best thing for the remedy."

"Previously my mother had the same complaint," said Chang Shun, "and although we tried a hundred medicines she got no better. At last we got a doctor named An Tao-ch'uan from Chien K'ang Fu[1] who knew the disease and cured her. I was very grateful to him, and whenever I got some money I sent it to him as gifts. I will ask him to come here and cure Sung Chiang. But it is a long journey, and will take some time to get the doctor here."

Wu Yung then mentioned Sung Chiang's dream of Ch'ao Kai the previous night, and said how Ch'ao Kai had suggested that a propitious star in Kiangnan (South of the Yangtze River) could relieve him of a coming calamity. "Can it be that this doctor, An Tao-ch'uan, is that very star?"

"Younger brother," said Sung Chiang, "send for this man at once, and save my life. There must not be the least delay in this matter."

Wu Yung got about one hundred ounces of silver for the doctor and handed them to Chang Shun. He also told him, "To-day we are all going back to Liang Shan Po, so you must bring the doctor there without any delay."

Chang Shun started off immediately.

Wu Yung then issued orders for a return to Liang Shan Po, and they started that very day, Sung Chiang being carried on his bed in a cart.

When Liang, the grand secretary, heard of the departure of the brigands he discussed matters with his generals, and decided not to pursue them as they considered this move might be some new plot of the brigands to get them out of Ta Ming Fu.

Chang Shun traveled day and night with all possible speed, but he found it somewhat difficult owing to the snow

[1] Modern Nanking.

on the ground. He braved both wind and snow without regard for his own safety. At last he reached the Yangtze River, but there was no boat available. He was very disappointed at this, but continued his way along the northern bank. He soon came to many reeds amid which he saw some smoke. He called out, "Lao Ta! quickly get your boat ready to take me across." A man emerged from the reeds wearing a broad straw hat and a grass raincoat. He asked, "Where do you want to go?"

"I want to go to Chien K'ang Fu, on urgent business," replied Chang Shun, "and I will pay you much money to row me across the river quickly."

"I can take you across," said the man, "but it is getting rather dark now, and there is no place on the opposite bank for you to sleep. You had better sleep in my boat here, and I will take you across to-morrow morning at daybreak."

Chang Shun agreed to this, and followed the man through the reeds to the bank where there was a boat with a young fellow on board warming himself at a fire. They went under cover on the boat, and Chang Shun took off his wet clothing, and the boatman handed it to his assistant to dry at the fire. Chang Shun undid his baggage, took his quilt, and wrapping it round himself lay down. He then asked the boatman whether it was possible to get some wine, and was informed there was none. Chang Shun ate some rice, and then lay down again. He had had such a hard day traveling that he was very tired and soon fell asleep.

The assistant, seeing this, pulled his lips awry towards Chang Shun, and whispered to the boatman, "Brother, do you see?" The boatman crept forward silently and felt at Chang Shun's bundle. He then went back, and told his assistant to quietly row the boat into the middle of the river where they would kill the passenger. The assistant jumped ashore, and untied the boat. Then pushing with a bamboo pole and then sculling, he took the boat into the middle of the river. While this was being done the boatman had quietly bound the sleeper with cords, and now carried him from underneath the cover on to the open deck. Chang Shun was now awake, but found himself bound hand and foot. The boatman took a knife in one hand, and put the other hand on Chang Shun.

"Please spare my life," appealed Chang Shun. "I will give you all the money I have."

"I want both your money and your life," replied the boatman.

"Then do not kill me, but only drown me," appealed Chang Shun, "and then my spirit will not trouble you afterwards."

"That I can do," said the boatman. He then took Chang Shun and threw him into the water. Taking the bundle he opened it and was surprised to find such a lot of money. He frowned at this, and called his assistant. When the latter came inside, the boatman seized him, and taking the knife killed him on the spot. He then threw the body overboard. He washed the blood from the deck, and then sculled back to the bank.

When Chang Shun was in the water he soon bit the cords tying his hands, then freed his feet, and swam to the southern bank of the Yangtze River. There he saw a light among some trees, and going near he found that it was an inn where they were distilling wine in the night. He called out, and pushing open the door entered, and saluted an old man who was inside.

The old man said, "I can see that you have been robbed on the river, and have escaped by jumping into the water, and swimming ashore."

"I will be quite straight with you," said Chang Shun. "I am from Shantung, and am on my way to Chien K'ang Fu on urgent business. Last evening I got on a boat to cross the river, and did not suspect that the boatmen were bad fellows. They took all my silver and clothes, and threw me into the water. But I swam across to this side, and so saved my life. I appeal for your assistance."

The men led Chang Shun into a room at the back, and gave him dry clothes for a change. He then produced food and wine. He asked for Chang Shun's name and his business.

Chang Shun gave his name, and explained that he wished to see an old friend Dr. An at Chien K'ang Fu.

"On your way here did you pass Liang Shan Po?" asked the man.

Chang Shun admitted this, and the man remarked, "At

that place there is a man named Sung Chiang who does not molest travelers, but acts as the 'agent of heaven.'"

"Yes," said Chang Shun, "he is a very honest and upright man. He does not injure the people, but is opposed to all corrupt officials."

"I have heard the same. His followers help the poor, and the old, and are quite different to the brigands about here. If he came to this place he would be welcomed by all the people."

Chang Shun then disclosed that he was one of the leaders at Liang Shan Po. That Sung Chiang was seriously ill with a boil on the back, and he (Chang Shun) had been given a hundred ounces of silver to go quickly for Dr. An. It was a misfortune that he had fallen asleep on the boat and been robbed.

The old man said, "As you are one of those leaders I will introduce my son to you." In a short time a young man came from the back room, and saluted Chang Shun. He said, "I am Wang Ting-liu, but the people call me, 'Living Pluto's Wife,' because I walk very quickly. I like swimming, but so far have not been able to get a good instructor to teach me the use of sticks, and have had to earn a living at this inn. I know those two thieves who assaulted you. One is Chang Wang, the River Devil, and the other is Sun the Fifth, the Oily Eel. They are always robbing travelers. If you would stay here for a few days you would see them come here, and then you could have your revenge."

"I am grateful for your offer," said Chang Shun, "but I cannot delay my important affair. So to-morrow I will go to the town, and after finding Dr. An I will see you again on my way back."

This was agreed to, and the following day Wang Ting-liu gave Chang Shun new clothes and ten ounces of silver. It was a fine day, and the snow had stopped. Chang Shun soon reached the town, and found Dr. An's place close to the Ash Tree Bridge. He entered the dispensary, and saluted Dr. An Tao-ch'uan.

Immediately Dr. An remembered him, and said, "I have not seen you for many years. What wind has blown you here?"

Chang Shun went into the inner room, and there told the doctor his business. He explained how he had been robbed in crossing the Yangtze River, and therefore arrived without money.

"As Sung Chiang, the uprighteous hero, is sick, it is important that he should be cured quickly," said Dr. An. "But unfortunately my wife died recently, and as I have no relative to look after my business here I cannot go to any distant place."

Chang Shun pleaded earnestly for a long time for the doctor to go, and at last said he would not return without the doctor. Thus after much discussion Dr. An agreed to go.

In the town was a prostitute named Li Chiao-nu who was on very familiar terms with Dr. An, and the latter took Chang Shun to see her. Food and wine were provided, and during the meal Dr. An spoke, "I will sleep here to-night, but early to-morrow morning I will start on my journey to Shantung. I will return however in about a month."

"I do not like you to leave me," said the woman. "If you do not listen to me now you need not trouble to come here again to see me."

"I have made all preparations to start to-morrow," said Dr. An, "and I will come back as quickly as possible, so you must not worry."

The woman threw all discretion on one side, and leaning on his breast said, "If you go and forget me, I will curse you to your destruction."

Chang Shun was very much annoyed with the woman. As it was now late in the evening, Dr. An was drunk, and he went into the woman's room, and lay down. The woman spoke to Chang Shun, "You can go now, as I have no place here for you to sleep."

"I will wait here until the doctor is sober," said Chang Shun, "and then we will depart together."

As she could not get him to go, the woman at last gave him a small room to sleep in.

Chang Shun was annoyed at what had happened, and could not sleep. Shortly afterwards he heard a knock at the house door, and looking through a crack in his own room, he saw the door open and a man enter. The man spoke something to the woman who opened the door for him and she asked him, "Where have you been lately? I have not seen you for a long time. The doctor is drunk inside, so you cannot stay here to-night."

"I have ten ounces of gold here to be made into hair-pins for your mistress. Please ask her to come here and talk with me now," said the man.

"Come into my room," said the woman, "and I will bring her there."

Chang Shun now recognized the man as Chang Wang, the River Devil, who had robbed him, and became excited. But he still watched what was happening as he did not want to delay his own affair by attacking this thief. The prostitute came, and sat drinking wine with Chang Wang. About midnight the woman and two servants in the kitchen were quite drunk. Then Chang Shun left his room, and went into the kitchen where he found a knife there. He killed the woman, but although he wanted to kill the two servants he found that the edge of the knife was not sharp enough. He took a wood chopper and killed them with that as they were going to call out. The prostitute in the inner room hearing the noise, opened the door, and met Chang Shun with the wood chopper in his hand. He dealt her a blow with it, and killed her on the spot. Chang Wang, the robber, seeing this happen, jumped up, opened a window, and escaped that way. Chang Shun was annoyed at this as the man might raise an alarm. He, however, tore a strip of cloth from the woman's clothing and dipping it in the pool of blood he wrote on the wall, "I, Dr. An, have killed these people." He wrote this in several places with the blood. About daybreak Dr. An awoke, and Cheng Shun said to him, "Please keep quiet but look at your lover here." Dr. An got up, and seeing the four corpses he was dumbfounded and trembled with fear.

"Brother, do you see what you have written on the walls?" asked Chang Shun.

"You have seriously implicated me and endangered my life," said Dr. An.

"There are two ways lying before you," said Chang Shun. "You can cry out for help in which case I shall run away, and leave you to your fate. Or you can ignore this affair, go to your shop for your medicines, and escape with me to Liang Shan Po to cure Sung Chiang. Which do you prefer?"

"You have been too malicious in your actions," said Dr. An, but he agreed to go.

It was still dark, and they both left the house. Upon reaching the doctor's shop they opened the door, got the medicines and bundle, and started off at once. They left the town, and duly reached the inn owned by Wang Ting-liu on the bank of the Yangtze River. When he saw Chang Shun he said, "It was a pity that you were not here yesterday when Chang Wang happened to come here."

"I saw him yesterday," said Chang Shun, "but I was too busy to attend to him. My business is so pressing that I have no time even for revenge."

Just as he finished saying this Wang Ting-liu exclaimed, "Why, here is Chang Wang coming now!"

"Do not alarm him! We will just see where he goes," said Chang Shun.

Chang Wang walked to the bank of the river, and was evidently looking around for his boat. So Wang Ting-liu called out, "Brother, wait a little, and you can take two of my guests across who are waiting here now."

"I want to cross at once," said Chang Wang. "Tell your guests to come quickly."

Wang Ting-liu informed Chang Shun of this, and Chang Shun asked Dr. An to change clothes with him. "What is your idea?" asked Dr. An. "That is my affair," said Chang Shun, "and you had better not ask any questions."

They exchanged clothing, and then went with Wang Ting-liu to the bank where Chang Wang's boat was waiting. They all three got in the boat. Chang Shun went to the stern, and lifting up a plank took out a knife that was there. He hid himself under the cover of the boat. Chang Wang shoved the boat off, and yalued (sculled) towards the middle of the river. Chang Shun now took off his clothes and called out, "Lao Ta, come here! There are stains of blood on the planks."

"Sir, please do not joke with me," replied Chang Wang. So saying he left the oar, and went towards the center of the boat. Then Chang Shun seized hold of him, and said, "Thief! Don't you recognize me? Don't you remember the passenger who came on your boat the other night when it was snowing?"

Chang Wang looked up, but could not speak.

"You took all my money," said Chang Shun, "and tried to kill me. Where is your assistant now?"

"Sir," said Chang Wang, "when I saw such a lot of money I was afraid that he would want an equal share, so I killed him and threw his body in the river."

"Previously I lived at Chiang Chou," said Chang Shun, "and earned a living as a wholesale fish dealer. But now I live at Liang Shan Po under our leader Sung Chiang, and we are feared everywhere. You falsely decoyed me on your boat, and while asleep you bound me, and threw me into the river. If I had not been an expert swimmer I should have been drowned. We are now enemies, and I must kill you." He then pulled Chang Wang on to the deck, bound him hand and foot, and threw him into the river.

Wang Ting-liu heaved a sigh at this. Chang Shun found where his money was stored, and took it back. They brought the boat to the northern bank, and there Chang Shun spoke to Wang Ting-liu, "You have been very good to me, and I shall never forget it. But if you do not think yourself above us, we should be very glad if you and your father would come and join us at Liang Shan Po."

"What you say is just my own idea," said Wang Ting-liu.

They then took leave of each other, and Chang Shun and Dr. An continued on their way. But Dr. An was a literary man, and was not accustomed to traveling, so after walking about ten miles he could not go any further. Chang Shun found an inn, and they went inside to rest a while. While they were eating a meal they noticed a man coming in who spoke to Chang Shun, "Brother, how is it that you are so late?" Chang Shun recognized the man as Tai Tsung, the Flying Prince. Chang Shun introduced Dr. An, and then asked about Sung Chiang.

"He is still very sick," said Tai Tsung, "and cannot take any food. It looks as though he might die."

Chang Shun weeped at this. Dr. An asked what was the state of the patient's complexion.

Tai Tsung replied, "His skin is quite dry and wrinkled. He cries out with pain, and we are afraid that he is about to die."

"As he feels the pain I think we can cure him," said Dr. An. "But we must not delay our journey, but get there quickly."

"That is easy," said Tai Tsung. He took two of his magic greaves, and fastened them on Dr. An's legs. He then shouldered the Doctor's satchel and spoke to Chang Shun, "I will go with Dr. An first, and you may follow us slowly." They then went outside the inn, and the two flew away.

Chang Shun stayed at the inn for three days, and then he was joined by Wang Ting-liu and his father. They traveled together to Liang Shan Po.

Tai Tsung and Dr. An reached the mountain stronghold that night, and were at once taken in to see Sung Chiang. The doctor found the patient breathing very feebly, and felt his pulse. Dr. An spoke to the leaders, "You need not be afraid, as it is not a serious illness, and I think I can cure him, so that he will be all right again in about ten days." The doctor then took some artemisia, and spread it on the boil to draw out the poisonous matter. He also gave him some medicine to take. After about ten days of this treatment Sung Chiang's skin looked quite rosy, and was not so dry and warm as before. He also began to take nourishment.

As he got better, however, he began to worry and weep about Shih Hsiu and Lu Tsun-i being still prisoners in Ta Ming Fu. Dr. An, however, objected to his being moved, or doing anything as he was only convalescent.

"Brother," said Wu Yung, "you can leave matters in my hands while you yourself obey the doctor's orders. It is now springtime, and I will undertake an attack on Ta Ming Fu, and release our brothers from prison."

"If you avenge the wrong done to our brothers," said Sung Chiang, "I shall die in peace."

All the leaders were summoned to the Loyalty and Justice Hall where Wu Yung announced his plans for an attack on Ta Ming Fu.

> City changed to fiery furnace,
>   Mass of spears like forest trees;
> Corpses piled up high as mountain,
>   Blood in pools as wide as seas;
> Loyal heroes with their laughter
>   Make the devils turn and flee.

CHAPTER 65

SHIH CH'IEN SETS FIRE TO THE BLUE CLOUD TOWER; WU YUNG TAKES TA MING FU WITH A SUBTLE PLAN

"I am very glad that you are getting better," said Wu Yung to Sung Chiang. "While you have been sick I have sent many spies to Ta Ming Fu, and they have reported that Liang, the grand secretary, is still very anxious and afraid that we will soon renew our attack. I have also had anonymous posters secretly put up in the city and the surrounding villages assuring the people that 'they need not be afraid when the Liang Shan Po heroes appear again. Our hatred is directed against our enemy only, and the creditor will only collect the debt from the debtor. Our army is only for our enemies.' Liang has got our posters, which have upset him very much. At the Eastern Capital the royal tutor feels much disgrace because of the disaster to the imperial troops under General Kuan Sheng. Many letters have been sent to the grand secretary ordering him not to execute the two prisoners Lu Tsun-i and Shih Hsiu and that he must endeavor to placate us at Liang Shan Po that we may come over on friendly terms to their side."

Sung Chiang upon hearing this urged Wu Yung to depart at once to attack Ta Ming Fu.

"Now the winter is over and spring is drawing near," said Wu Yung. "It will soon be the Lantern Feast (15th day of the first month), when there will be a great display of lanterns in Ta Ming Fu. I am going to embrace the opportunity of the festival to get many of our men in disguise into the city, and then they can coöperate when our men attack the city from outside."

"A splendid plan!" said Sung Chiang, "I wish you success."

"It is of first importance," said Wu Yung, "that many buildings should be set on fire inside the town as a signal to our men outside. Who is willing to go inside the town and set the place ablaze?"

A man stepped forward and said he was willing to go. This man was Shih Ch'ien, the Flea on the Drum. He said, "When I was young I lived in Ta Ming Fu. In the city is a tower called the Blue Cloud Tower, and there are over a hundred rooms there. At the Feast of Lanterns the city will be crowded, and on that night I will set fire to the Tower, and then our men outside can march in, and take the city."

This was agreed to, and it was arranged for Shih Ch'ien to leave the following day. Hsieh Chen and Hsieh Pao were ordered to be dressed up as hunters, carrying games to Ta Ming Fu, to be presented to the officials at the yamen. They had orders that at the Feast of Lanterns when they saw the Blue Cloud Tower burst into flames they must station themselves near the entrance to the yamen to prevent any messenger from conveying the news to the officials inside.

Wu Yung also ordered Tu Chien and Sung Wan to be disguised as merchants with a cart of rice to go into the city, and to stay at an inn. When they saw the fire they were to go to the East Gate, kill the guard there, and take their place.

He also instructed Kung Ming and Kung Liang to go to the city as servants. They were to act as messengers.

Li Ying and Shih Chin were to go as travelers, and stay at an inn outside the East Gate. They were to assist in capturing the East Gate.

Lu Ta and Wu Sung were to be dressed as priests, and were to stay at a monastery outside the city. When the fire broke out they were to go to the Southern Gate, and prevent the soldiers from leaving the town by that way.

Tsou Yuan and Tsou Jen were to stay at an inn inside the town as merchants selling lamps, and when the fire broke out they were to go to the prison.

Liu Tang and Yang Hsiung were to go as minor officials, and stay at an inn close to the yamen. On the night of the fire they were to prevent messengers from conveying orders from the yamen.

THE FEAST OF LANTERNS

Kung-Sun Sheng was to enter the town as a mendicant Taoist with Ling Chen as his assistant, and to stay at some quiet spot. They were to carry fireworks with them, and when the fire broke out they were to burn the fireworks and make as much noise as possible.

Chang Shun and Yen Ch'ing were to enter the town by the water gate, and when they saw the signal they were to kill Li Ku and the adulterous wife of Lu Tsun-i.

Wang Ying and his wife, the Amazon Miss Hu, Sun Hsin and his wife Ku Ta-sao, Chang Ching and his wife Sun Erh-niang, were to go into the town as country folks who went to view the sights. They were to set fire to Lu Tsun-i's house.

Squire Ch'ai Chin and Yueh Ho were to enter the town as military officers, and when the fire took place they were to go to the house of the head jailer Tsai and arrange for the safety of the two prisoners.

All these arrangements having been made by Wu Yung the leaders mentioned above took their leave.

In Ta Ming Fu, Liang, the grand secretary, had called a conference of generals Li Ch'eng, Wen Ta, and Wang the governor to discuss the celebration of the Feast of Lanterns. He said, "It is a custon that lanterns are in display to celebrate the occasion in the same as they do in the Eastern Capital. By this we let the people enjoy themselves with us. But this year there are exceptional circumstances. The bandits of Liang Shan Po have attacked us twice, and I am afraid that they are only waiting for an opportunity to attack us again. I therefore think it would be better if we postpone this festival this year."

"I think," said General Wen Ta, "that the brigands have all gone back to Liang Shan Po, and although they have secretly posted up notices, yet I think they have no plan of attack, and that we need not worry about them. If we prohibit the lanterns show on the 15th of the first moon, the brigands, upon hearing of this, will laugh at us and conclude that we are afraid of them. I think we may issue an order that this year the people are encouraged to display lanterns and discharge fireworks. That we allow them five whole nights for this, from the 13th to the 17th, without interruption and that at the crossroads two additional large mountains of lanterns may be built up. The governor must see to it that this order is observed. You yourself will also celebrate the occasion in order to share the happiness with the people. As a precautionary measure against the bandits I will lead a company of cavalry out of the city to the Flying Tiger Gully in order to guard the town on that side. General Li Cheng may have his men marching about the town to quell any disturbance."

The grand secretary was very much pleased at this proposal, and after further discussion General Wen Ta's plans were adopted and put into execution.

On the north of the Yellow River (Huang Ho), Ta Ming Fu was the most important town. It was also a great metropolis and was the center for all government and trade activities. Therefore it was expected that many people from the surrounding country would come to enjoy the festivities of the Feast of Lanterns. The Ti Pao in every part of the town supervised the preparations that were being made. The people entered into the spirit of the festival and there was keen rivalry as to who should have the best display. Mat sheds were erected at all the big houses with festoons of curiously shaped lanterns. Door screens were covered with lanterns of all varieties of colors. There were hung large numbers of scrolls of writings and drawings by famous hands. At the governor's yamen there was a mountain of lanterns, with two red and yellow dragons with lanterns representing the scales, and arrangements for ejecting water into the river. Lanterns were innumerable, and covered the entire paper mountain. In front of the Bronze Buddha Temple there was an erection covered with a thousand lanterns. In front of the Blue Cloud Tower was another erection of lanterns with a white dragon similar to the others.

The tower was the most famous inn to the north of the Yellow River. It had threefold eaves, and all the beams were engraved with fancy designs in bright colors. There were over a hundred rooms for guests, and every day there was the sound of music and laughter in the building.

The spies from Liang Shan Po duly reported this to the stronghold. Wu Yung was much pleased at the prospects, and discussed matters minutely with Sung Chiang. The latter was very keen on going to Ta Ming Fu to direct the attack but Dr. An would not allow this, so Wu Yung offered to go in his stead. Arrangements were made for most of the men to leave Liang Shan Po and travel to the town by eight different routes, and they were all to reach the town on the time of the Feast of Lanterns.

Shih Ch'ien duly arrived at Ta Min Fu on his mission, but as the inns would not admit single individuals he contented himself with walking about during the daytime, and slept at a temple for the night. During the next few days he came across seven of the leaders from Liang Shan Po who were in the town on secret service.

When the Feast of Lanterns was near at hand Liang, the grand secretary, issued an order for General Wen Ta to take soldiers to the Flying Tiger Gully and establish an outpost there. On the day before the Festival, General Li Cheng assembled five hundred soldiers, and marched them about the town. The festival day broke with splendid weather, and the grand secretary was quite happy and contented. In the evening there was the full moon in a clear sky, and the bright moonlight made the city look as though it was made of silver and gold. On the streets were crowds of men and women of all ages strolling about; fireworks were burnt on all sides; and everybody was enjoying the sights which were the best they had ever seen.

In the city jail the head jailer Ts'ai Fu told his brother Ts'ai Ching to take charge as he wanted to go home. When he had been at his home a few minutes two men came—one dressed as a military officer and the other as his orderly. Upon looking closely he recognized the first as Squire Ch'ai Chin, and the orderly was Yueh Ho whom Ts'ai Fu did not know. Ts'ai Fu requested them to come into a room where refreshments were already spread out, and there he offered them wine and cakes.

"We need not partake of wine," said Squire Ch'ai Chin, "I have come here to-day to discuss an important matter with you. You have treated very well both Lu Tsun-i and Shih Hsiu, and I wish to thank you for this. As this is the Feast of Lanterns I should particularly like to go inside the jail and see my friends there. I hope that you will agree with us."

Ts'ai Fu was a yamen runner, and he at once understood that there would be some trouble, and the lives of all his family would be endangered if he refused to do as they wished. So he got some old clothes, and gave them to the two men so that they could disguise as members of the prison staff. He then conducted them to the prison.

When the drum in the tower sounded the second watch, Shih Ch'ien took a basket filled with brimstone and saltpeter covered with paper flowers, and entered the Blue Cloud Tower. He saw that in the rooms were parties of people singing and chatting, while flutes and stringed instruments filled the night with a melody of music. He went upstairs stopping at various rooms as a hawker trying to sell paper flowers and butterflies. He soon met Hsieh Chen and Hsieh Pao who were dressed as hunters, and carried hares stuck on the end of forks over their shoulders. He spoke to them, "The time is now due. Have you seen anything outside?"

"Just now while we were looking outside we saw some scouts going to the yamen. We expect they are reporting the arrival of our troops. You had better get your work done at once."

Just then they heard great noise in front of the Tower, and they heard people shouting, "The brigands from Liang Shan Po are outside the West Gate."

"Hurry up!" said Hsieh Chen to Shih Ch'ien. "Let us go to the yamen now and do our bit there." Upon reaching the yamen they found the defeated troops of General Wen Ta had entered the city in disorder. They said, "The brigands attacked our camp, and drove us out. They followed us to the gate of the city."

General Li Cheng had heard the news, and had already dispatched his soldiers to guard the gates. Wang, the governor, had taken one hundred soldiers to quell any disorder on the streets, and to arrest anybody attempting to make trouble. When he heard the news he returned to the yamen.

In the yamen Liang, the grand secretary, had been drinking, and was slightly intoxicated. When he heard the news he treated it lightly. When the defeated cavalry began to arrive he became dumbfounded, but at last ordered his horse to b. got ready. Just then the Blue Cloud Tower burst into flames, and lit up the whole town in a blaze of light. He quickly mounted his horse and started off. When he reached the street, however, two big men tried to stop him, but he avoided them and galloped towards the East Gate which, however, was guarded by Li Ying and Shih Chin.

Upon reaching the East Gate, Liang was attacked by four big men Li Ying, Shih Chin, Tu Chien, and Sun Wan, and realizing that his soldiers there had been overcome he turned his horse and galloped off towards the South Gate. On the way however he heard people shouting that a big fat priest armed with an iron priest's staff had got in through the South Gate and was killing people on the way. The grand secretary therefore again turned his horse towards the yamen, but when near that place he saw two big men were running amuck on the street so that he could not pass. Just then he saw the Governor Wang attacked by two brigand leaders (Yang Hsiung and Liu Tang) who struck Wang on the head with a pole and killed him on the spot.

The grand secretary turned his horse again, and raced off towards the West Gate. On the way however he heard a loud explosion in the Temple of the City God. There the two brigand leaders Tsou Yuan and Tsou Jen had long bamboo poles with torches on the ends, and were quickly setting fire to the houses about there. There was general confusion in the town, and the people were shrieking and crying with fear. There were fires in all parts of the town.

Near the West Gate the grand secretary happened to meet General Li Cheng, who rushed with him to the South Gate. Upon reaching there they ascended the city wall and went to the gate tower. From there they saw that there were many brigands on the streets with banners bearing the characters "General Kuan Sheng, the Big Sword." In the blaze of light they could see Kuan Sheng mounted on a horse in a defiant attitude. He was supported by other leaders on horseback and they were fighting and killing as they came towards the gate. Liang, the grand secretary, and General Li Cheng seeing the weakness of their position descended from the Gate Tower, mounted their horses, and went towards the North Gate. Upon getting near that place they saw so many brigands in charge of Lin Ch'ung that they again turned, and went towards the East Gate. But that was no better as there were about a thousand brigands entering the city in charge of Mu Heng. So they turned to the South Gate. But on the way they met Li K'wei and a number of other leaders, and when Li K'wei saw them he ran forward wielding his two axes. General Li Cheng went in front with the grand secretary behind, and together they cut their way through the brigands. They, however, were attacked from the left by a large number of brigands led by Huyen Sho. General Li Cheng fought with Huyen Sho, but after about two bouts Li Chen retreated as he realized that fighting was useless because other leaders were arriving. Among them was Hwa Jung who shot an arrow which wounded the adjutant of General Li Cheng. General Li Cheng seeing his adjutant fall galloped off, but soon ran into another party of brigands under Chin Ming.

Li Cheng and the grand secretary, however, succeeded in getting through the South Gate, having killed so many men that they and their horses were covered with blood. Thus they rode off.

We will now return and see what was happening inside the city. In the jail Squire Ch'ai Chin and Yueh Ho, seeing the fires breaking out, spoke to the head jailer Ts'ai Fu, "Do you see those fires? What time are you waiting for?" The main entrance of the jail just then was smashed in, and a crowd of brigands entered shouting. Ch'ai Chin drew out his weapon, and breaking the cangues released Lu Tsun-i and Shih Hsiu without waiting for the head jailer. Then he told Ts'ai Fu, "You had better take me to your home, where I will protect your family." This was done.

Li Ku was at Lu Tsun-i's home, and seeing the fires and hearing the uproar on the streets he discussed escape with the late wife of Lu Tsun-i. They quickly made up bundles containing jewelry and valuables, with the idea of escaping, but they could not leave by the front gate as there was much noise and uproar there. So they went to the back door, and getting out, turned round corners, and at last reached the bank of the river. But Chang Shun was there, and upon seeing them he shouted out, "Where is that woman going?" Li Ku did not reply, but jumped on a boat. A man on the boat, however, caught hold of him, and called out, "Li Ku! Do you recognize me?" Li Ku recognized Yen Ch'ing by his voice, and replied, "Younger brother, we are not enemies. Let me go!"

But Yen Ch'ing did not reply. He took Li Ku, and Chang Shun took the woman, to the East Gate as prisoners.

This had just happened when Lu Tsun-i arrived at his home. As he could not find Li Ku and his wife at once gave orders that all his movable wealth was to be packed and placed on carts to be conveyed to Liang Shan Po.

Head jailer Ts'ai Fu also packed up his things and got his family ready to start for Liang Shan Po. He then addressed Squire Ch'ai Chin, "I request you to use your influence to spare the lives of the people in the city." Squire Ch'ai Chin agreed to this, and went to see Wu Yung about it. Wu Yung concurred and issued orders to that effect but a great many people had already been killed or wounded.

It was now daybreak, and Wu Yung gave the signal for his men to assemble.

Liang, the grand secretary, and General Li Cheng happened to meet with General Wen Ta as they fled from the town. They had not gone far, however, before their progress was stopped by a party of brigands blocking their way.

Pardoned man again arrested,
Vile disease returns again.

CHAPTER 66

SUNG CHIANG REWARDS HIS MEN; KUAN SHENG MAKES TWO GENERALS SURRENDER

WHEN the grand secretary and his generals and their followers found themselves surrounded by brigands they desperately fought their way out and escaped towards the West. The brigand leaders could not catch them so they returned to Ta Ming Fu to await further orders.

In the town Wu Yung had ordered his men to help put out the fires. He also had the treasury opened, and had all the loot loaded up. The public grain stores were all opened, and much rice was given to the people, and the remainder was loaded up and sent to Liang Shan Po. Li Ku and Lu Tsun-i's former wife were confined in prisoner's carts to be conveyed to the mountain stronghold. The brigands then were formed into three bodies, and so returned to Liang Shan Po, Tai Tsung having already been dispatched to inform Sung Chiang of their complete victory.

Upon reaching their stronghold the brigand leaders were welcomed by Sung Chiang and all assembled in the Loyalty and Justice Hall. When he saw Lu Tsun-i, Sung Chiang kotowed, and Lu Tsun-i did likewise.

"I was very careless," said Sung Chiang, "when I requested you to stay at Liang Shan Po. I did not think that it would cause so much misery to you. The hardships you underwent made me feel as though a sword had pierced my heart. But Heaven helped us, and so to-day we can see you here again."

Lu Tsun-i saluted and replied, "I am indebted to you for your powerful assistance, and am grateful to all the leaders for their heroism. Your united strength has rescued me from death. Even if my brains and kidney were rubbed on the ground I could not recompense you for your kindness." He then introduced Ts'ai Fu and Ts'ai Ching, and continued,

"I owe a great deal to these jailers who kept me alive and treated me so well."

Sung Chiang then offered to abdicate his position to Lu Tsun-i who was surprised, and said, "What am I to accept your offer? I am only fit to hold your whip and stirrup, and act as an ordinary retainer."

Sung Chiang however insisted upon his offer being accepted.

"Brother, you are not straightforward," interposed Li K'wei. "You previously consented to occupy this position, but now you want to yield to another man. This chiar must be made of real gold that you always regard it as a present. If you keep on yielding it, you will make me resort to my knife."

"You, fellow!" shouted Sung Chiang.

Lu Tsun-i hurriedly saluted, and said, "If you still press me to take the position I must leave here."

"If Sung Chiang became emperor," said Li K'wei, "and Lu Tsun-i the prime minister and all of us were now sitting in the gold palace it would be worth while for us to act in these polite ways. But as a matter of fact we are only brigands, so it is better for us to conduct ourselves as such."

Wu Yung interposed, "Would it not be better if we treated Lu Tsun-i as a guest, and ask him to live temporarily in the rooms on the east side. When he has done some meritorious deed we could then press him to accept the position of commander in chief."

Sung Chiang agreed to this. He then ordered a feast to be prepared for all the men. The leaders had their feast in the Loyalty and Justice Hall where they all enjoyed themselves. During the feast Lu Tsun-i stood up, and addressed Sung Chiang, "The adulterer and the adulteress are our prisoners here and await your disposal."

Sung Chiang laughed and replied, "I have forgotten about them. Let the prisoners be brought in."

The prisoners were taken out of the cart, and tied up to posts in front of the hall.

Sung Chiang then said, "There is no need to question them as to their crime. We can leave Lu Tsun-i to deal with them."

Lu Tsun-i took a sword, and going outside he cut both of

them open and took out their hearts. He then sliced their bodies into small pieces.

When Liang, the grand secretary, heard the news that the brigands had gone back to Liang Shan Po he went back to Ta Ming Fu with his generals and their few remaining soldiers. There they found what enormous damage had been done, and how their own families and property had been wiped out. He wrote a dispatch to the royal tutor at the Eastern Capital giving particulars of the disaster, and requesting that troops be at once dispatched to safeguard the district. Of the civilians about five thousand, and of the soldiers about 30,000, had been killed.

Upon reaching the Eastern Capital the messenger delivered the dispatch. Upon considering the matter the royal tutor at first thought that it would be a good plan to induce the brigands to join the imperial army, but on second thoughts he saw that was impossible as the brigands had gained such a victory, and as everybody would soon know about it and therefore he was determined to attack the brigands and reëstablish the name of the imperial troops.

The following morning when the emperor had his usual audience with his ministers at daybreak, the Royal Tutor Ts'ai presented a memorial about this disaster. When the emperor read the same he showed surprise. The Censor Chao Ting stepped forward, and addressed the throne, "Many troops have been dispatched, but they have all been defeated. The brigands have the advantageous positions and so are invincible. My humble opinion is that Your Majesty issue an edict pardoning them for their crimes, and conferring upon their leaders official ranks, if they will reform, and help you to restore order in the country."

The Royal Tutor Ts'ai was very angry at this, and spoke, "The censor's suggestion would endanger the moral dignity of the emperor. Your crazy proposal makes you worthy of death."

"In that case," said the emperor, "he may retire from the court."

The censor withdrew, and was duly deprived of his office. After that who would dare to offer any suggestion or reproof about the case?

The emperor then asked Ts'ai Ching, "As these brigands are so truculent, who can be deputed to subdue them?"

"I think these brigands have not much power," replied Ts'ai Ching, "and therefore we need not dispatch a very big army against them. At Ling Chou there are two men—one is Colonel Shan Ting-kwei and the other is Colonel Wei Ting-kwo. I recommend that your majesty issue a decree ordering them to take command of an expedition against Liang Shan Po."

The emperor was pleased at this, and had the edict written at once. He then left the court, and all the officials dispersed. Many of them regarded this event as a laughing-stock among themselves. The following day the edict was duly dispatched to Ling Chou to summon the two colonels.

At the stronghold on Liang Shan Po the brigands continued their feasting in celebration of their victory. One day during the feast Wu Yung spoke to Sung Chiang, "As we have done great damage at Ta Ming Fu you may be sure that the grand secretary must write a dispatch to the Eastern Capital so that we cannot treat the matter as entirely settled. I expect that it will not be long before we are again attacked by the imperial troops."

"I quite agree with your view," said Sung Chiang. "Wny we don't send spies to Ta Ming Fu to find out what is being done, and prepare our men here for the coming attack?"

Wu Yung laughed and said, "I have already sent a spy, and he will soon be back." Duly as they were speaking before the feast was over the spy arrived, and reported that Liang, the grand secretary, had sent a dispatch to the Eastern Capital asking for reënforcements. He also told them what had occurred at court, and how troops at Ling Chou had been ordered to attack Liang Shan Po.

"What shall we do?" asked Sung Chiang.

"Let them come," said Wu Yung. "We shall arrest them all."

Here Kuan Sheng stood up and addressed them, "Since I arrived at Liang Shan Po I have done nothing yet. I know both of these colonels who are in command of the expedition against us. Colonel Shan Ting-kwei is fond of flooding the enemies camp by breaking the dams of rivers. For this reason people call him the Water God General. Colonel Wei Ting-kwo is skillful at the use of fire attack, and therefore is nicknamed the Fire God General. If you will let me have five thousand men I will go and meet them on their way from Ling Chou before they can reach here. If they will surrender, that would be all right. If they do not surrender, I will bring them to you as captives. I do not need any other leaders to assist me in this matter as I can manage it myself."

Sung Chiang was pleased at this offer, and instructed Hsuan Tsan and Hao Ssu-wen to accompany Kuan Sheng under whom they had previously served. The following day they left with five thousand men.

When they had left, the leaders again assembled in the Loyalty and Justice Hall, and there Wu Yung said to Sung Chiang, "Kuan Sheng has gone, but you cannot guarantee his heart (i.e., loyalty) so we had better send a reliable man to watch his movements, but ostensibly to assist him."

"As I know," said Sung Chiang, "Kuan Sheng is quite loyal to us. From first to last he is always the same. You need not harbor any suspicion of him."

"I am afraid that he is not of the same mind as you," said Wu Yung. "I suggest that we dispatch another five thousand men in charge of Lin Ch'ung and three other leaders to follow Kuan Sheng."

"I also want to go," interposed Li K'wei.

"We do not need you this time," said Sung Chiang, "as we have capable leaders for this work."

"If I am idle I shall soon be sick," said Li K'wei. "If you do not let me go, then I will go myself."

"If you disobey my order," said Sung Chiang, "I will have your head cut off."

Li K'wei did not reply to this, but left the hall with a very downhearted spirit.

The men under Lin Ch'ung duly left the next day, and when they had gone a menial reported that the previous night Li K'wei had left the mountain by himself with his two axes. Sung Chiang was annoyed at this. He said, "Yesterday I injured his feeling and he must have gone somewhere else."

"Though he is a rough fellow," said Wu Yung, "yet he is very faithful, and I do not think he will desert us. You need not worry, he will return in a few days." But Sung Chiang was anxious, and sent Tai Tsung to find out where he had gone to. In addition he sent Shih Ch'ien and three other leaders to look for him.

Li K'wei had as a matter of fact taken the direct road to Ling Chou, and on the way he thought, "Those two colonels are only small officers, and I cannot understand why we should send so many men to attack them. I will go myself into the town of Ling Chou, and kill those officers with my axes, one ax for each man, and that will surprise my brother Sung Chiang. Then I shall be able to argue the point with him to my advantage." He walked for half day, and then felt very hungry. He had left the mountain without any money. He soliloquized, "I must look out for a traveler and kill him." Soon he came to an inn, and entering he ordered a jug of wine and three pounds of meat. He sat down and having eaten the food walked out. But the waiter demanded payment, and Li K'wei said, "I have some business to transact, and when I come back I will pay you for the food." Just then he saw a big man approaching who shouted to him, "You nigger, you have some cheek! You eat our food, and won't pay for it. To whom do you think this inn belongs?"

Li K'wei glared at the man, and replied, "Wherever I go I never pay for my food."

"If I tell you who I am you would be very afraid," said the man. "I am Han Po-lung of Liang Shan Po, and this inn is provided by Sung Chiang."

Li K'wei was amused at the man's impudence and thought, "I do not know this fellow at our stronghold." The fact was that this man had tried to join them at Liang Shan Po, but as Sung Chiang was sick at the time he could not see him. Therefore, Chu Kwei told him to open an inn at this point, and await further instructions. Li K'wei took an ax out of his belt, and said, "I will leave this in pawn with you for payment." Han Po-lung thought this was a genuine offer, and held out his hand for the ax, but Li K'wei lifted it up and cleaved open his head. When the waiters saw this they ran away.

Li K'wei went into the inn, and took all the cash about there. He then set fire to the inn which was only made of straw matting. He went on his way, and the following day he met a big man who looked him over very minutely.

Li K'wei asked him, "Why are you looking at me like that?"

"Who are you?" asked the man.

Li K'wei did not reply, but went forward to attack the man. The man avoided the blow, and hit Li K'wei with his fist so that the latter was forced to crouch. Li K'wei had felt the great strength of the man, so he sat down, and looking upwards asked, "What is your name?"

The man standing over him replied, "I have no name, but if you want to fight I'll fight with you. Dare you get up?"

Li K'wei was angry at this, and jumped up, but at the same moment received a kick in the stomach which sent him sprawling on the ground.

"I cannot overcome you," said Li K'wei, and getting up was walking off. But the man stopped him, calling out, "What is your name and where do you come from?"

"You have beaten me," said Li K'wei, "and I do not care to tell you my name. Seeing that you are a fine fellow, however, I will not deceive you. I am Li K'wei, from Liang Shan Po."

"Are you speaking the truth now?" asked the man. "You need not lie to me."

"You may not believe me," said Li K'wei, "but you can see these two axes."

"As you are from Liang Shan Po where are you going alone like this?" asked the man.

"I had a dispute with our commander in chief, because I wanted to go to Ling Chou to kill those two officers, Shan and Wei."

"I have heard that some men have already left Liang Shan Po. Can you say the name of the leader in charge of them?" asked the man.

"Kuan Sheng is in charge of the first body of men, and Lin Ch'ung is supporting him with another body of men."

Upon hearing this the man saluted Li K'wei, who then asked, "Will you not tell me your name now?"

The man said, "I am a Chung Shan Fu man, and my great grandfather was a great wrestler. My father trained me to fight with the fists, and we have never adopted a pupil. My name is Chiao Ting but I am called the Disliked One.

FIRE ATTACK

A few days ago I heard that at Dead Tree Mountain in Keu Chou there is a strong brigand named Pao Hsu, nicknamed Ill-Omened Devil, who is very fond of killing people. I was thinking of going there and joining him."

"But instead of that," said Li K'wei, "why not go to Liang Shan Po, and assist Sung Chiang."

"I have thought of that too," said Chiao Ting, "but I do not know anybody there who would introduce me. But to-day as I have met you I am willing to accompany you."

"I left the mountain in an angry dispute with Sung Chiang," said Li K'wei, "and as I have not yet killed those army officers I cannot very well go back with you. I suggest that we now go to the Dead Tree Mountain and get Pao Hsu to join us in killing those two colonels, Shan and Wei, and then, we can go to Liang Shan Po."

"At Ling Chou there is a large army," said Chiao Ting, "and we two by ourselves can do nothing. It would be suicidal for us to go there alone. The best plan is for us to go to the Dead Tree Mountain and get Pao Hsu to join us at Liang Shan Po."

Just then they were interrupted by Shih Ch'ien who came up and spoke to Li K'wei, "Our commander, Sung Chiang, was very anxious about your disappearing, and sent us in all directions to look for you, and bring you back to Liang Shan Po."

Li K'wei introduced Chiao Ting to Shih Ch'ien. He then told Shih Ch'ien of his plan, and said he would first go with Chiao Ting to the Dead Tree Mountain. Shih Ch'ien could not get Li K'wei to change his mind, and so at last he went back to Liang Shan Po to report the matter while the other two continued on their way.

Kuan Sheng and his five thousand men duly reached Ling Chou. Inside the town colonels Shan and Wei had received their orders from the prefect, and had made all arrangements for a march on Liang Shan Po. When they heard of the arrival of the brigands they were angry, and marched out their soldiers to oppose them. When the two armies met Kuan Sheng rode forth. Immediately a man also rode out from the imperial army. He wore a square iron helmet surmounted by a large plume, his armor was of bearskin covered with iron plates; under which was a black silk gown embroidered with kingfisher-blue flowers; he wore a pair of leather shoes decorated with a design in white; and a leather belt studded with metal plates engraved with lions. He rode a coal-black horse, and was armed with a bow and quiver full of arrows, and a spear. Behind him was a soldier carrying a black flag on which were seven characters in silver, "Shan Ting-kwei, the Water God General."

Another officer also rode forth from the imperial troops, and he wore a vermilion-colored helmet with a design in gold surmounted by a red plume; mail armor decorated with rings in which were animals done in metals, and under that a red silk gown embroidered with animals and clouds in colors; his leather boots were decorated with a Chilin in kingfisher blue. He was armed with a bow, arrows, and a sword, and rode a roan-colored horse. In front of him marched a soldier bearing a red flag on which were seven characters in silver, "Wei Ting-kwo, the Fire God General."

Kuan Sheng sitting on his horse addressed these two colonels, "It is a long time since we parted."

The two colonels laughed, and abused him saying, "You inefficient upstart and rebellious profligate! You have been ungrateful to the emperor's benevolence, and your ancestors would be ashamed of you. You have no modesty. You bring these armed men here now. What have you to say?"

"You two generals are mistaken," replied Kuan Sheng. "At present the emperor is a weakling, traitorous ministers are in power, only relatives are employed, and officials are impeached for petty personal enmity. Our commander Sung Chiang is benevolent, just, loyal, and sincere, and is acting according to the commands of Heaven. He has instructed me to come here and invite both of you to join him at Liang Shan Po."

Both colonels were very angry at this speech, and dashed forward to attack him. They looked like a black cloud and a red cloud threatening a storm. Before they came near Hao Ssu-wen and Hsuan Tsan rode forth from both sides of Kuan Sheng and engaged the opposing men. Sword clashed with sword and spear clanked with spear that there seemed to be chilly flashes of bloody struggle. Kuan Sheng looked on, and admired the great skill displayed by all the combatants. During the fight, however, both colonels turned their horses at the same time, and withdrew. Hao Ssu-wen pursued Shan Ting-kwei right into the army where the latter turned to the left. Hsuan Tsan pursued Wei Ting-kwo who turned to the right. When they had nearly caught up to the generals they suddenly found themselves surrounded by soldiers armed with hooked poles who closed in, pulled them off their horses, and made them prisoners. The prisoners were at once dispatched to Ling Chou, while the main body of soldiers moved forward to attack the brigands. Kuan Sheng was surprised at the quick defeat and ordered his men to retreat. But they had only gone a short distance when Kuan Sheng saw another body of brigands in charge of Lin Ch'ung, and they joined in the fight against the imperial troops, who soon retreated to their camp.

The two prisoners were placed in a cart, and dispatched at once to the Eastern Capital while the two colonels were rewarded for the success attained. The prisoners were escorted by three hundred soldiers, and on the way they passed close to the Dead Tree Mountain. There they were attacked by brigands in front of whom was their new leader Li K'wei with his two axes, and close behind him was Chiao Ting. Turning round to escape the captain of the escort found that in their rear was a big man with a complexion like a copper kettle—no other than Pao Hsu—armed with a double-edged sword. Pao Hsu hacked the captain on the spot and the escort all began to run away, and in a minute there was nobody left with the prisoner's cart.

Li K'wei released the prisoners, and asked for an explanation of their having been captured. Hsuan Tsan also asked Li Kwei how he had come that way and Li Kwei told them how he had made friends with Pao Hsu at the Dead Tree Mountain, and how came down the mountain to attack the the escort of Hsuan Tsan and Hou Ssu-wen.

Pao Hsu invited them all to come to his stronghold on the mountain where he provided a feast. During the festivities Hao Ssu-wen said that as Pao Hsu and his men were willing to join with the brigands at Liang Shan Po they should first join in the attack on Ling Chou. Pao Hsu agreed to this, and arrangements were made accordingly.

When the news of the disaster to the escort reached Ling Chou Colonel Shan Ting-kwei was angry, and said, "If we arrest those two men this time, we must execute them here, and not send them to the Eastern Capital." Just then another report came that Kuan Sheng was advancing to attack the town. Immediately Colonel Shan Ting-kwei mounted his horse, and led his five hundred soldiers outside the town. When near the brigands, the flags separated; and Colonel Shan rode forward by himself, and shouted at Kuan Sheng, "You disgrace to your country! You defeated general. You are deserving death!"

Kuan Sheng hearing this urged his horse forward, whirling his sword aloft. After about fifty bouts Kuan Sheng turned his horse, and galloped off followed closely by Colonel Shan Ting-kwei.

Kuan Sheng led Colonel Shan a long distance away from his troops, and then turning his head he called out, "Why not dismount and submit now? What time are you waiting for?" But instead of doing this Colonel Shan attempted to stab Kuan Sheng in the back with his spear, but Kuan Sheng seeing the movement shouted "Go down," and cut the spear with his sword, and this upset the balance of Colonel Shan who fell off his horse. Kuan Sheng sprang from his horse, and ran to raise his enemy and said, "Please forgive me!" Colonel Shan replied, "I humbly submit to you."

"When I was at Liang Shan Po," said Kuan Sheng, "I very often spoke highly of you to Sung Chiang. So I have specially come here to request both of you to join us in the cause of justice."

"I am willing to do my best and coöperate with you in carrying out the Heaven's wish," said Colonel Shan.

They then mounted their horses, and rode off abreast. When Lin Ch'ung saw them riding together like this he asked for an explanation.

Now Kuan Sheng did not want to say anything about the defeating of Colonel Shan so he replied, "In this secluded spot, we talk about our old friendship and I try to induce him to join us."

They were all pleased at this, Colonel Shan then went back to his troop, and waving his hand called out, "Let all my men come over here," and his five hundred black

FIRE ATTACK

jackets all joined the brigands. Those who did not wish to do so returned to the town, and reported this matter to the governor.

In the town Colonel Wei Ting-kwo was exceedingly angry when he heard of this desertion, and the following day he led his men outside the town and challenged the brigands to battle. In front of the brigands he saw Colonel Shan Ting-kwei and Kuan Sheng and Lin Ch'ung so he rode forward, and shouted at them, "You have forgotten the graciousness of our ruler, and have become mean rebels."

At this Kuan Sheng only laughed, and whipping his horse dashed forward, and fought with Colonel Wei Ting-kwo. After about ten bouts Colonel Wei turned his horse, and ran away followed by Kuan Sheng. But Colonel Shan called out "Do not pursue him!" and immediately Kuan Sheng stopped his horse. Just then the ranks of the soldiers opened and about fifty carts rushed out. These were piled up with burning reeds and grass. They were pushed by soldiers who carried on their backs iron calabash containing sulphur emitting large volumes of smoke. As they came near the brigands, all fell down on all sides, men and horses. Kuan Sheng seeing this gave orders for a general retreat, and after withdrawing his men for about three miles he called a halt.

Colonel Wei seeing the brigands retreating marched his soldiers back to the town. But as he drew near he was surprised to see the town on fire in various parts.

This was because when Colonel Wei left the town with his soldiers another body of brigands from the Dead Tree Mountain in charge of Pao Hsu and Li K'wei entered the town by the north gate, and started to loot and set fire to the houses.

Colonel Wei dared not enter the town, and just as he was going to withdraw Kuan Sheng and his brigands had come upon him. So he decided to retreat to a neighboring town Chung Ling Hsien which he duly reached. Kuan Sheng had however closely followed him, and surrounded the town with his brigands. But Colonel Wei did not offer to fight, and kept the gates carefully defended and guarded.

Seeing this Colonel Shan spoke to Kuan Sheng and Lin Ch'ung, "This man is very brave, and would rather die than submit to a defeat. We must therefore take a broad view of the position and not press him too closely. Instead of fighting I will go by myself into the town, and pursuade him to join us. I can talk him over and induce him to submit to you without fighting."

Kuan Sheng was much pleased, and agreed to the proposal.

Shan Ting-kwei went into the town alone, and was duly announced, and taken in to see Colonel Wei Ting-kwo. He said, "Just now the court is misguided, and stupid ministers are in power. So it would be better for us both join Sung Chiang at Liang Shan Po, and there wait until corrupt officials retire when we may change our course and surrender to the court."

Wei Ting-kwo was turning this over in his mind for some time before he spoke. "If they really wish me to surrender Kuan Sheng himself should come here and make the proposal. If he does not come I would rather die than go."

Shan Ting-kwei then took his leave, and duly reported the conversation to Kuan Sheng, who said, "I am not an important person, but he holds me in such a wrong esteem." He at once mounted his horse and was ready to go to the town.

But Lin Ch'ung remonstrated with them, "It is hard to know men's intentions, and you had better think the matter over carefully before acting."

"He is my old friend so you need not suspect anything," said Kuan Sheng.

So he set off, and when Colonel Wei saw him he was much pleased, and at once agreed to submit and go with them. He invited him to dine and during the meal they talked about old times when they were colleagues. That evening Colonel Wei left the town with his five hundred soldiers, and surrendered to the brigands. The next day they all set out for Liang Shan Po.

We will now relate what important news had reached Liang Shan Po.

> Our feelings know that language fine,
>   Is subtle; like a hook on line;
> The hook is cast, and soon the man,
>   Is captured by the courtesan.

CHAPTER 67

SUNG CHIANG CONDUCTS A NIGHT ATTACK ON TSENG T'OU SHIH; LU TSUN-I TAKES SHIH WEN-KUNG AS PRISONER

COLONEL WEI and his men had reached Liang Shan Po, and were making arrangements for the men to cross the lake when Lin Ch'ung saw one of their leaders, Tuan Ching-chu, also arrive, and asked him where he had been.

Tuan Ching-chu replied, "I went with Yang Lin and Shih Yung to the north to buy some horses. We bought two hundred very fine animals, and were bringing them here when we were stopped near Ching Chou by some brigands under the leadership of Yü Pao-ssu, whose nickname is the Colossal Spirit. They seized all our horses and took them off to Tseng T'ou Shih (i.e., the Tseng village). Yang Lin and Shih Yung went away somewhere I did not know, so I hurriedly came here by myself to report the matter."

Lin Ch'ung saw the importance of the matter, and at once took Tuan Ching-chu across the lake to the stronghold to report matter to Sung Chiang. The two colonels from Ling Chou were also introduced to Sung Chiang and the other leaders. Li K'wei also introduced Pao Hsu and his men from the Dead Tree Mountain.

Sung Chiang was very angry at the horses having been stolen, and said, "It is these thieves who shot Ch'ao Kai to death, and so far no punishment has been inflicted upon them. As they have now robbed our horses again we shall be disgraced if we do not take our revenge."

"As it is now springtime," said Wu Yung, "and we have not much to do, we can arrange to attack them. When Cha'o Kai was fighting, he lost the advantageous position, but this time we must use some strategy. Shih Ch'ien is excellent in scaling walls so we can send him as a spy, to detect the position inside Tseng T'ou Shih." This was agreed to, and Shih Ch'ien took his departure. In a few days Yang Lin and Shih Yung returned to Liang Shan Po, and reported that at Tseng T'ou Shih, Shih Wen-kung was very boastful, and declared that they would not live under the same heaven with the brigands at Liang Shan Po. Sung Chiang upon hearing this wanted to dispatch his men to attack Tseng T'ou Shih, but Wu Yung objected, and urged that they must wait until Shih Ch'ien came back. Sung Chiang, however, was in a towering rage at this insult, and wanted immediate revenge. He sent Tai Tsung to go there and quickly return with the latest news.

In a few days Tai Tsung returned, and reported, "The leading family at Tseng T'ou Shih are preparing for an attack on Liang Shan Po, and have established a big encampment at the Fa Hwa Temple."

The following day Shih Ch'ien arrived and reported, "I got inside the village and made careful inquiries. The villagers are divided into five companies under the command of Shih Wen-kung. Yü Pao-ssu keeps our horses in the Fa Hwa Temple."

Upon hearing this Wu Yung held general conference of all the leaders and addressed them: "As these men are divided into five companies so we can divide our forces in the same way, and proceed to the village by five different roads."

Lu Tsun-i stood up, and said, "You saved my life, but since then I have had no opportunity of recompensing you. I am willing to risk my life on this expedition, but I don't know what is your opinion."

Sung Chiang asked Wu Yung whether he could agree to Lu Tsun-i doing this, and Wu Yung replied, "The roads between here and Tseng T'ou Shih are very rugged and wild, and we could not allow Lu Tsun-i to lead the vanguard. He had better lead a body of men in ambush on the open field, and when he hears the sound of our bombs, he can come and join in the fight."

Sung Chiang instructed Lu Tsun-i to act in this way. The other leaders were then divided into five detachments, and altogether 22,000 men were placed under their charge. They were given full instructions.

A DESERTED CAMP

In the village of Tseng T'ou Shih the scouts duly reported the approach of the brigands, the headman of Tseng T'ou Shih sent for Shih Wen-kung and Su Ting, the two military instructors, for a discussion. Shih Wen-kung said, "We must dig pits and traps for these brigands." The headman of the village ordered all the people to make pits in the different places and cover them over with soil. The village guard was to be stationed near these traps.

Before the Liang Shan Po brigands drew near the village, Shih Ch'ien was sent in advance as a spy. He found out the whereabouts of these hidden pitfalls, and duly reported the matter to Sung Chiang.

Upon hearing this Wu Yung laughed and said, "That is not important." He gave orders for the men to move forward, and they soon reached the outskirts of the village. It was about noon, and a horse galloped towards them with copper bells tinkling, and with a long plume on its tail. Its rider had white clothes and a black hat, and carried a short spear. The brigands wanted to rush forward and fight with him, but Wu Yung forbade this, and ordered encampment there. He also ordered that trenches were to be dug all around their position, and these were to be protected by iron palisades. He instructed the five detachments raise defensive works accordingly around thir separate camps.

They encamped there for three days, but the soldiers in the village did not show themselves. So Wu Yung instructed Shih Ch'ien to enter the village again as a spy, and to find out what was happening. He was also to locate exactly where the hidden pits were. Shih Ch'ien did this, and within a day had found out all about the hidden pits, and duly reported the details to Wu Yung.

This information was made known to all the leaders, and Wu Yung then ordered that a body of men was to be armed with hoes, and that a hundred carts were to be loaded with grass and reeds, and all these were to be concealed in the center of the camp. This was done, and then Wu Yung issued orders that at 10 a.m. the next day an attack would be made on the village on the west and east sides my foot soldiers only. On the north side, however, other bounted men were to be on parade with flags flying and drums beating, but they were not to move forward.

The following day Shih Wen-kung heard the noise of bombs and was informed of the approaching of the brigands on all four sides, but he held his men back waiting for the brigands to advance and fall into the hidden pits. But Wu Yung gave orders for his men to attack the soldiers at the South Gate from two sides instead of a frontal attack. This was done, and they not only avoided the hidden pits, but actually drove the soldiers into their own traps.

Shih Wen-kung upon seeing this brought soldiers to the South Gate to repel the attack, but Wu Yung had given orders for all the carts to advance (avoiding the pits), and when near the gates the dry grass and reeds were all set on fire. The flames spread to the gate tower, and so set that on fire, and Kung-Sun Sheng having control of the wind caused a south wind to blow, which carried the flames into the village.

When Wu Yung saw this desired result he withdrew his men to their camp while Shih Wen-kung inside the village had the fires put out, and during the following night endeavored to repair the damage done at the South Gate.

The following day a son of the headman Tseng Tu expressed his opinion to Shih Wen-kung that if they did not capture the chief leader of the brigands they would have no chance in defeating them. He therefore proposed to take some men to fight outside, while Shih Wen-kung guarded the South Gate. This was agreed to.

When Sung Chiang was informed that Tseng Tu had come out to fight he accepted the challenge, and rode forth accompanied by Lu Fang and Kuo Sheng. When he saw Tseng Tu he was angry, and pointing at him with his whip called out, "Who will fight with that fellow and revenge the death of our late commander?"

Upon hearing this Lu Fang whipped his horse and galloped forward. The two men fought for about thirty bouts. Kuo Sheng then noticed that Lu Fang would be defeated as his opponent proved more skillful. Lu Fang was showing weakness, and was making mistakes. He was acting entirely on the defensive. So Kuo Sheng whipped his horse, and galloped forward with his halberd in hand to engage Tseng Tu. Both of the two brigands had leopard tails fastened to the end of their halberds, and as they both lunged at Tseng Tu he in a flash took his spear to ward off the halberds.

But the spear happened to catch the two leopard tails and so the three weapons were entangled. All three men pulled in order to free their weapons without success. Hwa Jung seeing this realized that Tseng Tu had the advantage so taking his bow he shot an arrow which hit Tseng Tu in the shoulder and sent him off his horse. Lu Fang and Kuo Sheng now drove their halberds into Tseng Tu, and killed him immediately.

This fatality was reported to the village and when the headman heard of his son's death he cried. But a younger son, Tseng Sheng, was very angry, and called for his horse, and shouted out that he would avenge the death of his elder brother. Tseng Sheng would not heed his father's objections, and rode out to the South Gate. There he met Shih Wen-kung who said, "You must not treat these men too lightly, as they are very talented and skillful warriors."

But Tseng Sheng was determined. "They have killed my brother, and I must have revenge." He rode forward accompanied by about ten men on horseback.

Chin Ming was in charge of the brigands' advance post, and he was ready to accept the challenge when he saw that Li K'wei with his axes had already gone forth. The Tsen troops recognized Li K'wei, and Tseng Sheng ordered his archers to shoot at him. An arrow hit Li K'wei on the leg, and he fell down. Tseng Sheng ordered his cavalry to capture Li K'wei, but the brigand leaders Chin Ming, Hwa Jung, and four others, also moved forward at the same time to rescue him. Tseng Sheng seeing so many opponents ordered his cavalry to retire, and so Li K'wei was rescued.

The following day Shih Wen-kung again was opposed to any offensive, but Tseng Sheng was still keen on having revenge, so at last Shih Wen-kung put on his uniform and mounted his horse. The brigands were ready for action, and Chin Ming rode forward to fight with Shih Wen-kung. But after about twenty bouts Chin Ming felt being overcome, and turned his horse to retire, but Shih Wen-kung was too quick for him, and wounded Chin Ming in his leg, so the latter fell off his horse. Four brigand leaders, however, rushed to his rescue, and took him back to the camp. The defeated brigands retreated about three miles where they encamped. Chin Ming was placed in a cart and sent back to Liang Shan Po. Reënforcements under Kuan Sheng and three other leaders were at the same time called for from the mountain stronghold.

Sung Chiang burnt incense and prayed to the spirits, and secretly caste lots to divine the further proceeding of the battle. Wu Yung read the indication of the lots and said to him, "Congratulations, as there is no need for fear. This night I am sure the villagers will again press their attack. We must warn our leaders of this, and divide our men into two camps to the east and west of this place. The mounted men must be stationed all around, and wait for orders." This was done accordingly.

That night the moon shone brightly. There was neither wind nor cloud. Shih Wen-kung spoke to Tseng Sheng, "We have wounded two of the brigand leaders to-day, and as they have retired after being defeated they will be afraid of us now, so we must press forward our attack." Orders were given for a march that night. Horses were not to carry bells, and all was to be done in silence. About 11 p.m. they started off, but upon reaching the place where the brigands had stopped, they found nobody there. Suspecting some trick, Shih Wen-kung gave orders for all to return to the village. But they had not gone far when they were attacked from both sides. Fires were set up by the brigands on all sides, and the fighting went on till midnight when Shih Wen-kung got back to the village and wrote a note to Sung Chiang admitting defeat, and offering to surrender. It read as follows:

"Tseng Lung, headman of the Tseng T'ou Shih village, sends greetings to Sung Chiang, commander of the army. Previously my son seized your horses, and offended you by his ignorance. When Ch'ao Kai came here we ought to have surrendered to him. Unfortunately one of our soldiers sent a stray shot which wounded Ch'ao Kai, and we recognize the seriousness of that offense, and can offer no excuse for same. Allowance may however be made of the fact that it was done without orders. My two sons have been killed, and I plead with you for peace. If you will withdraw your men I will return to you all the horses. I will also send you money, for distribution among your men. By peace we shall avoid further bloodshed. I write this with all due respects, and hope for your kind consideration."

When Sung Chiang read this letter he seemed to be angry and tore it into pieces. He said to Wu Yung, "How can we settle things in this way when they have killed our leader? We must wipe them out."

The messenger heard this, and trembled on the ground in fear.

Wu Yung exhorted Sung Chiang, "I think you may be wrong. In this fight both sides were merely in a display of temper. Now that they desire peace we should be in the wrong if we refuse to consider their proposal." After fruther discussion he wrote at once a reply, and handed it to the messenger with ten ounces of silver.

The messenger duly returned, and handed the reply to Shih Wen-kung and Tseng Lung who read it as follows:

"Sung Chiang, commander at Liang Shan Po, replies to Tseng Lung, headman of the Tseng T'ou Shih. It has always been a fact that a country without confidence among the people must become extinct in the end; without propriety soon become of no account. Unjust gains must be robbed, generals without bravery must soon be defeated. These are definite laws. Liang Shan Po and your village had no enmity before, and we both guarded our own domains respectively. But recently you did a wicked thing, and so we are now enemies. If, however, you wish to have peace then you must return to us the horses you stole, and also hand over to us Yü Pao-ssu who stole the horses. You must also give money to our men. If you are sincere you must not treat lightly the proper procedure."

When they read this both men were surprised. But the following day they sent a messenger to talk with Sung Chiang that if Yü Pao-ssu was handed over to the brigands they must also hand over a man in exchange.

When Sung Chiang received this message he agreed, and sent not one man, but five of his leaders to be exchanged for Yü Pao-ssu. Shih Ch'ien and Li K'wei were two of the five, and before they left Wu Yung gave Shih Ch'ien secret instructions what to do in case of treachery.

When they reached the village they were taken before Tseng Lung and Shih Ch'ien said to him that they had come to arrange peace. But Shih Wen-kung replied, "As Wu Yung has sent you five men to arrange peace I think he must have some trick."

Li K'wei was very angry at this, and seized hold of Shih Wen-kung to fight, but Tseng Lung interposed.

Shih Ch'ien also spoke, "This man, Li K'wei, is very rough but he is a personal friend of Sung Chiang. You need not suspect him as Sung Chiang specially sent him here."

Tseng Lung wanted peace, and would not listen to Shih Wen-kung's remarks. He ordered a meal for the five men from the brigands and provided them a room in the Fa Hwa Temple, and placed a guard of 500 soldiers to look after them.

Tseng Sheng and Yü Pao-ssu were duly dispatched to discuss peace with Sung Chiang. They took with them all the stolen horses, and also a cartload of silver and embroidered cloth. When Sung Chiang saw the horses he noticed that the splendid white race horse presented to Liang Shan Po by Tuan Ching-chu was not among them and therefore asked why it had not been returned also.

"That horse is now ridden by Shih Wen-kung," replied Tseng Sheng.

"Then you quickly write a letter at once demanding the immediate return of that horse," said Sung Chiang.

Tseng Sheng did this, and sent the letter off by a messenger. When Shih Wen-kung read the letter he spoke to the messenger, "I will not return the horse, but am quite willing to send another horse instead of it."

The messenger went back with this message, but was soon back again with the word that the identical horse must be returned. Shih Wen-kung then spoke, "As Sung Chiang insists upon the horse being returned, I will return it, but only on the condition that he first withdraws his men from the environs of our village."

When this message was delivered to Sung Chiang he consulted Wu Yung, and while they were talking a scout arrived, and reported that imperial troops were approaching by two roads from Ching Chou and Ling Chou. Sung Chiang said, "If Shih Wen-kung gets to know this he will probably change his mind, so we must keep the matter secret." He then divided his men into two bodies, and gave orders that they were to march along the two roads to oppose the coming troops on the way. He then summoned Yü Pao-ssu and said, "We have a very important commission for you to carry through, and if you succeed I will promote you to a position as leader at Liang Shan Po. I will take a solemn oath by this arrow that I will bear no more grudge to your taking my horse. But if you do not agree I shall recommence the attack on Tseng T'ou Shih."

Yü Pao-ssu agreed to do what he was requested. Wu Yung then said to him: "You must enter the village quietly as though you have secretly left us, and tell Shih Wen-kung that you think we do not really desire peace, but that Sung Chiang will try to get back the white race horse by some deception. That as soon as he gets the horse, his attitude towards the village will change. That as troops are approaching here from Ching Chou and Ling Chou, the brigands are in great terror and the villegers may now embrace the opportunity to attack Sung Chiang."

Yü Pao-ssu left with these orders, and duly came back to Tseng T'ou Shih. When Shih Wen-kung heard the news he decided to recommence his attack on the brigands. Tseng Lung however objected to a renewed attack as it would endanger the life of his son Tseng Sheng who was then staying with the brigands. But Shih Wen-kung said that when they had seized the brigands' camp Tseng Sheng would be saved. Shih Wen-kung then gave orders for all the men to be ready for an attack that very night.

Yü Pao-ssu knowing all this went secretly to the Fa Hwa Temple, and told Shih Ch'ien and the other leaders there what had been arranged.

In the brigands' camp Sung Chiang asked Wu Yung whether their plan would be carried out.

"If he does not return," said Wu Yung, "then we can assume that Shih Wen-kung suspects us. We may expect them to attack us this night, but we will not oppose them, but retreat and lay in ambush on both sides of their road. At the same time we may dispatch our men to their village while it is depleted of soldiers, and so we can establish ourselves there. That plan is called, 'Drawing the wild dog from its hole. It generally succeeds."

That night Shih Wen-kung got his men together, and marched out of the village. There was little moonlight. When they reached the brigands' camp they were surprised to find the gate open and the place quite deserted. Shih Wen-kung now suspected a plot and ordered a retreat. But they had not gone far when they heard bombs being fired in their village, and also heard the large bell in the Fa Hwa Temple booming. From the noise it seemed that the brigands had got into the village.

In the Fa Hwa Temple Li K'wei and the other three leaders were armed, and rushing out with swords in their hands. When the headman, Tseng Lung, heard that the brigands had got into the village he committed suicide by hanging himself. His son, Tseng Mi, was killed in resisting the brigands on the west side of the village. Another son, Tseng Kwei, was also killed in the confused fighting on the east side. Su Ting was killed near the North Gate where he found himself opposed by Lu Ta and three other leaders. Many of the villagers met their death by falling into the traps while trying to escape from the village.

Shih Wen-kung being mounted on the white race horse reached the village before any of his soldiers, but seeing the confused mass of fighting in the streets he immediately left by the West Gate. There was a great deal of mist that night, and in the dark and confusion he was soon uncertain where he actually was. He had gone about two miles when he heard a gong sounded in a forest, and soon he saw a body of about five hundred men. In front of them was their leader armed with a cudgel. He ran up to Shih Wen-kung and struck his horse with the cudgel. But the horse leapt over his head and carried Shih Wen-kung off. The mist here however was extremely thick, and it was blown about by a very strong cold wind. He thought he saw the spirit of Ch'ao Kai everywhere in the mist, so he turned his horse and went back by the same road. He soon met Yen Ch'ing, the servant of Lu Tsun-i. He then met Lu Tsun-i himself who called out, "Thief! Where are you going?" So saying he wounded Shih Wen-kung in the leg with his sword. The latter fell off his horse, was immediately seized, bound with ropes, and taken back to Tseng T'ou Shih as a prisoner. The coveted horse had also been captured and brought to the village.

Sung Chiang was excited to get the horse again. He

gave orders that every member of the Tseng family must be executed, including Tseng Sheng who was a prisoner. The whole village was then looted, all valuables and rice being loaded on carts, and transported to Liang Shan Po.

The troops from Ching Chou and Ling Chou were attacked and defeated, and then all the brigands returned to Liang Shan Po. In the Loyalty and Justice Hall all the leaders assembled, dressed in mourning, and held a memorial service to the spirit of Ch'ao Kai. A prayer was written addressed to Ch'ao Kai, and then burnt as a sacrifice. Shih Wen-kung was executed, and his heart was also offered as a sacrifice.

After this Sung Chiang raised the question for discussion as to who should now be the commander-in-chief at Liang Shan Po.

"You should remain in that position," said Wu Yung, "and Lu Tsun-i should be your assistant. All the other leaders can remain as before."

"But we must not forget the will of Ch'ao Kai," said Sung Chiang. "He said that whoever should capture Shih Wen-kung should be our commander-in-chief, no matter who he was. As Lu Tsun-i captured that thief and avenged the injury to Ch'ao Kai, he must be our head without any question."

"My virtue is insignificant, and my ability is meager, so how dare I accept the position? Even if I occupy the lowest position my abilities would hardly be enough for that work," said Lu Tsun-i.

"It is not for the sake of modesty that I decline the honor," said Sung Chiang, "but because Lu Tsun-i is superior to me in three things. First, I am of smaller stature and have a sallow complexion, while he has a majestic bearing, and nobody can be compared to him. Secondly, I was once only a petty official and became your head only through the generosity and kindness of the brothers here; while he was a very wealthg and important person and was famous for his heroism. Thirdly, I had no influence in pacifying the country and am without military knowledge. I could not even capture a chicken. In my body there is not even an inch of merit, while he has the power to oppose ten thousand men, and is very well versed in both ancient and modern affairs. Having these abilities he is very suitable for the job. If the emperor wants us to return, and help him to achieve meritorious deeds then we shall be honored, and shall be able to gain promotion in official rank. These are my firm convictions, and I hope that you will raise no objections."

Lu Tsun-i kotowed, and said, "Your talk is useless, because even if you threaten to kill me I cannot accept the position."

"We all recognized you, brother, as our leader," said Wu Yung, "with Lu Tsun-i as your assistant. If you do not accept this, I am afraid that our men will regard you as being cold-hearted." So saying he glanced round inviting the approval of all the others.

Li K'wei instantly called out, "I risked my life at Chiang Chou in your service and we all admitted you as our commander. You issued all the orders, so it is now useless for you to be hypocritical as to abdicate your post in another's favor. If there is any change I shall create a disturbance, so that everybody has to leave."

Wu Sung had noticed Wu Yung appealing for support, so he now stood up and said, "We have many ex-military officers, and I am sure they all wish you to remain as our commander-in-chief. We are unwilling to have any other man in that position."

Liu Tang then spoke, "When we first came here, there were only seven brothers, and we unanimously elected you as our chief. Why do you now think of another man for that position?"

Lu Ta spoke in a loud voice, "If you, brother, still stand on politeness we must disband."

"You need not say anything else," said Sung Chiang; "I have an alternative. We must discover the will of Heaven in this matter, and follow that."

"What is your own exalted view?" asked Wu Yung. "Please tell us."

"There are two things to be done," said Sung Chiang.

Liang Shan Po gains two more heroes,
Tung Ping Fu becomes scene of remorse.

CHAPTER 68

SHIH CHIN IS IMPRISONED AT TUNG PING FU; SUNG CHIANG RELEASES TUNG PING

THE leaders would not agree to Sung Chiang's handing over the command to Lu Tsun-i, and Sung Chiang did not like to disobey Ch'ao Kai's dying wish so he addressed them, "Just now we are short of money and rice, but there is a good supply of those things at the cities to the east of Liang Shan Po. The cities I refer to are Tung Ping Fu and Tung Chang Fu. We have never troubled those towns, so I think we may go there now, and borrow some rice from them. We will write the two names on slips of paper, and Lu Tsun-i and myself will draw lots. Whoever takes his city first will take command here."

"A good plan," said Wu Yung.

"That will not do," said Lu Tsun-i. "Sung Chiang is our commander, and I prefer to obey his order only."

But the assembled heroes would not agree to Lu Tsun-i's suggestion. The slips of paper were written out, and after offering incense to the gods, the lots were drawn. Lu Tsun-i drew Tung Chang Fu while Sung Chiang drew Tung Ping Fu. That evening Sung Chiang divided the leaders and men. He took Lin Ch'ung and twenty-four other leaders and altogether ten thousand men. Lu Tsun-i took Wu Yung and an equal number of leaders and men.

Everything was soon ready, and both forces left the mountain on the first day of the third month. The weather was warm with a refreshing wind blowing, and the fresh grass was of brilliant green color. The prospects for a campaign could not have been better.

Sung Chiang led his force to within thirteen miles of Tung Ping Fu, and encamped there at a village called An Shan Chen. Sung Chiang addressed his leaders, "I know that the prefect here is Cheng Wan-li, and that with him is a great warrior who can face ten thousand men without defeat. He is called Tung Ping, and his nickname is the Two Spears General, because he can use two spears at the same time. If we attack his town we must be polite, and inform him of our intention, so I will now write such a letter and send it to him. If he is willing to surrender, then all the fighting will be avoided. But if he is unwilling, then he cannot complain about the results. Who will take the letter?"

Yü Pao-ssu stepped forward and said, "I know the Lieutenant General Tung Ping, and am willing to take the letter to him."

But Wang Ting-liu also stepped forward and said, "I am a newcomer, and so far have not done anything to show my merits. So I should like to go on this mission."

This was agreed to, and after the letter had been written asking for the loan of some rice, the two men departed.

In Tung Ping Fu the prefect discussed with the lieutenant general upon hearing of the arrival of the brigands at An Shan Chen. While they were conferring, the letter from Sung Chiang arrived, and the messengers were called in. Yü Pao-ssu and Wang Ting-liu duly presented the letter. The prefect read the letter, and then spoke to the lieutenant general, "The brigands want to borrow some rice. What do you think about it?"

The general was very angry, and ordered that the two messengers be taken outside and executed.

But the prefect objected to this. He said, "There is an ancient rule, 'When two countries are at war, the delegates must not be killed.' That is only proper. The most we could do would be to give them ten blows each with the bamboo and send them back."

The lieutenant general was still angry, but he argeed to this, and gave orders accordingly.

When the two messengers returned and reported the matter with tears Sung Chiang was very angry. Shih Chin came forward and said, "When I lived in Tung Ping Fu I was on very intimate terms with a woman there named Li Shui-lan. Now I can take some money to the town and stay at that woman's house. When you are ready you can attack the town, and I will set fire to the Drum Tower inside the town. By working together, both inside and outside, we can accomplish our object."

Sung Chiang approved of this plan. Money was given to Shih Chin, and he left that day for the town. He duly reached the house of Li Shui-lan, and she asked Shih Chin, "I have not seen you for a long time. I heard that the officials wanted to arrest you, and that you had escaped to Liang Shan Po where you became a leader among the brigands. These two days there has been a great stirring on the streets because the brigands are coming to attack us. Why have you come here?"

"I will tell you the truth," replied Shih Chin. "I am a leader of the brigands, but so far I have done no meritorious deed. Just now they have come to borrow some rice from the town, and I have told them all about you. I come here really as a spy and here is a parcel of money for you. You must not let anybody know of my arrival. When the thing is finished, I will bring you to the mountain stronghold to enjoy pleasures."

The woman assented, and received the money. She then entertained Shih Chin with wine. During the meal she went down below, and spoke to the proprietor, "This man was previously a good visitor here, and so we admitted him. But he has now become a bad man, and is wanted by the officials, I think we may be implicated by his coming here."

The man said, "These brigands are very fierce, and never failed to take the town they attacked. If we betray this Shih Chin, they will kill us when they enter the town."

The woman who took charge of the prostitute said, "How stupid you are! You do not know very much! An old proverb says, 'If a bee is on the breast, loosen the clothes immediately.' This is a rule. If we inform the officials about this man, then we are free from blame. You had better go to the yamen at once, and tell them about this man. They will arrest him, and so we shall avoid any trouble."

The man said, "But he has given us plenty of money so we cannot treat him that way."

The woman abused him, "You brute! Your talk is simply nonsense! Our business here injures a countless number of men, not to say a single man. If you do not do as I tell you, then I will go to the yamen myself, and inform against you as well."

The pimp said, "Do not be so hasty. Shui-lan must entertain and keep him here. We must not beat the grass to drive away the snake. I will go to the yamen, and inform them to have him arrested."

When Li Shui-lan came upstairs again after this conversation Shih Chin noticed her face was changing colors so he asked her, "What has upset you like this?"

The girl replied, "I am somewhat upset because in coming up the staircase I missed my footing, and nearly fell down."

They had hardly had time to drink a cup of tea, when they heard the noise of men down below. About ten policemen entered the room, and seized Shih Chin, bound him with cords, and took him to the yamen.

When the prefect saw Shih Chin he abused him, "Your courage appears to be bigger than your body. You come here as a spy all by yourself. If the father of the girl Li Shui-lan had not informed against you, you might have done much injury to the people. Tell us quickly what you have to say in defense. What instructions did Sung Chiang give you?"

Shih Chin did not speak, so the lieutenant general said, "This kind of thief will not confess without a sound beating." The prefect ordered that the prisoner be beaten. The attendants brought a pail of cold water, and after pouring it over the legs of the prisoner they gave him about a hundred blows on the same parts.

But still Shih Chin would not speak. The lieutenant general, Tung Ping, therefore, ordered that the prisoner be taken to the jail.

When Shih Chin had left for the town Sung Chiang wrote a letter to Wu Yung (who was in charge of the brigands attacking Tung Chang Fu) informing him what had been done. When Wu Yang read the letter he was very surprised, and told Lu Tsun-i that he (Wu Yung) must go at once to see Sung Chiang. This was agreed to, and Wu Yung traveled all that night. When he reached Sung Chiang's camp Wu Yung asked him who had given the order for Shih Chin to go as a spy.

"He was willing to go, and made the proposal himself," replied Sung Chiang. "He was previously very friendly with a girl Li Shui-lan there."

"Brother, you have not thought the matter over," said Wu Yung. "If I had been here he would not have gone. Those girls injure many good men, and prefer new to old acquaintances. They have dispositions as changeable as water, and are quite controlled by their proprietors. I am sure that Shih Chin will have met trouble there."

Sung Chiang asked Wu Yung whether he had any plans to rescue Shih Chin. Wu Yung sent for Ku Ta-sao and spoke to her, "There is a troublesome affair which I want you to take in hand. I want you to dress as an old woman, and stealthily get into the town as a beggar. You must get the latest news there, and quickly return with it. If Shih Chin is already in prison, then go and speak to the jailer that the prisoner helped you sometime before, and therefore you want to bring him some food. When you are allowed to see Shih Chin you must tell him secretly that at the end of the month we shall come during the night and attack the town. He must find a place where he can afterwards escape that night. He must set fire to the buildings as a beacon for us to attack the town. Turning to Sung Chiang he said, "You, brother, must take your men, and attack Wen Shang Hsien, a town near-by, and the people there will escape to Tung Ping Fu. Ku Ta-sao will easily enter the town as one of the refugees without any suspicion being aroused. Then you can do what I have already told you."

When this plan had been arranged Wu Yung mounted his horse and returned to Tung Chang Fu. Sung Chiang then gathered his men together and marched on Wen Shang Hsien. The people in that town fled to Tung Ping Fu for protection as anticipated.

Ku Ta-sao joined the refugees as an old woman with hair and dress in great disorder. Upon entering Tung Ping Fu with the others she began to beg for food on the streets. She soon found out that Shih Chin was in prison. The next day she got a basket of food, and went to the entrance of the prison. Soon a jailer came out, and Ku Ta-sao weeping bitterly saluted him, and the jailer asked her what she was crying about.

Ku Ta-sao replied, "My old master, Shih Chin, has been imprisoned; I have not seen him now for ten years. I heard that he was living as merchant, and do not know how he came to get imprisoned. I see that nobody gives him anything to eat, so I have brought him some food. I sak you to allow me to present this gift. By doing this your merit will be enormous (literally as big as a seven-storied pagoda)."

"That man is a brigand from Liang Shan Po," said the jailer, "and his crime deserves his execution. Who would dare allow you to see him?"

"If he has committed such a crime then he must answer for it," said Ku Ta-sao. "I pray you have pity on me and allow me offer him this food to show my gratitude to him." So saying she began to weep again.

The jailer thought, "If this were a man I would not dare to take him into the prison, but as it is only an old woman perhaps I might do it." So he told her to follow him, and took Ku Ta-sao to the cell where Shih Chin was chained up. Shih Chin recognized her, but although surprised dared not say a word. Ku Ta-sao burst into tears again, and gave Shih Chin some food. Other attendants seeing this called out, "That is a bad man waiting for execution. Why give him food? Get out of this place at once, or we will beat you with the bamboo." As Ku Ta-sao saw no means of staying, so she whispered to Shih Chin, to struggle by the night of the end of the month. Ku Ta-sao was then jostled out of the prison so that Shih Chin could not ask for further information as he had only caught the three words, "The night of the end of the month." It was the third month, and had 30 days, but on the 29th day he heard two jailers talking, and one asked, "What is the date?" The other man evidently made a mistake for he replied, "To-day is the last day of the month, and I must buy some paper money and sacrifice to the spirits."

Shih Chin was not aware of the mistake in the date, and for the rest of the day was anxiously waiting for the coming of the night. That evening the jailer was half drunk, and when he took Shih Chin to the place where the paper money was to be burnt Shih Chin called out, "Who are those men at your back?" The jailer looked round to see, and Shih Chin seized his cangue, tore it off his neck, and knocked the jailer down with it. He then seized a stone, and broke the wooden fetters fastened to his feet. He then rushed into the guard-room where many of the jailers happened to be drunk, and using his wooden cangue he killed a number of them while some ran out of the room. He opened the prison gate expecting the brigands to be somewhere near at hand, but as nobody was there he entered the prison and released about sixty prisoners. There was now a great uproar from the released brutes.

When the prefect heard of the disturbance in the jail he summoned General Tung Ping who expressed his opinion that the trouble must have been caused by a spy who had got into the town. He immediately issued an order for the soldiers to turn out and capture the spy. He also ordered other soldiers to march out of the town and attack the brigands. He asked the prefect to defend the town and dispatch guards to the prison to prevent the prisoners from escaping.

The prison was soon surrounded, and Shih Chin was still inside, daring not to venture out. Ku Ta-sao was outside, and was sad because she could not get in.

The lieutenant general and his soldiers marched out to attack the brigands' camp about 3 a. m. When Sung Chiang heard the news he assumed that Ku Ta-sao must have been arrested and their plans discovered. He however ordered all his men to get ready for the coming attack.

It was the hour just before dawn. The two forces soon met and halted, when General Tung Ping rode forth. He was very intellectual and was well acquainted with the three religions (Confucianism, Taoism, and Buddhism), and also the nine schools of philosophy. He was also a skilled musician. Sung Chiang noticed his stylish manner, and was very glad to meet such a man. He noticed that his quiver was full of arrows, and from it was also sticking out a small flag with the characters, "Heroic Two Spears General, Marquis over 10,000 families." Sung Chiang ordered Han Tao to give battle to the challenger.

Han Tao was armed with a long handled mace, while Tung Ping used his iron spears with great skill. After they had been fighting for some time Sung Chiang thought that Han Tao stood no chance of victory so he ordered Hsu Ning to relieve Han Tao. This was done, but after Hsu Ning had fought about fifty bouts he had not gained any advantage. So Sung Chiang being afraid that Hsu Ning might be defeated ordered a gong to be sounded as a signal for him to return.

Upon seeing this Tung Ping raised both spears, and dashed after Hsu Ning right into the brigands. Sung Chiang signaled for his men to surround the foe, while he himself took his position on a mound so as to overlook the conflict. If Tung Ping tried to escape to the east Sung Chiang signaled for his men to block that route and the same if Tung Ping tried another way. But Tung Ping used his spears with deadly effect every time, so that he could not be captured. After fighting like a rat in a trap he at last found a means of escape, and cut his way through the brigands. He had had enough fighting for that day so ordered his soldiers to retire to the town.

But that evening Sung Chiang ordered an advance on the town according to his original plan. They surrounded the town, but Ku Ta-sao, although she saw this, dared not set fire to any building. Shih Chin also had no courage to venture out.

Now the Prefect Cheng had a daughter who was very beautiful, and General Tung Ping being single had several times sent a go-between to try and arrange a marriage. But his offers had always been rejected by the prefect. For this reason the general secretly did not like the prefect, although openly they were friends. When Tung Ping got back to the town that evening he remembered this old grudge and sent a go-between to reopen negotiations for the marriage.

Prefect Cheng replied that the proposal was an excellent one, but on account of the present dangerous crisis he could not agree to the marriage as people would only be amazed and jump to wrong conclusions. But he would be pleased to discuss the matter when the brigands were driven away from the town.

The go-between reported this to Tung Ping, who ostensibly accepted the prefect's idea but in his heart he was really dissatisfied as he was afraid that the prefect would eventually decline his offer.

That night, however, the brigands attacked the town and the prefect again ordered Tung Ping to defend the town. General Tung Ping was very angry at this renewed attack, and taking three regiments of soldiers he left the town.

Sung Chiang was on horseback in front of his men, and when he saw Tung Ping he called out, "How dare you an unsupported general fight with my overwhelming strength, but if you submit I may spare your life."

Tung Ping was angry, and shouted, "You were only a petty clerk, so how dare you talk to me like this!" So saying he whipped his horse and dashed towards Sung Chiang. But Hwa Jung and Lin Ch'ung were on both sides of Sung Chiang, and they both galloped forward to fight with Tung Ping. After several bouts the two brigand leaders suddenly galloped away as if defeated, and in accordance with Sung Chiang's previous orders the bandits upon seeing this scattered in all directions. Seeing this Tung Ping was elated, and wished to show off his abilities further, and whipping his horse galloped after the now retreating bandits under Sung Chiang. After racing for about three miles like this they came to a village with a single road between two rows of straw huts. Across the road the brigands had laid several ropes covered with a thin layer of earth to catch the enemy's horse. As Tung Ping dashed up the street a gong was sounded, the doors opened, and the ropes were stretched across the road as soon as he was going to pass. Tung Ping had hardly rushed forward, but his horse was tripped by the rope, and fell. The brigands leapt out of the huts, and seizing Tung Ping bound him with ropes. He was disarmed, and taken before Sung Chiang who had pulled up his horse under a poplar tree. When Tung Ping came up Sung Chiang pretended to be angry, and shouted, "I told you to invite general Tung Ping to come, why you tied him with ropes like this?" He hurriedly dismounted, released the prisoner, and then saluted him. Tung Ping also saluted in response. Sung Chiang then spoke to him, "If you do not disdain us we shall be pleased to receive you as a commander of our stronghold."

Tung Ping replied, "I am your prisoner, and deserve nothing more than death, but if you will forgive me, then

I shall be very fortunate. But as you ask me to become your leader it makes me astonished."

"In our stronghold we are short of grain, and came to Tung Ping Fu to borrow some, and had no other intention," replied Sung Chiang.

"That fellow, Cheng Wan-li, the prefect," said Tung Ping, "was previously a tutor in the family of His Excellency Tung Kwan, and that was how he got the office of prefect at Tung Ping. If you like I could return to Tung Ping, and by false pretenses get the gate of the town opened so that your men could enter, and so get all you require."

Sung Chiang was very pleased at this offer and accepted same. He ordered the prisoner's arms, mail armor, and helmet to be returned to him. They mounted their horses with Tung Ping riding in front, and soon reached the town. Tung Ping called out for the gate to be opened. It was still dark, and the gatekeeper lit a torch to see who it was, and when he saw Tung Ping he at once opened the gate, and lowered the drawbridge. Tung Ping entered and killed the gatekeeper, and Sung Chiang and his brigands flocked through the open gate, and were soon in control of the town. Sung Chiang ordered his men not to kill the civilians, or set fire to the houses. Tung Ping went to the yamen, and killed the prefect and all his family with the exception of the daughter whom he kept for himself. Sung Chiang ordered the jail to be opened, and rescued Shih Chin. He also seized the treasury, and looted the gold and silver there. The town granary was also looted, and the grain was sent to Liang Shan Po. Shih Chin took the men to the house of the woman Li Shui-lan and killed everybody there. Sung Chiang distributed all the goods in the prefect's house among the people. He also issued a proclamation, "We have killed the officials who injured you people, so that now you may continue your avocations without fear." He then ordered his men to leave the town and return to Liang Shan Po. When they were on the way however, Pai Sheng arrived with news as to how the expedition to Tung Chang Fu had progressed.

     Generals throwing stones which hit
     Quite another target.

CHAPTER 69

THE FEATHERLESS ARROW THROWS STONES AT THE HEROES; SUNG CHIANG ABANDONS GRAINS TO CAPTURE A BRAVE MAN

WHILE the brigands were on their way to Liang Shan Po, Pai Sheng arrived and reported to Sung Chiang, "Lu Tsun-i attacked Tung Chang Fu twice, but was twice defeated. In that town there is a very fierce general named Chang Ching who is a Chang Te Fu man, and is a very skillful horseman. He is unexcelled at throwing stones, and hits his mark every time. He is nicknamed, 'Featherless Arrow.' He has two capable adjutants: Kung Wang, nicknamed 'Spot-necked Tiger,' because his skin is all tattooed like the tigers. He wears a tiger's head, and on horseback throws his spear with great speed and precision. The other adjutant is called Ting Te-sun nicknamed 'Archer-Tiger.' Both his face and neck are scarred. On horseback he throws his three-pronged fork.

"Lu Tsun-i arrived Tung Chang Fu with his men, but for the first ten days the troops in the town did not come outside. Two days ago, however, General Chang Ching came out with his army, and was challenged by Hao Ssu-wen but after a few bouts Chang Ching was going to retire into the town. Hao Ssu-wen pursued him on horseback, but Chang Ching threw a stone which knocked Hao Ssu-wen off his horse. But Yen Ch'ing had also followed them, and he now shot an arrow which wounded Chang Ching's horse, and so saved Hao Ssu-wen's life.

"The next day Hsiang Chung and two others of our leaders went out to challenge combat, and adjutant Ting Te-sun came out to fight them, but he threw his three-pronged fork, and wounded Hsiang Chung in the back. Hsiang Chung then retired, and that was our second defeat.

"Those two wounded leaders are being attended to on our boats. Wu Yung however told me to come and request you to bring all your men to Tung Chang Fu to help him."

When Sung Chiang heard this he was sad, and exclaimed, "Lu Tsun-i has had bad luck! I never anticipated this! We must all go and help him." He at once gave orders for all his men to march to Tung Chang Fu.

The two forces were soon united, but while the leaders were discussing the situation a scout arrived and reported that General Chang Ching and his soldiers had again left the town for a fight. The leaders at once mounted their horses and proceeded to an open field. The two forces faced each other with drums beating. General Chang Ching was attended by his adjutants Ting Te-sun and Kung Wang. All three rode forward, and when they halted General Chang Ching pointed at Sung Chiang and said, "You water thief! Shall we have a fight?"

"Who will fight this man?" asked Sung Chiang to his leaders.

Immediately one of his heroes dashed forward armed with a hooked spear, and Sung Chiang saw that it was Hsu Ning, the Spear Expert. Sung Chiang was pleased as he knew that this man would be a suitable match for General Chang Ching.

The two men fought, but after about five bouts General Chang Ching retired. Hsu Ning chased him on horseback, but General Chang Ching put his spear to his left hand and held a stone in his right hand, and when Hsu Ning drew near he (Chang Ching) turned in his saddle and threw the stone which struck Hsu Ning in the face and knocked him off his horse. Both the adjutants galloped forward to capture Hsu Ning, but at the same time Lu Fang and Kuo Sheng also rode forward, and they succeeded in reaching Hsu Ning first, and rescuing him, carried him back on their horses.

Sung Chiang now asked for another volunteer, and at once another horseman dashed forward. He was Yen Shun, the Sleek Tiger. He fought with General Chang Ching for several bouts, but then realizing that he had no chance of winning he withdrew. General Chang Ching pursued him, and threw a stone which struck Yen Shun in the back so hard that the latter rode with pain. A man shouted, "Who is afraid of this man?" and rode forward holding his long mace. This was Han Tao, the Hundred Victories General. Han Tao wished to display his skill before Sung Chiang so he did his best. After about ten bouts General Chang Ching withdrew. Han Tao did not pursue him as he suspected that he (Chang Ching) would throw a stone as before. General Chang Ching did turn round, but seeing that his opponent was not following him he wheeled his horse round and returned. But just as he neared he threw a stone which hit Han Tao on the nose, and caused blood to flow, so that Han Tao hurriedly retreated.

Upon seeing this Peng Chi, without waiting for orders, dashed forward, but before the two could fight General Chang Ching suddenly threw another stone which struck Peng Chi right in the face, and made him drop his sword and ride back to the brigands' ranks.

Sung Chiang was rather annoyed at these repeated repulses, and was inclined to withdraw all his men. But just then a man called out from behind, "If we were repelled to-day, how can we fight to-morrow? Will he hit me with a stone as well?"

General Sung Chiang saw that it was Hsuan Tsan, the Disgraced Son-in-law. General Chang Ching called out, "They come and go, one by one, but it would be just the same if they come in pairs. Do you know how I throw stones?"

"You have hit others, but you cannot hit me," said Hsuan Tsan.

He had not finished saying this when he was struck in the mouth by a stone, and fell off his horse. The adjutants Kung Wang and Ting Te-sun were going to take him prisoner but they were outnumbered by the brigands who rushed forward and took Hsuan Tsan back.

Sung Chiang was very angry at this, and drawing his sword he swore an oath, "If I do not capture this man I will not return."

Huyen Sho interposed, "If you take this oath of what use are we?" He at once whipped his horse, and galloped forward. He called out, "You proud one! You have strength without wisdom. Do you recognize the great General Huyen Sho?"

"You are a disgrace to our country and a deserter! You want also to suffer at my hand!" replied General Chang Ching. So saying he again suddenly threw a stone, but Huyen Sho put up his whip and received the stone on his wrist. His whip fell to the ground, so he wheeled his horse and retired.

Sung Chiang called out, "All our mounted men have been repulsed, so now a foot-soldier had better have a try."

Liu Tang now stepped forward armed with a sword, but General Chang Ching laughed at him, and said, "You, defeated bandits, your horsemen have suffered at my hand, not to say you a footman."

Liu Tang was very angry and advanced, but General Chang Ching declined to fight with him and turned back to his army. But Liu Tang ran forward, and struck the general's horse with his sword. The horse kicked Liu Tang, and knocked him down while General Chang Ching threw another stone. Liu Tang was arrested and taken prisoner.

"Who will rescue Liu Tang?" shouted Sung Chiang. Yang Chih now dashed forward on horseback, and General Chang Ching pretended to defend himself with his spear, but as Yang Chih thrust with his sword General Chang Ching merely evaded the blow. Before Yang Chih could recover his position he was struck on the head by a stone, and he quickly retreated.

Chu Tung now turned to Lei Heng, and said, "Men are beaten singly, but we two might succeed."

Lei Heng agreed, and they both advanced on foot, armed with swords. General Chang Ching laughed when he saw them, and said, "One alone was useless so an extra one is added. But why don't they play for safety and send ten?" He secretly got two stones in his hand, and suddenly threw one at Lei Heng whom it hit on the forehead and knocked him down. Chu Tung ran to assist Lei Heng, but another stone hit the former. In the ranks of the brigands Kuan Sheng was angry when he saw this further repulse, and whipping his horse he galloped forward to rescue the two leaders. As he got near, however, General Chang Ching threw a stone, but Kuan Sheng received it on his sword so that it fell to the ground. Kuan Sheng rescued the two leaders, and took them back into safety.

Tung Ping, the Two Spears General, thought, "I have only recently joined these brigands, and it is now a suitable opportunity to show my skill. If I don't do something here, I shall have no distinction at the mountain stronghold." So he rode forth and charged General Chang Ching who called out to him, "We were in command in neighboring towns, and assisted each other in a common cause. Why do you now oppose me? You are a disgrace!"

Tung Ping was annoyed at this, and they fought. The four arms and three spears whirled around and flashed, as numerous lunges were made. After about seven bouts however General Chang Ching retired.

"You threw stones at the others," said Tung Ping, "so why not at me?"

General Chang Ching put his spear in its buckle, and taking a stone threw it at his opponent. But Tung Ping knocked the stone to one side with the haft of his spear. The general threw another stone, but this time Tung Ping crouched and avoided it. This rather disappointed the general, and made him afraid as Tung Ping was now quite close. Tung Ping lunged with his spear as the two horses galloped one behind the other, but General Chang Ching evaded the blow. The two horses were now level, so General Chang Ching seized Tung Ping with both arms, but failed to pull Tung Ping off his horse. The two men and two horses were now close together in one mass.

So Ch'ao seeing this dashed forward with his ax to help Tung Ping, but on the other side the adjutants Kung Wang and Ting Te-sun also galloped forward to intercept the fresh opponents. Now there were two separate groups of fighters. Among the brigands Lin Ch'ung and three other leaders rode forth. Upon seeing that he was outnumbered General Chang Ching released his hold on Tung Ping and retreated. But Tung Ping pursued him right among the soldiers, having forgotten at the moment about the stones. General Chang Ching reigned in his horse, and when Tung Ping was near he suddenly threw a stone. But Tung Ping saw the move, ducked, evaded the stone, wheeled his horse, and galloped away in safety. The general now threw a stone at So Ch'ao which struck that man in the face, so that he at once wheeled his horse and retreated.

The other six horsemen were still fighting in two groups. At last Kung Wang was captured by Lin Ch'ung while Yen Ch'ing on the brigands' side took his crossbow and shot an arrow which wounded adjutant Ting Te-sun's horse, and he (Ting) was immediately made prisoner. General Chang Ching would have liked to rescue his adjutants, but decided not to do so as the opposing force was greater than his. So he ordered his army to return to Tung Chang Fu. Upon reaching the town the prisoner Liu Tang was sent to prison, and the prefect entertained General Chang Ching at a feast.

On the other side adjutants Ting Te-sun and Kung Wang were sent to Liang Shan Po as prisoners.

Sung Chiang was conferring with Wu Yung and Lu Tsun-i when he said, "I have read that during the Five Dynasties (A.D. 907) there was a man named Wang Wen-chang who defeated thirty-six generals in about an hour. To-day this General Chang Ching has done almost the same thing, having defeated fifteen of our leaders in about the same time. He is undoubtedly a doughty warrior. But it is evident that he depends a great deal on the assistance of his two adjutants, but as we have captured them we can capture him with some strategy."

"You need not worry about him," said Wu Yung. "I have carefully noticed his method of fighting; I have long had a plan to capture him. We must now send all our wounded leaders back to Liang Shan Po and then order Lu Ta and four other leaders to arrange carts and boats to proceed by land and water to induce Chang Ching into our trap.

In the town General Chang Ching said to the prefect, "Although we have twice defeated the brigands yet we have not entirely crippled their activities. We must send spies to find out what they are doing."

This was done, and it was not long before a scout returned and reported, "On the northwest side there are about a hundred carts and about fifty boats on the river. They are evidently all loaded with rice, but I do not know where they came from—but they are approaching the town."

"I am afraid that this is some plot of those brigands," said the prefect. "We had better send a spy to find out whether it is really rice or not."

This was done, and the following day the scout returned and reported, "The carts are covered with straw, but I saw some grain fell from the cart, and found that it was rice. The boats have covers over the hatches, but I could see the sacks inside evidently filled with rice."

"I will take soldiers to-night, and capture both those carts and boats," said General Chang Ching.

The prefect agreed to this, and arrangements were made accordingly. That night a thousand soldiers left the town very quietly. There was not much moonlight, but the sky was clear of clouds and the stars were numerous. After going about three miles the advance guard saw a train of carts bearing a flag, "Grain for the Loyalty and Justice Hall at Liang Shan Po," General Chang Ching saw Lu Ta walking in front with his priest's staff over his shoulder. Lu Ta pretended not to be aware of the arrival of General Chang Ching, and for the moment had forgotten about the stone that was to be expected. General Chang Ching suddenly threw a stone, which struck Lu Ta on the head, made a serious wound, and knocked him down. The soldiers now all shouted and rushed forward. Wu Sung was there with a sword, and abandoned the carts, and rushed to rescue Lu Ta. General Chang Ching seized the carts and was much pleased to find that they really contained rice, so he did not pursue Lu Ta, but took the carts into the town with his men. He then left with his army for the South Gate, where from the wall he saw many boats on the river loaded with rice.

He ordered the gate to be opened, and when they marched out they found there was a thick dark mist obscuring their view so that the men could hardly see each other. This was conjured up by Kung-Sun Sheng. General Chang Ching decided to return, but was now uncertain as to which way to go. Just then there came loud shouts from the brigands, but he could not know where the brigands were. In trying to evade the brigands he found himself in the water, and was surrounded by brigand leaders who soon arrested him, and took him as prisoner to their camp. When this news was reported to Sung Chiang he ordered a vigorous attack on the town.

The prefect found himself helpless. The city gate was open, and there was sound of bombs outside the town. The brigands were soon in the town, and at once took the prison and released Liu Tang. They also looted the public granary and treasury, and sent half of the rice and money to Liang Shan Po on carts—the other half being distributed among the people. As the brigands had no fault to find with the prefect they did not touch him. The leaders assembled in the yamen and General Chang Ching was brought there as prisoner. Many of the leaders showed their anger at the general who had wounded many of their friends, and wished to have him executed. But Sung Chiang advanced, and saluted him saying, "We offended you unintentionally, we ask you to forgive us." He then conducted him to the hall. He had no sooner entered the hall than Lu Ta with his head bandaged up, stepped forward with his priest's staff to get his revenge. But Sung Chiang intervened, and protected General Chang Ching, who, seeing this exhibition of kindness to a defeated defenseless man, at once saluted Sung Chiang and agreed to join the brigands.

Sung Chiang now took an oath, broke an arrow, and scattered a cup of wine on the ground, and said, "If we seek revenge Heaven will not support us."

Nobody could say a word against this, and they all agreed to abandon all ideas of revenge. There was soon general rejoicing at this auspicious climax. The next day they all departed for Liang Shan Po.

Before departing, however, General Chang Ching introduced to Sung Chiang a famous veterinary surgeon who had a double surname Huang-pu and a personal name Tuan. He knew all diseases of horses, and could cure any sickness by either medicine or needle. He was a Yü Chou man, and had green eyes and light colored beard. He looked like a barbarian, and had got the nickname, "Purple Bearded Uncle." There was need for such a man at Liang Shan Po, and he was duly enrolled. He took his family with him to the bandits' stronghold.

Upon reaching Liang Shan Po an assembly was held in the Loyalty and Justice Hall, and there Sung Chiang talked very friendly with the two adjutants who were prisoners, and they also agreed to join the band. The new recruits were made leaders, and this brought the total number of the leaders to 108. We will now recount the speech made to the assembled leaders by Sung Chiang.

> Three dozen heavenly heroes replete,
> With earthly dozens six complete.

CHAPTER 70

A STONE TABLET IS FOUND WITH HEAVEN'S COMMANDS IN THE LOYALTY AND JUSTICE HALL

WHEN all the leaders (who now numbered 108) were all assembled in the Loyalty and Justice Hall Sung Chiang addressed them: "Since I escaped here as a consequence of some outrageous conduct at Chiang Chou I have ever been elected and supported as a leader by you heroic brothers. For that I shall always be grateful. Now I am very glad that we have assembled altogether 108 leaders. Since our late commander Ch'ao Kai passed away we by the help of the spirits have always been victorious in every conflict. This has been due to no person's ability but to the protection of the Providence. Some of our leaders have been imprisoned, and some wounded, but so far not a single one has been killed. There has never been such an assembly of heroes since the world began. We however have killed many men so I propose that we conduct a great sacrificial ceremony for the pacification of their souls, and also to thank Heaven for its great assistance to us. By this I wish you first get peace at heart. Second, I wish that the emperor will forgive us our crimes, that we may volunteer ourselves to the service of our country. Thirdly, I wish the early metempsychosis of our late leader Ch'ao Kai into a heavenly being that we may always be with him. Lastly I wish that all those who lost their lives in our fighting will be profited by our prayers. What do you think of this proposal?"

All the leaders approved of this, and Wu Yung said, "I think that the arrangements may be left to Kung-Sun Sheng, and we can get priests from everywhere to take part in the ceremony." The 15th day of the fourth month was selected as the first of the seven days of prayers. Sufficient money was appropriated from the treasury to cover the expenses.

TABLET WITH HEAVEN'S COMMAND

When the day was drawing near they erected two large flag-staffs in front of the hall, and also a three-storied terrace for the use of the service. Inside the hall they had the three Taoist idols, and on each side of them were the Signs of the Zodiac. The ten symbols of the Tien Kan were drawn in the hall and outside was erected a sacrificial altar. Four images were prepared, and dressed up in the characters of Tsui, Lu, Teng, and Tou. The priests invited for this service were altogether 49 including Kung-Sun Sheng and they duly arrived on the appointed date.

Sung Chiang and Lu Tsun-i took the leading part in the ceremony, and Wu Yung and all the other leaders were next to burn incense. Kung-Sun Sheng wrote the prayers which were distributed among the 48 priests for incantation. There were three services each day, and it took a whole week to finish the whole ceremony. On the last day about midnight Kung-Sun Sheng was on the first floor of the terrace, the 48 priests were on the second floor, while all the 108 leaders were on the third floor. All the brigands were kneeling around the terrace. They were all united in prayer to Heaven. About 1 a.m. a sharp noise was heard in the sky as though a huge piece of silk was being torn apart. Gazing upward the assembled mass saw in the sky a golden tray with two sides elongated. This was known as "Heaven's Gates Opened," or "Heaven's Eyes Opened." In the bright gap there shone a dazzling blaze of light. Circling around it were clouds of variegated colors. From the middle of the lights came a ball of fire which descended on the first floor of the terrace. It circled round the other two floors and then went to the south side where it disappeared. The Heaven's Gates were now closed. The priests and leaders descended from the terrace. Sung Chiang called for shovels and spades to dig the ground where the fire had disappeared. They had dug down only about three feet when they found a stone tablet on which characters were engraved. Orders were given for incense and paper to be offered to Heaven for this gift.

The following day the stone tablet was examined, but nobody could decipher the characters which were evidently of very ancient style. But among the priests was one named Ho Hsuan-tung who came forward and addressed Sung

Chiang, "At my home there is a very ancient book which might decipher these characters, and I have studied it a little." He examined the characters carefully for some time, and then said that he thought they were the names of the heroes of Liang Shan Po. Then turning to the right lateral side he made out the four characters, "Carrying out Heaven's wish," and on the other side were also four characters, "Loyalty and Justice Achieved." On the top side there was a drawing of the Charles's Wain. On the front of the stone were the names of the heroes which he said he could make out if Sung Chiang permitted him. Sung Chiang asked him to do this and hide nothing from him no matter what the message was. He then ordered Hsiao Jang to prepare ink and paper, and write down what Ho Hsuan-tung should decipher. The latter then deciphered one by one all the names of the 108 heroes of Liang Shan Po, each of whom represented a star in the heaven.

When this was all disclosed the leaders were astonished.

Sung Chiang addressed the assembly: "Who should know I, a humble clerk, am under a star, but you, my brothers, are also each under a star. Heaven evidently has intentionally brought us all together to uphold the rule of justice. Heaven has also given each of us our respective positions and responsibilities, so we can raise no disputes among us as to our duties."

All the leaders replied, "This is the decree of Heaven, and we will not disobey it."

Sung Chiang paid the priests, and they all left the mountain. He then assigned each leader his duties and also quarters. These were clearly written out on paper, sealed, and handed to each man.

Sung Chiang addressed the assembled leaders and impressed upon them the extreme importance of loyalty. He then told them that they were now all bound together, and must live and die as one body and that they must all support him to act up to the Heaven's wish.

All the assembled leaders took a solemn oath to observe these conditions and then all swore, "We are all united to-day, and so we will remain throughout this life. Any one among us who will turn out to be traitor or coward will be noticed by Heaven and be killed by sword or lightning and his soul will be banished to the Hades forever. They then pledged each other in wine in which blood had been mixed. So was achieved this great assembly of heroes sworn to unite to uphold justice.

That night Lu Tsun-i had a very dreadful dream in which he met a giant warrior who arrested him and brought him to a grand mansion where he and the other 107 leaders of Liang Shan Po were examined and sentenced to death. On the point of being executed he happened to look upward as he dreamt, and saw a tablet on the top of the door with four big characters meaning, "Universal peace throughout this kingdom."

> Mandarins lead an honest life,
>   Great peace reigns in empire's bounds;
> Far and wide no sound of strife,
>   Elders pass their time at feasts.
>
> People rejoice and regard
>   Music and proprieties as their heritage;
> They wish to voice their merriness,
>   With lavish songs and joyous ballads.
>
> Graves of fathers, in trees' shade,
>   Hundred years pass, we'll be dead;
> Emperor's taxes being all paid,
>   Sun's as warm as fur coat.
>
> Tzu Chien's fame sounds in vain,
>   Chuang Tsu held official as ox;
> Verses written when I'm drunk,
>   Attract no admiration when sung.